# MECHANICAL DETAILS FOR PRODUCT DESIGN

OTHER BOOKS BY DOUGLAS C. GREENWOOD

Mechanical Power Transmission

Product Engineering Design Manual

Engineering Data fo Product Design

Your Turn for Mathematics and Engineering

# MECHANICAL DETAILS FOR PRODUCT DESIGN

Edited by
**DOUGLAS C. GREENWOOD**
Associate Editor, *Product Engineering*

McGRAW–HILL BOOK COMPANY

*New York    Toronto    London*

MECHANICAL DETAILS FOR PRODUCT DESIGN

# PREFACE

This book is a completely new presentation of mechanical design aids that have never before appeared in book form. Since this volume relates to the same on-the-job problems as did my previous handbook, *Product Engineering Design Manual*, I feel I cannot do better than repeat, in general, its accompanying preface:

> Most advances in design engineering do not come about unaided. Even the most brilliant developments are based on the firm ground of existing, proven ideas. To this extent, therefore, improved mechanisms, better fastening and assembly methods, material savings, and design ingenuity in general are the result of an evolutionary process. One thing helps another and design takes a step forward.
>
> But to trigger the inventive processes that yield the new idea, there must be a catalyst. Two or more ideas—even though quite different—can then combine to produce a completely new and better method, device, component, or complete product. The catalyst in all design-engineering problems is experience and recallable knowledge. That is one reason why engineering offices and individual engineers compile a design file. Another reason is simply to have quickly available various alternative ways of solving some specific design problems. Accumulated in these files is material of special, long-term reference value. Indeed it can almost be said that one mark of an experienced design engineer is the quality and size of his design file.
>
> A treasurehouse of such material has appeared in the pages of *Product Engineering* magazine, and one of the saddest reflections of an engineering editor is the realization that permanent-value material has been lost to many readers in the no-longer available back issues of his magazine.
>
> To my knowledge, only in the pages of *Product Engineering* can be found such specially edited design-file material. The pages that contain such material are never reprinted—except by special arrangement. They have consequently been much sought after by engineers, many of whom have suggested their reproduction. This stimulating material has now been carefully sifted, condensed, and re-edited where necessary.

That book, incidentally, has now been translated into Spanish, and, shortly, a Japanese translation will be published.

All the latest *Product Engineering* mechanism spreads are presented in this volume. It contains material of the type for most of which you would search the usual engineering handbooks and textbooks in vain—material that is, nevertheless, the lifeblood of engineering design.

The illustrated mechanisms and other information have been supplemented, for additional design aid, with charts, formulas, and tables. For the experienced man this book will be recognized immediately as an essential supplement to the fund of knowledge he already possesses. To the younger engineer this represents the nearest thing to a ready-made experience that I can possibly imagine.

For all levels of product design engineers, it is intended that this book will be a solid package of practical how-to's and the catalyst for further progress through new ideas. It is an interesting sidelight, incidentally, that patent attorneys and inventors have found that this material is of tremendous help to them also.

Again I should like to thank my associates on the staff of *Product Engineering* for data and helpful suggestions, and also former staff members who originally edited some of the earlier pages. Most of all, credit is due the engineers who prepared the material and submitted it to *Product Engineering* for evaluation and publication. Finally, I dare not forget to thank my twin helpers, Janice and Joyce, who, like dutiful daughters, helped to assemble, collate, and even type where necessary, the many many articles and illustrations involved.

*Douglas C. Greenwood*

# CONTENTS

*Chapter 1*

# TABLES AND CHARTS

# Measurement Conversion Tables

**Angstrom Unit** ...... $10^{-10}$ meter
1/10,000 micron
0.003937 millionths of an inch

**B.t.u.** (*British Thermal Unit*) ............ 778 foot pounds
0.2930 watt hour
0.252 calorie

**Calorie** ............. 1 kilogram of water raised 1 degree Centigrade
3.97 B.t.u.

**Centare** (*square meter*).. 10.764 square feet

**Centimeter** ......... 0.3937 inch

**Cheval** (*French hp.*).... 0.986 horsepower

**Circular Mil** ........ Area of circle whose diameter is one mil or 1/1,000 inch.
0.000000785 square inch

**Cubic Centimeter** (*milliliter*) ........... 0.061 cubic inch

**Cubic Foot** .......... 1,728 cubic inches
60 pints
8/10 bushel
1,000 ounces of water, approx.
0.028 cubic meter
28.32 liters

**Cubic Inch** ......... 16.39 cubic centimeters

**Cubic Meter** ........ 35.315 cubic feet
1.308 cubic yards

**Cubic Yard** ......... 27 cubic feet
0.765 cubic meter

**Decimeter** .......... 3.937 inches

**Foot** ................ 12 inches
0.385 meter

**Foot Pound** ........ 0.1364 kilogrammeter

**Gallon** ............. 231 cubic inches
4 quarts
8 pints
3.785 liters
128 fluid ounces

**Gallon per Cubic Foot** 1.254 liters per cubic meter

**Gallon** (*British Imper'l*) 277.3 cubic inches
1.201 U. S. gallons
weight of 10 lb. water at 15°C.
4.546 liters

**Gallon of Water** ..... 8.33 pounds

**Grain** ............. 1/7000 lb. avoirdupois
0.0684 gram

**Grain per Cubic Foot**. 2.288 grams per cubic meter

**Gram** ............. 15.43 grains
0.0353 ounce
0.0022 pound

**Gram per Cubic Meter** 0.437 grains per cu. ft.

**Horsepower** ......... 33,000 ft. lb. per minute
42.41 B.t.u. per minute
1.014 cheval
746 watts

**Hundredweight** (*British*) ............ 112 pounds
50.80 kilograms

**Inch** ................ 39,540 ¼ wave lengths of red ray of cadmium
25.4 127/5 or millimeters

**Joule** ............... 1 watt second

**Kilogram** ........... 2.2046 pounds
35.274 ounces
15432.36 grains
0.0011 short ton
0.00098 long ton

**Kilogram per Cubic Meter** ............ 0.0624 lbs. per cu. ft.

**Kilogram per Square Centimeter** ....... 14.225 lbs. per sq. in.

**Kilogram per Square Meter** ............ 0.205 lbs. per sq. ft.

**Kilometer** ........... 1,000 meters
0.621 mile

**Kilowatt** ........... 1.34 horsepower
44,257 ft. lb. per min.
56.87 B.t.u. per minute

**Liter** ................ 1.000027 cubic decimeter
1.057 quart
0.264 gallon
61.02 cubic inches
.035 cubic feet
33.8147 fluid ounces
270.518 fluid drams

**Liter per Cubic Meter** 0.798 U.S. Gal. per cu.ft

**Liter per Second** ..... 2.12 cu. ft. per minute
0.474 U.S. gal. per min.

**Meter** ............... 39.37 inches
3.28 feet
1.09 yards
1,553,164.13 wavelengths of red ray of cadmium

**Metric Ton** .......... 2204.6 pounds
1.1023 short tons

**Micron** ............. 0.001 millimeter
10,000 Angstrom units
39.37 millionths of an in.

**Microgram** .......... 1/1000 milligram

**Mil** ................. 0.001 inch
25.4 microns
0.0254 millimeter

**Mile** ................ 1,760 yards
5,280 feet
1.61 kilometers

**Milligram** .......... 0.0154 grain

**Milliliter** ........... 1.000027 cu. centimeter
0.0610 cubic inch

**Myriameter** ......... 10,000 meters
6.2137 miles

**Ounce** .............. 437.5 grains
0.911 troy ounces
0.000446 long ton
28.35 gram

**Ounce,** (*Fluid*) ....... 1.805 cubic inches
29.573 milliliters

**Ounce,** (*Fine*) ....... Troy ounce
480 grains
31.104 grams

**Pied** (*French foot*) ..... 12 Paris inches
0.325 meter

**Pint** ................. 0.4732 liter

**Pound Avoirdupois** ... 16 ounces
7,000 grains
454 grams
0.454 kilogram
14.58 troy ounces

**Pound per Cubic Foot** 16.02 kilogram per cubic meter

**Pound per Sq. In.** ..... 0.434 x water head feet

**Pound per sq. In.** ..... 0.0703 kilogram per sq. centimeter

**Pound per Sq. Ft.** ..... 4.88 kilogram per square meter

**Quart** ............... 2 pints
¼ gallon
0.946 liter

**Quart** (*British quarter hundredweight*) ...... 28 pounds
12.70 kilograms

**Quintal** ............. 100 kilograms
220.46 pounds

**Stere** ................ 1 cubic meter

**Square Centimeter** ... 0.155 square inch

**Square Foot** ........ 0.093 square meter

**Square Inch** ........ 6.452 square centimeters

**Square Kilometer** .... 0.386 square mile

**Square Meter** (*centare*) 10.764 square feet
1.196 square yard

**Square Mil** .......... 0.000001 square inch
0.000645 sq. centimeter

**Square Mile** ......... 640 acres
3,097,600 square yards
2.59 square kilometers

**Square Millimeter** ... 0.00155 square inch

**Square Yard** ........ 0.836 square meter

**Stone** (*British*) ....... 14 pounds
6.35 kilograms

**Ton** (*short*) .......... 2,000 pounds
907 kilograms

(*long*) .............. 2,240 pounds
1,016 kilograms

**Tonne** (*metric*) ....... 1,000 kilograms
2204.62 pounds

**Yard** ................ 3 feet
36 inches
0.914 meter
1,420,212 wave lengths of red ray of cadmium

Courtesy of American Institute of Weights and Measures

# Measurement Conversion Tables
## English and Metric Factors

### U. S. System to Metric System

| | | |
|---|---|---|
| Pounds per lineal foot | × 1.488 | = kilos. per lineal metre |
| Pounds per lineal yard | × 0.496 | = kilos. per lineal metre |
| Tons per lineal foot | × 3333.33 | = kilos. per lineal metre |
| Tons per lineal yard | × 1111.11 | = kilos. per lineal metre |
| Pounds per mile | × 0.2818 | = kilos. per kilometre |
| Pounds per square inch | × 0.0703 | = kilos. per square centimetre |
| Tons per square inch | × 1.575 | = kilos. per square millimetre |
| Pounds per square foot | × 4.883 | = kilos. per square metre |
| Tons per square foot | × 10.936 | = tonnes per square metre |
| Tons per square yard | × 1.215 | = tonnes per square metre |
| Pounds per cubic yard | × 0.5933 | = kilos. per cubic metre |
| Pounds per cubic foot | × 16.020 | = kilos. per cubic metre |
| Tons per cubic yard | × 1.329 | = tonnes per cubic metre |
| Grains per U. S. gallon (3.785 litres) | × 0.017093 | = grammes per litre |
| Pounds (avoir.) per U. S. gallon (3.785 litres) | × 0.11955 | = kilos. per litre |
| U. S. gallons (3.785 litres) per square feet | × 40.742 | = litres per square metre |
| Foot-pounds | × 0.1382 | = kilogrammetres |
| Foot-tons | × 0.323 | = tonne-metres |
| Horsepower | × 1.0139 | = force de cheval |
| Pounds per H. P. | × 0.477 | = kilos. per cheval |
| Square feet per H. P. | × 0.0196 | = square metre per cheval |
| Cubic feet per H. P. | × 0.0279 | = cubic metre per cheval |
| Heat units (B. T. U.) | × 0.252 | = calories |
| Heat units (B. T. U.) per square foot | × 2.713 | = calories per square metre |

### Metric System to U. S. System

| | | |
|---|---|---|
| Kilos. per lineal metre | × 0.672 | = pounds per lineal foot |
| Kilos. per lineal metre | × 2.016 | = pounds per lineal yard |
| Kilos. per lineal metre | × 0.0003 | = tons per lineal foot |
| Kilos. per lineal metre | × 0.0009 | = tons per lineal yard |
| Kilos. per kilometre | × 3.548 | = pounds per mile |
| Kilos. per square centimetre | × 4.223 | = pounds per square inch |
| Kilos. per square millimetre | × 0.635 | = tons per square inch |
| Kilos. per square metre | × 0.2048 | = pounds per square foot |
| Tonnes per square metre | × 0.0914 | = tons per square foot |
| Tonnes per square metre | × 0.823 | = tons per square yard |
| Kilos. per cubic metre | × 1.686 | = pounds per cubic yard |
| Kilos. per cubic metre | × 0.0624 | = pounds per cubic foot |
| Tonnes per cubic metre | × 0.752 | = tons per cubic yard |
| Grammes per litre | × 58.4139 | = grains per U. S. gallon (3.785 litres) |
| Kilos. per litre | × 8.3459 | = Pounds (avoir.) per U.S. gallon (3.785 litres) |
| Litres per square metre | × 0.02453 | = U. S. gallons (3.785 litre) per square feet |
| Kilogrammetres | × 7.233 | = foot-pounds |
| Tonne-metres | × 3.088 | = foot-tons |
| Force de cheval | × 0.9863 | = horse-power |
| Kilos. per cheval | × 2.235 | = pounds per H. P. |
| Square metre per cheval | × 10.913 | = square foot per H. P. |
| Cubic metre per cheval | × 35.806 | = cubic feet per H. P. |
| Calories | × 3.968 | = heat units. (B. T. U.) |
| Calories per square metre | × 0.369 | = heat units (B. T. U.) per square foot |

Courtesy of the Heppenstall Company

# LENGTH OF MATERIAL FOR 90-DEG. BENDS

As shown in Fig. 1, when a sheet or flat bar is bent, the position of the neutral plane with respect to the outer and inner surfaces will depend on the ratio of the radius of bend to the thickness of the bar or sheet. For a sharp corner, the neutral plane will lie one-third the distance from the inner to the outer surface. As the radius of the bend is increased, the neutral plane shifts until it reaches a position midway between the inner and outer surfaces. This factor should be taken into consideration when calculating the developed length of material required for formed pieces.

The table on the following pages gives the developed length of the material in the 90-deg. bend. The following formulas were used to calculate the quantities given in the table, the radius of the bend being measured as the distance from the center of curvature to the inner surface of the bend.

1. For a sharp corner and for any radius of bend up to $T$, the thickness of the sheet, the developed length $L$ for a 90-deg. bend will be

$$L = 1.5708 \left( R + \frac{T}{3} \right)$$

2. For any radius of bend greater than $2T$, the length $L$ for a 90-deg. bend will be

$$L = 1.5708 \left( R + \frac{T}{2} \right)$$

3. For any radius of bend between $1T$ and $2T$, the value of $L$ as given in the table was found by interpolation.

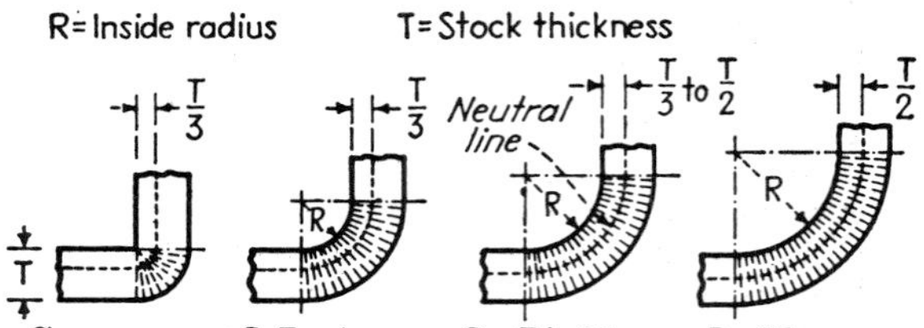

The developed length $L$ of the material in any bend other than 90 deg. can be obtained from the following formulas:

1. For a sharp corner or a radius up to $T$:

$$L = 0.0175 \left( R + \frac{T}{3} \right) \times \text{degrees of bend}$$

2. For a radius of $2T$ or more:

$$L = 0.0175 \left( R + \frac{T}{2} \right) \times \text{degrees of bend}$$

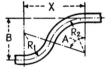

R = Inside radius  T = Stock thickness

Sharp corner  R = T or less  R = 1T to 2T  R = 2T or more

FIG. 1.

For double bends as shown in Fig. 2, if $R_1 + R_2$ is greater than $B$:

$$X = \sqrt{2B(R_1 + R_2 - B/2)}$$

With $R_1$, $R_2$, and $B$ known:

$$\cos A = \frac{R_1 + R_2 - B}{R_1 + R_2}$$
$$L = 0.0175(R_1 + R_2)A$$

where $A$ is in degrees and $L$ is the developed length.

If $R_1 + R_2$ is less than $B$, as in Fig. 3,

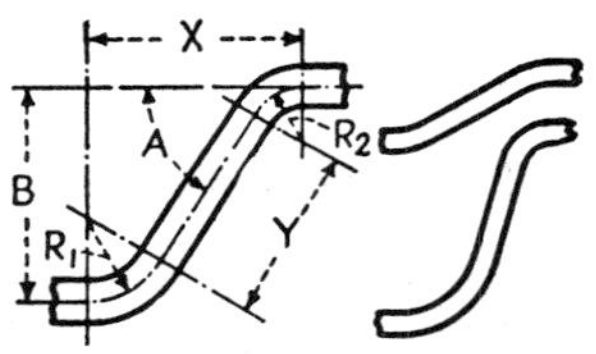

$$Y = B \csc A - (R_1 + R_2)(\csc A - \cot A)$$

The value of $X$ when $B$ is greater than $R_1 + R_2$ will be

$$X = B \cot A + (R_1 + R_2)(\csc A - \cot A)$$

FIG. 2.　　FIG. 3.

The total developed length $L$ required for the material in the straight section plus that in the two arcs will be

$$L = Y + 0.0175(R_1 + R_2)A$$

To simplify the calculations, the table on this page gives the equations for $X$, $Y$, and the developed length for various common angles of bend. The table on following pages gives $L$ for values of $R$ and $T$ for 90-deg. bends.

## EQUATIONS FOR $X$, $Y$, AND DEVELOPED LENGTHS

| Angle $A$, deg. | $X$ | $Y$ | Developed length |
|---|---|---|---|
| 15 | $3.732B + 0.132(R_1 + R_2)$ | $3.864B - 0.132(R_1 + R_2)$ | $3.864B + 0.130(R_1 + R_2)$ |
| 22½ | $2.414B + 0.199(R_1 + R_2)$ | $2.613B - 0.199(R_1 + R_2)$ | $2.613B + 0.194(R_1 + R_2)$ |
| 30 | $1.732B + 0.268(R_1 + R_2)$ | $2.000B - 0.268(R_1 + R_2)$ | $2.000B + 0.256(R_1 + R_2)$ |
| 45 | $B + 0.414(R_1 + R_2)$ | $1.414B - 0.414(R_1 + R_2)$ | $1.414B + 0.371(R_1 + R_2)$ |
| 60 | $0.577(B + R_1 + R_2)$ | $1.155B - 0.577(R_1 + R_2)$ | $1.155B + 0.470(R_1 + R_2)$ |
| 67½ | $0.414B + 0.668(R_1 + R_2)$ | $1.082B - 0.668(R_1 + R_2)$ | $1.082B + 0.510(R_1 + R_2)$ |
| 75 | $0.268B + 0.767(R_1 + R_2)$ | $1.035B - 0.767(R_1 + R_2)$ | $1.035B + 0.542(R_1 + R_2)$ |
| 90 | $R_1 + R_2$ | $B - R_1 - R_2$ | $B + 0.571(R_1 + R_2)$ |

# DEVELOPED LENGTH IN INCHES OF MATERIAL REQUIRED FOR 90-DEG. BEND

| Thickness of material, in. | Sharp corner | Inside radius of bend, in. | | | | | | | | | | | | | | |
| --- | --- | --- | --- | --- | --- | --- | --- | --- | --- | --- | --- | --- | --- | --- | --- | --- |
| | | 0.005 | 0.010 | 1/64 | 0.020 | 0.025 | 1/32 | 0.040 | 3/64 | 0.050 | 1/16 | 5/64 | 3/32 | 0.100 | 7/64 | 1/8 |
| 0.004 | 0.002 | 0.011 | 0.0188 | 0.028 | 0.035 | 0.042 | 0.052 | 0.066 | 0.077 | 0.082 | 0.101 | 0.126 | 0.150 | 0.160 | 0.175 | 0.200 |
| 0.005 | 0.003 | 0.011 | 0.0196 | 0.028 | 0.035 | 0.043 | 0.053 | 0.067 | 0.077 | 0.083 | 0.102 | 0.127 | 0.151 | 0.161 | 0.176 | 0.200 |
| 0.007 | 0.004 | 0.012 | 0.020 | 0.030 | 0.037 | 0.045 | 0.055 | 0.068 | 0.079 | 0.084 | 0.104 | 0.128 | 0.153 | 0.163 | 0.177 | 0.202 |
| 0.008 | 0.004 | 0.012 | 0.0206 | 0.031 | 0.034 | 0.046 | 0.055 | 0.069 | 0.080 | 0.085 | 0.105 | 0.129 | 0.154 | 0.163 | 0.178 | 0.203 |
| 0.010 | 0.005 | 0.013 | 0.0213 | 0.031 | 0.039 | 0.047 | 0.057 | 0.071 | 0.081 | 0.086 | 0.106 | 0.131 | 0.155 | 0.165 | 0.180 | 0.204 |
| 0.012 | 0.006 | 0.014 | 0.022 | 0.032 | 0.040 | 0.049 | 0.058 | 0.072 | 0.083 | 0.088 | 0.108 | 0.132 | 0.157 | 0.167 | 0.181 | 0.206 |
| 0.014 | 0.007 | 0.015 | 0.023 | 0.032 | 0.040 | 0.049 | 0.060 | 0.074 | 0.085 | 0.090 | 0.109 | 0.134 | 0.158 | 0.168 | 0.183 | 0.207 |
| 0.016 | 0.008 | 0.016 | 0.024 | 0.033 | 0.041 | 0.050 | 0.061 | 0.075 | 0.085 | 0.091 | 0.110 | 0.135 | 0.159 | 0.169 | 0.184 | 0.209 |
| 0.016 | 0.008 | 0.016 | 0.024 | 0.033 | 0.041 | 0.051 | 0.062 | 0.075 | 0.086 | 0.091 | 0.111 | 0.135 | 0.160 | 0.170 | 0.184 | 0.209 |
| 0.018 | 0.009 | 0.017 | 0.025 | 0.034 | 0.042 | 0.052 | 0.062 | 0.077 | 0.088 | 0.093 | 0.112 | 0.137 | 0.161 | 0.171 | 0.186 | 0.211 |
| 0.020 | 0.011 | 0.018 | 0.026 | 0.035 | 0.043 | 0.052 | 0.063 | 0.079 | 0.089 | 0.094 | 0.114 | 0.138 | 0.163 | 0.173 | 0.187 | 0.212 |
| 0.022 | 0.012 | 0.019 | 0.027 | 0.036 | 0.043 | 0.053 | 0.063 | 0.079 | 0.096 | 0.096 | 0.116 | 0.140 | 0.165 | 0.174 | 0.189 | 0.214 |
| 0.025 | 0.013 | 0.021 | 0.029 | 0.038 | 0.045 | 0.053 | 0.064 | 0.080 | 0.092 | 0.098 | 0.118 | 0.142 | 0.167 | 0.177 | 0.191 | 0.216 |
| 0.028 | 0.015 | 0.023 | 0.030 | 0.039 | 0.046 | 0.054 | 0.065 | 0.081 | 0.092 | 0.099 | 0.120 | 0.145 | 0.169 | 0.179 | 0.194 | 0.218 |
| 0.031 | 0.016 | 0.024 | 0.032 | 0.041 | 0.048 | 0.056 | 0.065 | 0.081 | 0.093 | 0.100 | 0.123 | 0.147 | 0.172 | 0.182 | 0.196 | 0.221 |
| 0.032 | 0.017 | 0.025 | 0.032 | 0.041 | 0.048 | 0.056 | 0.066 | 0.082 | 0.094 | 0.100 | 0.123 | 0.148 | 0.172 | 0.182 | 0.197 | 0.222 |
| 0.035 | 0.018 | 0.026 | 0.034 | 0.043 | 0.050 | 0.058 | 0.067 | 0.082 | 0.095 | 0.101 | 0.124 | 0.150 | 0.175 | 0.185 | 0.199 | 0.224 |
| 0.038 | 0.020 | 0.028 | 0.035 | 0.044 | 0.051 | 0.059 | 0.069 | 0.083 | 0.096 | 0.102 | 0.125 | 0.152 | 0.177 | 0.185 | 0.201 | 0.226 |
| 0.040 | 0.021 | 0.029 | 0.037 | 0.045 | 0.052 | 0.060 | 0.070 | 0.084 | 0.097 | 0.102 | 0.126 | 0.153 | 0.179 | 0.189 | 0.203 | 0.228 |
| 0.042 | 0.022 | 0.030 | 0.038 | 0.047 | 0.053 | 0.061 | 0.071 | 0.085 | 0.097 | 0.103 | 0.126 | 0.154 | 0.180 | 0.190 | 0.205 | 0.229 |
| 0.044 | 0.023 | 0.031 | 0.039 | 0.047 | 0.054 | 0.062 | 0.072 | 0.086 | 0.097 | 0.103 | 0.127 | 0.154 | 0.182 | 0.191 | 0.206 | 0.231 |
| 0.045 | 0.024 | 0.031 | 0.039 | 0.048 | 0.055 | 0.063 | 0.073 | 0.086 | 0.099 | 0.104 | 0.127 | 0.154 | 0.183 | 0.192 | 0.207 | 0.232 |
| 0.049 | 0.026 | 0.034 | 0.041 | 0.050 | 0.057 | 0.065 | 0.075 | 0.088 | 0.099 | 0.105 | 0.128 | 0.155 | 0.183 | 0.196 | 0.210 | 0.235 |
| 0.051 | 0.027 | 0.034 | 0.042 | 0.051 | 0.058 | 0.066 | 0.076 | 0.083 | 0.100 | 0.105 | 0.129 | 0.155 | 0.184 | 0.196 | 0.212 | 0.236 |
| 0.057 | 0.030 | 0.038 | 0.046 | 0.054 | 0.061 | 0.069 | 0.079 | 0.093 | 0.103 | 0.108 | 0.130 | 0.156 | 0.185 | 0.198 | 0.214 | 0.241 |
| 0.058 | 0.030 | 0.038 | 0.046 | 0.055 | 0.062 | 0.070 | 0.079 | 0.093 | 0.104 | 0.109 | 0.130 | 0.157 | 0.185 | 0.198 | 0.215 | 0.242 |
| 0.063 | 0.033 | 0.041 | 0.048 | 0.057 | 0.064 | 0.072 | 0.082 | 0.096 | 0.106 | 0.111 | 0.131 | 0.158 | 0.186 | 0.199 | 0.216 | 0.245 |
| 0.064 | 0.034 | 0.041 | 0.049 | 0.058 | 0.065 | 0.073 | 0.083 | 0.096 | 0.107 | 0.112 | 0.132 | 0.159 | 0.187 | 0.200 | 0.217 | 0.246 |
| 0.065 | 0.034 | 0.042 | 0.050 | 0.058 | 0.065 | 0.073 | 0.083 | 0.097 | 0.107 | 0.113 | 0.132 | 0.159 | 0.187 | 0.200 | 0.218 | 0.246 |
| 0.072 | 0.038 | 0.046 | 0.053 | 0.062 | 0.069 | 0.077 | 0.087 | 0.100 | 0.111 | 0.116 | 0.136 | 0.161 | 0.189 | 0.202 | 0.220 | 0.248 |
| 0.078 | 0.041 | 0.049 | 0.057 | 0.065 | 0.072 | 0.080 | 0.090 | 0.104 | 0.114 | 0.119 | 0.139 | 0.163 | 0.190 | 0.204 | 0.223 | 0.250 |
| 0.081 | 0.042 | 0.050 | 0.058 | 0.067 | 0.074 | 0.082 | 0.091 | 0.105 | 0.116 | 0.121 | 0.140 | 0.165 | 0.191 | 0.205 | 0.224 | 0.250 |
| 0.083 | 0.043 | 0.051 | 0.059 | 0.068 | 0.075 | 0.083 | 0.092 | 0.106 | 0.117 | 0.122 | 0.141 | 0.166 | 0.192 | 0.205 | 0.225 | 0.251 |
| 0.091 | 0.047 | 0.055 | 0.063 | 0.072 | 0.080 | 0.087 | 0.096 | 0.110 | 0.121 | 0.126 | 0.146 | 0.170 | 0.194 | 0.207 | 0.227 | 0.254 |
| 0.094 | 0.049 | 0.057 | 0.065 | 0.074 | 0.080 | 0.088 | 0.098 | 0.112 | 0.123 | 0.128 | 0.147 | 0.172 | 0.196 | 0.208 | 0.227 | 0.255 |
| 0.095 | 0.050 | 0.058 | 0.065 | 0.074 | 0.081 | 0.089 | 0.099 | 0.113 | 0.123 | 0.128 | 0.148 | 0.172 | 0.197 | 0.209 | 0.228 | 0.256 |
| 0.102 | 0.053 | 0.061 | 0.069 | 0.078 | 0.085 | 0.092 | 0.102 | 0.116 | 0.127 | 0.132 | 0.151 | 0.176 | 0.200 | 0.210 | 0.230 | 0.258 |
| 0.109 | 0.057 | 0.065 | 0.073 | 0.082 | 0.088 | 0.096 | 0.106 | 0.120 | 0.131 | 0.136 | 0.155 | 0.180 | 0.204 | 0.214 | 0.232 | 0.261 |
| 0.120 | 0.063 | 0.071 | 0.079 | 0.087 | 0.094 | 0.102 | 0.112 | 0.126 | 0.136 | 0.141 | 0.161 | 0.186 | 0.210 | 0.220 | 0.235 | 0.265 |
| 0.125 | 0.065 | 0.073 | 0.081 | 0.090 | 0.097 | 0.105 | 0.114 | 0.128 | 0.139 | 0.144 | 0.164 | 0.188 | 0.213 | 0.222 | 0.237 | 0.267 |
| 0.141 | 0.074 | 0.081 | 0.089 | 0.098 | 0.105 | 0.113 | 0.123 | 0.136 | 0.147 | 0.152 | 0.172 | 0.196 | 0.221 | 0.231 | 0.245 | 0.270 |
| 0.156 | 0.082 | 0.090 | 0.097 | 0.106 | 0.113 | 0.121 | 0.131 | 0.145 | 0.155 | 0.160 | 0.180 | 0.204 | 0.229 | 0.239 | 0.253 | 0.278 |
| 0.172 | 0.090 | 0.098 | 0.106 | 0.114 | 0.121 | 0.129 | 0.139 | 0.153 | 0.163 | 0.168 | 0.188 | 0.213 | 0.237 | 0.247 | 0.262 | 0.286 |
| 0.188 | 0.098 | 0.106 | 0.114 | 0.123 | 0.130 | 0.137 | 0.147 | 0.161 | 0.172 | 0.177 | 0.196 | 0.221 | 0.245 | 0.255 | 0.270 | 0.295 |
| 0.203 | 0.106 | 0.114 | 0.122 | 0.131 | 0.138 | 0.146 | 0.155 | 0.169 | 0.180 | 0.185 | 0.204 | 0.229 | 0.253 | 0.263 | 0.278 | 0.303 |
| 0.219 | 0.115 | 0.122 | 0.130 | 0.139 | 0.146 | 0.154 | 0.163 | 0.177 | 0.188 | 0.193 | 0.213 | 0.237 | 0.262 | 0.272 | 0.286 | 0.311 |
| 0.234 | 0.123 | 0.130 | 0.138 | 0.147 | 0.154 | 0.162 | 0.172 | 0.185 | 0.196 | 0.201 | 0.221 | 0.245 | 0.270 | 0.280 | 0.294 | 0.319 |
| 0.250 | 0.131 | 0.139 | 0.147 | 0.155 | 0.162 | 0.170 | 0.180 | 0.194 | 0.204 | 0.209 | 0.229 | 0.254 | 0.278 | 0.288 | 0.303 | 0.327 |
| 0.281 | 0.147 | 0.155 | 0.162 | 0.172 | 0.178 | 0.186 | 0.196 | 0.209 | 0.221 | 0.225 | 0.245 | 0.270 | 0.294 | 0.304 | 0.319 | 0.345 |
| 0.313 | 0.164 | 0.171 | 0.179 | 0.188 | 0.195 | 0.203 | 0.213 | 0.226 | 0.237 | 0.242 | 0.262 | 0.286 | 0.311 | 0.321 | 0.335 | 0.360 |
| 0.344 | 0.180 | 0.188 | 0.196 | 0.204 | 0.211 | 0.219 | 0.229 | 0.243 | 0.253 | 0.258 | 0.278 | 0.303 | 0.327 | 0.337 | 0.352 | 0.376 |
| 0.375 | 0.196 | 0.204 | 0.212 | 0.221 | 0.228 | 0.236 | 0.245 | 0.259 | 0.270 | 0.275 | 0.295 | 0.319 | 0.344 | 0.353 | 0.368 | 0.393 |
| 0.438 | 0.229 | 0.237 | 0.245 | 0.254 | 0.260 | 0.268 | 0.278 | 0.292 | 0.303 | 0.308 | 0.327 | 0.352 | 0.376 | 0.386 | 0.401 | 0.425 |
| 0.500 | 0.262 | 0.270 | 0.277 | 0.286 | 0.293 | 0.301 | 0.311 | 0.325 | 0.335 | 0.340 | 0.360 | 0.384 | 0.409 | 0.419 | 0.433 | 0.458 |
| 0.563 | 0.295 | 0.302 | 0.310 | 0.319 | 0.326 | 0.334 | 0.344 | 0.357 | 0.368 | 0.373 | 0.393 | 0.417 | 0.442 | 0.452 | 0.466 | 0.491 |
| 0.625 | 0.328 | 0.335 | 0.343 | 0.352 | 0.359 | 0.367 | 0.377 | 0.390 | 0.401 | 0.406 | 0.426 | 0.450 | 0.475 | 0.484 | 0.499 | 0.524 |
| 0.688 | 0.360 | 0.368 | 0.376 | 0.384 | 0.391 | 0.399 | 0.409 | 0.423 | 0.433 | 0.438 | 0.458 | 0.483 | 0.507 | 0.517 | 0.532 | 0.556 |
| 0.750 | 0.393 | 0.400 | 0.408 | 0.417 | 0.424 | 0.432 | 0.442 | 0.456 | 0.466 | 0.471 | 0.491 | 0.515 | 0.540 | 0.550 | 0.564 | 0.589 |
| 0.813 | 0.425 | 0.433 | 0.441 | 0.450 | 0.457 | 0.465 | 0.474 | 0.488 | 0.499 | 0.504 | 0.524 | 0.548 | 0.573 | 0.583 | 0.597 | 0.622 |
| 0.875 | 0.458 | 0.465 | 0.473 | 0.483 | 0.489 | 0.497 | 0.507 | 0.520 | 0.532 | 0.536 | 0.556 | 0.581 | 0.605 | 0.615 | 0.630 | 0.654 |
| 0.938 | 0.491 | 0.499 | 0.507 | 0.515 | 0.522 | 0.530 | 0.540 | 0.554 | 0.564 | 0.569 | 0.589 | 0.614 | 0.638 | 0.648 | 0.663 | 0.687 |
| 1.000 | 0.524 | 0.531 | 0.539 | 0.548 | 0.555 | 0.563 | 0.573 | 0.586 | 0.597 | 0.602 | 0.622 | 0.646 | 0.671 | 0.681 | 0.695 | 0.720 |

| Thickness of material, in. | Inside radius of bend, in. | | | | | | | | | | | | | |
|---|---|---|---|---|---|---|---|---|---|---|---|---|---|---|
| | 5/32 | 3/16 | 7/32 | 1/4 | 5/16 | 3/8 | 7/16 | 1/2 | 5/8 | 3/4 | 7/8 | 1 | 1 1/4 | 1 1/2 |
| 0.004 | 0.249 | 0.298 | 0.347 | 0.396 | 0.494 | 0.592 | 0.690 | 0.789 | 0.985 | 1.181 | 1.376 | 1.574 | 1.967 | 2.359 |
| 0.005 | 0.249 | 0.299 | 0.348 | 0.397 | 0.495 | 0.593 | 0.691 | 0.789 | 0.986 | 1.182 | 1.378 | 1.575 | 1.967 | 2.360 |
| 0.007 | 0.251 | 0.300 | 0.349 | 0.398 | 0.496 | 0.595 | 0.693 | 0.791 | 0.987 | 1.184 | 1.380 | 1.576 | 1.969 | 2.362 |
| 0.008 | 0.252 | 0.301 | 0.350 | 0.399 | 0.497 | 0.595 | 0.694 | 0.792 | 0.988 | 1.184 | 1.381 | 1.577 | 1.970 | 2.362 |
| 0.010 | 0.253 | 0.302 | 0.351 | 0.401 | 0.499 | 0.597 | 0.695 | 0.793 | 0.990 | 1.186 | 1.382 | 1.579 | 1.971 | 2.364 |
| 0.012 | 0.255 | 0.304 | 0.353 | 0.402 | 0.500 | 0.599 | 0.697 | 0.795 | 0.991 | 1.188 | 1.384 | 1.580 | 1.973 | 2.366 |
| 0.014 | 0.256 | 0.306 | 0.355 | 0.404 | 0.502 | 0.600 | 0.698 | 0.796 | 0.993 | 1.189 | 1.385 | 1.582 | 1.974 | 2.367 |
| 0.016 | 0.258 | 0.307 | 0.356 | 0.405 | 0.503 | 0.601 | 0.699 | 0.798 | 0.994 | 1.190 | 1.387 | 1.583 | 1.976 | 2.368 |
| 0.016 | 0.258 | 0.307 | 0.356 | 0.405 | 0.503 | 0.602 | 0.700 | 0.798 | 0.994 | 1.191 | 1.387 | 1.583 | 1.976 | 2.369 |
| 0.018 | 0.260 | 0.309 | 0.358 | 0.407 | 0.505 | 0.603 | 0.701 | 0.800 | 0.996 | 1.192 | 1.389 | 1.585 | 1.978 | 2.370 |
| 0.020 | 0.261 | 0.310 | 0.359 | 0.408 | 0.507 | 0.605 | 0.703 | 0.801 | 0.998 | 1.194 | 1.390 | 1.587 | 1.979 | 2.372 |
| 0.022 | 0.263 | 0.312 | 0.361 | 0.410 | 0.508 | 0.606 | 0.705 | 0.803 | 0.999 | 1.195 | 1.392 | 1.588 | 1.981 | 2.373 |
| 0.025 | 0.265 | 0.314 | 0.363 | 0.412 | 0.511 | 0.609 | 0.707 | 0.805 | 1.001 | 1.198 | 1.394 | 1.590 | 1.983 | 2.376 |
| 0.028 | 0.267 | 0.317 | 0.366 | 0.415 | 0.513 | 0.611 | 0.709 | 0.807 | 1.004 | 1.200 | 1.396 | 1.593 | 1.985 | 2.378 |
| 0.031 | 0.270 | 0.319 | 0.368 | 0.417 | 0.515 | 0.614 | 0.712 | 0.810 | 1.006 | 1.203 | 1.399 | 1.595 | 1.988 | 2.381 |
| 0.032 | 0.271 | 0.320 | 0.369 | 0.418 | 0.516 | 0.614 | 0.712 | 0.811 | 1.007 | 1.203 | 1.400 | 1.596 | 1.989 | 2.381 |
| 0.035 | 0.273 | 0.322 | 0.371 | 0.420 | 0.518 | 0.617 | 0.715 | 0.813 | 1.009 | 1.206 | 1.402 | 1.598 | 1.991 | 2.384 |
| 0.038 | 0.275 | 0.324 | 0.373 | 0.422 | 0.520 | 0.619 | 0.717 | 0.815 | 1.011 | 1.208 | 1.404 | 1.600 | 1.993 | 2.386 |
| 0.040 | 0.277 | 0.326 | 0.375 | 0.424 | 0.522 | 0.621 | 0.719 | 0.817 | 1.013 | 1.210 | 1.406 | 1.602 | 1.995 | 2.388 |
| 0.042 | 0.278 | 0.328 | 0.377 | 0.426 | 0.524 | 0.622 | 0.720 | 0.818 | 1.015 | 1.211 | 1.407 | 1.604 | 1.996 | 2.389 |
| 0.044 | 0.280 | 0.329 | 0.378 | 0.427 | 0.525 | 0.623 | 0.722 | 0.820 | 1.016 | 1.212 | 1.409 | 1.605 | 1.998 | 2.391 |
| 0.045 | 0.281 | 0.330 | 0.379 | 0.428 | 0.526 | 0.624 | 0.723 | 0.821 | 1.017 | 1.213 | 1.410 | 1.606 | 1.999 | 2.392 |
| 0.049 | 0.284 | 0.333 | 0.382 | 0.431 | 0.529 | 0.628 | 0.726 | 0.824 | 1.020 | 1.217 | 1.413 | 1.609 | 2.002 | 2.395 |
| 0.051 | 0.285 | 0.334 | 0.383 | 0.433 | 0.531 | 0.629 | 0.727 | 0.825 | 1.022 | 1.218 | 1.414 | 1.611 | 2.003 | 2.396 |
| 0.057 | 0.290 | 0.339 | 0.388 | 0.438 | 0.536 | 0.634 | 0.732 | 0.830 | 1.027 | 1.223 | 1.419 | 1.616 | 2.008 | 2.401 |
| 0.058 | 0.291 | 0.340 | 0.389 | 0.438 | 0.536 | 0.635 | 0.733 | 0.831 | 1.027 | 1.224 | 1.420 | 1.616 | 2.009 | 2.402 |
| 0.063 | 0.294 | 0.344 | 0.393 | 0.442 | 0.540 | 0.638 | 0.736 | 0.834 | 1.031 | 1.227 | 1.423 | 1.620 | 2.013 | 2.405 |
| 0.064 | 0.296 | 0.345 | 0.394 | 0.443 | 0.541 | 0.639 | 0.738 | 0.836 | 1.032 | 1.228 | 1.425 | 1.621 | 2.014 | 2.406 |
| 0.065 | 0.296 | 0.346 | 0.395 | 0.444 | 0.542 | 0.640 | 0.738 | 0.837 | 1.033 | 1.229 | 1.426 | 1.622 | 2.015 | 2.407 |
| 0.072 | 0.302 | 0.351 | 0.400 | 0.449 | 0.547 | 0.646 | 0.744 | 0.842 | 1.038 | 1.235 | 1.431 | 1.627 | 2.020 | 2.413 |
| 0.078 | 0.306 | 0.356 | 0.405 | 0.454 | 0.552 | 0.650 | 0.749 | 0.847 | 1.043 | 1.239 | 1.436 | 1.632 | 2.025 | 2.417 |
| 0.081 | 0.307 | 0.358 | 0.407 | 0.456 | 0.554 | 0.653 | 0.751 | 0.849 | 1.045 | 1.242 | 1.438 | 1.634 | 2.027 | 2.420 |
| 0.083 | 0.308 | 0.360 | 0.409 | 0.458 | 0.556 | 0.654 | 0.752 | 0.851 | 1.047 | 1.243 | 1.440 | 1.636 | 2.029 | 2.421 |
| 0.091 | 0.312 | 0.366 | 0.415 | 0.464 | 0.562 | 0.660 | 0.758 | 0.857 | 1.053 | 1.249 | 1.446 | 1.642 | 2.035 | 2.427 |
| 0.094 | 0.313 | 0.368 | 0.417 | 0.466 | 0.564 | 0.663 | 0.761 | 0.859 | 1.055 | 1.252 | 1.448 | 1.644 | 2.037 | 2.430 |
| 0.095 | 0.314 | 0.369 | 0.418 | 0.467 | 0.566 | 0.664 | 0.762 | 0.860 | 1.056 | 1.253 | 1.449 | 1.645 | 2.038 | 2.431 |
| 0.102 | 0.316 | 0.370 | 0.424 | 0.473 | 0.571 | 0.669 | 0.767 | 0.865 | 1.062 | 1.258 | 1.454 | 1.651 | 2.043 | 2.436 |
| 0.109 | 0.319 | 0.371 | 0.429 | 0.478 | 0.577 | 0.675 | 0.773 | 0.871 | 1.067 | 1.264 | 1.461 | 1.656 | 2.049 | 2.442 |
| 0.120 | 0.322 | 0.371 | 0.433 | 0.487 | 0.585 | 0.683 | 0.782 | 0.880 | 1.076 | 1.272 | 1.469 | 1.665 | 2.058 | 2.450 |
| 0.125 | 0.324 | 0.373 | 0.434 | 0.491 | 0.589 | 0.687 | 0.785 | 0.884 | 1.080 | 1.276 | 1.473 | 1.669 | 2.062 | 2.454 |
| 0.141 | 0.328 | 0.378 | 0.439 | 0.495 | 0.601 | 0.700 | 0.798 | 0.896 | 1.092 | 1.289 | 1.485 | 1.681 | 2.074 | 2.467 |
| 0.156 | 0.332 | 0.384 | 0.444 | 0.500 | 0.614 | 0.712 | 0.810 | 0.908 | 1.104 | 1.301 | 1.497 | 1.693 | 2.086 | 2.479 |
| 0.172 | 0.335 | 0.389 | 0.449 | 0.505 | 0.619 | 0.724 | 0.822 | 0.920 | 1.117 | 1.313 | 1.509 | 1.706 | 2.098 | 2.491 |
| 0.188 | 0.344 | 0.394 | 0.454 | 0.510 | 0.624 | 0.736 | 0.834 | 0.933 | 1.129 | 1.325 | 1.522 | 1.718 | 2.111 | 2.503 |
| 0.203 | 0.352 | 0.401 | 0.459 | 0.515 | 0.627 | 0.741 | 0.847 | 0.945 | 1.141 | 1.338 | 1.534 | 1.730 | 2.123 | 2.516 |
| 0.219 | 0.360 | 0.409 | 0.463 | 0.519 | 0.633 | 0.746 | 0.859 | 0.957 | 1.153 | 1.350 | 1.546 | 1.742 | 2.135 | 3.528 |
| 0.234 | 0.368 | 0.417 | 0.466 | 0.524 | 0.638 | 0.751 | 0.864 | 0.969 | 1.166 | 1.362 | 1.558 | 1.755 | 2.147 | 2.540 |
| 0.250 | 0.376 | 0.425 | 0.474 | 0.529 | 0.643 | 0.756 | 0.869 | 0.982 | 1.178 | 1.374 | 1.571 | 1.767 | 2.160 | 2.553 |
| 0.281 | 0.393 | 0.442 | 0.491 | 0.540 | 0.652 | 0.766 | 0.879 | 0.992 | 1.202 | 1.399 | 1.595 | 1.792 | 2.184 | 2.577 |
| 0.313 | 0.409 | 0.458 | 0.507 | 0.556 | 0.662 | 0.776 | 0.889 | 1.002 | 1.227 | 1.423 | 1.620 | 1.816 | 2.209 | 2.602 |
| 0.344 | 0.425 | 0.474 | 0.523 | 0.573 | 0.671 | 0.786 | 0.899 | 1.012 | 1.236 | 1.448 | 1.644 | 1.841 | 2.233 | 2.626 |
| 0.375 | 0.442 | 0.491 | 0.540 | 0.589 | 0.687 | 0.797 | 0.909 | 1.022 | 1.247 | 1.473 | 1.669 | 1.865 | 2.258 | 2.651 |
| 0.438 | 0.474 | 0.524 | 0.573 | 0.622 | 0.720 | 0.818 | 0.928 | 1.043 | 1.266 | 1.492 | 1.718 | 1.914 | 2.307 | 2.700 |
| 0.500 | 0.507 | 0.556 | 0.605 | 0.654 | 0.753 | 0.851 | 0.949 | 1.061 | 1.285 | 1.511 | 1.737 | 1.964 | 2.356 | 2.749 |
| 0.563 | 0.540 | 0.589 | 0.638 | 0.687 | 0.785 | 0.884 | 0.982 | 1.080 | 1.304 | 1.529 | 1.755 | 1.982 | 2.405 | 2.798 |
| 0.625 | 0.573 | 0.622 | 0.671 | 0.720 | 0.818 | 0.916 | 1.014 | 1.113 | 1.323 | 1.548 | 1.774 | 2.001 | 2.454 | 2.847 |
| 0.688 | 0.605 | 0.654 | 0.703 | 0.753 | 0.858 | 0.949 | 1.047 | 1.145 | 1.342 | 1.566 | 1.793 | 2.019 | 2.472 | 2.896 |
| 0.750 | 0.638 | 0.687 | 0.736 | 0.785 | 0.884 | 0.982 | 1.080 | 1.178 | 1.374 | 1.585 | 1.812 | 2.038 | 2.491 | 2.945 |
| 0.813 | 0.671 | 0.720 | 0.769 | 0.818 | 0.916 | 1.014 | 1.113 | 1.211 | 1.407 | 1.603 | 1.831 | 2.056 | 2.510 | 2.964 |
| 0.875 | 0.703 | 0.753 | 0.802 | 0.851 | 0.949 | 1.047 | 1.145 | 1.243 | 1.440 | 1.636 | 1.850 | 2.075 | 2.529 | 2.983 |
| 0.938 | 0.736 | 0.785 | 0.834 | 0.884 | 0.982 | 1.080 | 1.178 | 1.276 | 1.473 | 1.669 | 1.865 | 2.094 | 2.547 | 3.002 |
| 1.000 | 0.769 | 0.818 | 0.867 | 0.916 | 1.014 | 1.113 | 1.211 | 1.309 | 1.505 | 1.702 | 1.898 | 2.112 | 2.566 | 3.021 |

# DEVELOPED LENGTH IN INCHES OF MATERIAL REQUIRED FOR 90-DEG. BEND (*Continued*)

| Thickness of material, in. | Inside radius of bend, in. | | | | | | | | | | | | | |
|---|---|---|---|---|---|---|---|---|---|---|---|---|---|---|
| | 1¾ | 2 | 2¼ | 2½ | 2¾ | 3 | 3¼ | 3½ | 3¾ | 4 | 4½ | 5 | 5½ | 6 |
| 0.004 | 2.752 | 3.145 | 3.537 | 3.930 | 4.323 | 4.716 | 5.108 | 5.501 | 5.894 | 6.286 | 7.072 | 7.857 | 8.643 | 9.428 |
| 0.005 | 2.753 | 3.146 | 3.538 | 3.931 | 4.324 | 4.716 | 5.109 | 5.502 | 5.894 | 6.287 | 7.073 | 7.858 | 8.643 | 9.429 |
| 0.007 | 2.754 | 3.147 | 3.540 | 3.932 | 4.325 | 4.718 | 5.111 | 5.503 | 5.896 | 6.289 | 7.074 | 7.859 | 8.645 | 9.430 |
| 0.008 | 2.755 | 3.148 | 3.541 | 3.933 | 4.326 | 4.719 | 5.111 | 5.504 | 5.897 | 6.289 | 7.075 | 7.860 | 8.646 | 9.431 |
| 0.010 | 2.757 | 3.149 | 3.542 | 3.935 | 4.328 | 4.720 | 5.113 | 5.506 | 5.898 | 6.291 | 7.076 | 7.862 | 8.648 | 9.433 |
| 0.012 | 2.758 | 3.151 | 3.544 | 3.936 | 4.329 | 4.722 | 5.115 | 5.507 | 5.900 | 6.293 | 7.078 | 7.863 | 8.549 | 9.434 |
| 0.014 | 2.760 | 3.153 | 3.545 | 3.938 | 4.331 | 4.723 | 5.116 | 5.509 | 5.901 | 6.294 | 7.080 | 7.865 | 8.650 | 9.436 |
| 0.016 | 2.761 | 3.154 | 3.547 | 3.939 | 4.332 | 4.725 | 5.117 | 5.510 | 5.903 | 6.295 | 7.081 | 7.866 | 8.652 | 9.437 |
| 0.016 | 2.761 | 3.154 | 3.547 | 3.940 | 4.332 | 4.725 | 5.118 | 5.510 | 5.903 | 6.296 | 7.081 | 7.867 | 8.652 | 9.437 |
| 0.018 | 2.763 | 3.156 | 3.548 | 3.941 | 4.334 | 4.727 | 5.119 | 5.512 | 5.905 | 6.297 | 7.083 | 7.868 | 8.654 | 9.439 |
| 0.020 | 2.765 | 3.157 | 3.550 | 3.943 | 4.335 | 4.728 | 5.121 | 5.514 | 5.906 | 6.299 | 7.084 | 7.870 | 8.655 | 9.441 |
| 0.022 | 2.766 | 3.159 | 3.552 | 3.944 | 4.337 | 4.730 | 5.122 | 5.515 | 5.908 | 6.300 | 7.086 | 7.871 | 8.657 | 9.442 |
| 0.025 | 2.769 | 3.161 | 3.554 | 3.947 | 4.339 | 4.732 | 5.125 | 5.517 | 5.910 | 6.303 | 7.088 | 7.874 | 8.659 | 9.444 |
| 0.028 | 2.771 | 3.164 | 3.556 | 3.949 | 4.342 | 4.734 | 5.127 | 5.520 | 5.912 | 6.305 | 7.091 | 7.876 | 8.661 | 9.447 |
| 0.031 | 2.773 | 3.166 | 3.559 | 3.952 | 4.344 | 4.737 | 5.130 | 5.522 | 5.915 | 6.308 | 7.093 | 7.879 | 8.664 | 9.449 |
| 0.032 | 2.774 | 3.167 | 3.559 | 3.952 | 4.345 | 4.738 | 5.130 | 5.523 | 5.916 | 6.308 | 7.094 | 7.879 | 8.665 | 9.450 |
| 0.035 | 2.776 | 3.169 | 3.562 | 3.954 | 4.347 | 4.740 | 5.133 | 5.525 | 5.918 | 6.311 | 7.096 | 7.881 | 8.667 | 9.452 |
| 0.038 | 2.779 | 3.171 | 3.564 | 3.957 | 4.350 | 4.742 | 5.135 | 5.527 | 5.920 | 6.313 | 7.098 | 7.883 | 8.669 | 9.454 |
| 0.040 | 2.780 | 3.173 | 3.566 | 3.958 | 4.351 | 4.744 | 5.137 | 5.529 | 5.922 | 6.315 | 7.100 | 7.885 | 8.671 | 9.456 |
| 0.042 | 2.782 | 3.175 | 3.567 | 3.960 | 4.353 | 4.745 | 5.138 | 5.531 | 5.923 | 6.316 | 7.102 | 7.887 | 8.672 | 9.458 |
| 0.044 | 2.783 | 3.176 | 3.569 | 3.961 | 4.354 | 4.747 | 5.139 | 5.532 | 5.924 | 6.318 | 7.103 | 7.888 | 8.674 | 9.459 |
| 0.045 | 2.784 | 3.177 | 3.570 | 3.962 | 4.355 | 4.748 | 5.140 | 5.533 | 5.926 | 6.319 | 7.104 | 7.889 | 8.675 | 9.460 |
| 0.049 | 2.787 | 3.180 | 3.573 | 3.965 | 4.358 | 4.751 | 5.144 | 5.536 | 5.929 | 6.322 | 7.107 | 7.892 | 8.678 | 9.463 |
| 0.051 | 2.789 | 3.181 | 3.574 | 3.967 | 4.360 | 4.752 | 5.145 | 5.538 | 5.930 | 6.323 | 7.109 | 7.894 | 8.679 | 9.465 |
| 0.057 | 2.794 | 3.186 | 3.579 | 3.972 | 4.365 | 4.757 | 5.150 | 5.543 | 5.935 | 6.328 | 7.113 | 7.899 | 8.684 | 9.470 |
| 0.058 | 2.794 | 3.187 | 3.580 | 3.973 | 4.365 | 4.758 | 5.151 | 5.543 | 5.936 | 6.329 | 7.114 | 7.900 | 8.685 | 9.470 |
| 0.063 | 2.798 | 3.191 | 3.583 | 3.977 | 4.369 | 4.761 | 5.154 | 5.547 | 5.940 | 6.332 | 7.118 | 7.903 | 8.688 | 9.474 |
| 0.064 | 2.799 | 3.192 | 3.585 | 3.977 | 4.370 | 4.763 | 5.155 | 5.548 | 5.941 | 6.333 | 7.119 | 7.904 | 8.690 | 9.475 |
| 0.065 | 2.800 | 3.193 | 3.585 | 3.978 | 4.371 | 4.763 | 5.156 | 5.549 | 5.942 | 6.334 | 7.120 | 7.905 | 8.690 | 9.476 |
| 0.072 | 2.805 | 3.198 | 3.591 | 3.984 | 4.376 | 4.769 | 5.162 | 5.554 | 5.947 | 6.340 | 7.125 | 7.911 | 8.696 | 9.481 |
| 0.078 | 2.810 | 3.203 | 3.596 | 3.988 | 4.381 | 4.774 | 5.166 | 5.559 | 5.952 | 6.344 | 7.130 | 7.915 | 8.701 | 9.486 |
| 0.081 | 2.812 | 3.205 | 3.598 | 3.990 | 4.383 | 4.776 | 5.169 | 5.561 | 5.954 | 6.347 | 7.132 | 7.917 | 8.703 | 9.488 |
| 0.083 | 2.814 | 3.207 | 3.599 | 3.992 | 4.385 | 4.778 | 5.170 | 5.563 | 5.956 | 6.348 | 7.134 | 7.919 | 8.705 | 9.490 |
| 0.091 | 2.820 | 3.213 | 3.605 | 3.998 | 4.391 | 4.784 | 5.176 | 5.569 | 5.962 | 6.354 | 7.140 | 7.925 | 8.711 | 9.496 |
| 0.094 | 2.822 | 3.215 | 3.608 | 4.001 | 4.393 | 4.786 | 5.179 | 5.571 | 5.964 | 6.357 | 7.142 | 7.928 | 8.713 | 9.498 |
| 0.095 | 2.824 | 3.216 | 3.609 | 4.002 | 4.394 | 4.787 | 5.180 | 5.572 | 5.965 | 6.358 | 7.143 | 7.929 | 8.714 | 9.499 |
| 0.102 | 2.829 | 3.122 | 3.614 | 4.007 | 4.400 | 4.792 | 5.185 | 5.578 | 5.971 | 6.363 | 7.149 | 7.934 | 8.719 | 9.505 |
| 0.109 | 2.835 | 3.227 | 3.620 | 4.013 | 4.405 | 4.798 | 5.191 | 5.583 | 5.976 | 6.369 | 7.154 | 7.940 | 8.725 | 9.510 |
| 0.120 | 2.843 | 3.236 | 3.629 | 4.021 | 4.414 | 4.807 | 5.199 | 5.592 | 5.985 | 6.377 | 7.163 | 7.948 | 8.734 | 9.519 |
| 0.125 | 2.847 | 3.240 | 3.632 | 4.025 | 4.418 | 4.811 | 5.203 | 5.596 | 5.989 | 6.381 | 7.167 | 7.952 | 8.738 | 9.523 |
| 0.1406 | 2.859 | 3.252 | 3.645 | 4.037 | 4.430 | 4.823 | 5.216 | 5.608 | 6.001 | 6.394 | 7.179 | 7.964 | 8.750 | 9.535 |
| 0.1562 | 2.872 | 3.264 | 3.657 | 4.050 | 4.442 | 4.835 | 5.228 | 5.620 | 6.013 | 6.406 | 7.191 | 7.977 | 8.762 | 9.547 |
| 0.1718 | 2.884 | 3.277 | 3.669 | 4.062 | 4.455 | 4.847 | 5.240 | 5.633 | 6.025 | 6.418 | 7.204 | 7.989 | 8.774 | 9.560 |
| 0.188 | 2.896 | 3.289 | 3.681 | 4.074 | 4.467 | 4.860 | 5.252 | 5.645 | 6.038 | 6.430 | 7.216 | 8.001 | 8.787 | 9.572 |
| 0.203 | 2.908 | 3.301 | 3.694 | 4.086 | 4.479 | 4.872 | 5.265 | 5.657 | 6.050 | 6.443 | 7.228 | 8.013 | 8.799 | 9.584 |
| 0.219 | 2.921 | 3.313 | 3.706 | 4.099 | 4.491 | 4.884 | 5.277 | 5.669 | 6.062 | 6.455 | 7.240 | 8.025 | 8.811 | 9.596 |
| 0.234 | 2.933 | 3.325 | 3.718 | 4.111 | 4.503 | 4.896 | 5.289 | 5.682 | 6.074 | 6.467 | 7.252 | 8.038 | 8.823 | 9.609 |
| 0.250 | 2.945 | 3.338 | 3.731 | 4.123 | 4.516 | 4.909 | 5.301 | 5.694 | 6.087 | 6.480 | 7.265 | 8.050 | 8.836 | 9.621 |
| 0.281 | 2.970 | 3.362 | 3.755 | 4.148 | 4.540 | 4.933 | 5.326 | 5.719 | 6.111 | 6.504 | 7.289 | 8.075 | 8.860 | 9.646 |
| 0.313 | 2.994 | 3.387 | 3.780 | 4.172 | 4.565 | 4.958 | 5.350 | 5.743 | 6.136 | 6.529 | 7.314 | 8.099 | 8.885 | 9.670 |
| 0.344 | 3.019 | 3.411 | 3.804 | 4.197 | 4.590 | 4.982 | 5.375 | 5.768 | 6.160 | 6.553 | 7.339 | 8.124 | 8.909 | 9.695 |
| 0.375 | 3.043 | 3.436 | 3.829 | 4.222 | 4.614 | 5.007 | 5.400 | 5.792 | 6.185 | 6.578 | 7.363 | 8.149 | 8.934 | 9.719 |
| 0.438 | 3.092 | 3.485 | 3.878 | 4.271 | 4.663 | 5.056 | 5.449 | 5.841 | 6.234 | 6.627 | 7.412 | 8.198 | 8.983 | 9.768 |
| 0.500 | 3.142 | 3.584 | 3.927 | 4.320 | 4.712 | 5.105 | 5.498 | 5.891 | 6.283 | 6.676 | 7.461 | 8.247 | 9.032 | 9.818 |
| 0.563 | 3.191 | 3.583 | 3.976 | 4.369 | 4.761 | 5.154 | 5.547 | 5.940 | 6.332 | 6.725 | 7.510 | 8.296 | 9.081 | 9.867 |
| 0.625 | 3.240 | 3.632 | 4.025 | 4.418 | 4.811 | 5.203 | 5.596 | 5.989 | 6.381 | 6.774 | 7.560 | 8.345 | 9.130 | 9.916 |
| 0.688 | 3.289 | 3.681 | 4.074 | 4.467 | 4.860 | 5.252 | 5.645 | 6.038 | 6.430 | 6.823 | 7.609 | 8.394 | 9.179 | 9.965 |
| 0.750 | 3.338 | 3.731 | 4.123 | 4.516 | 4.909 | 5.301 | 5.694 | 6.087 | 6.480 | 6.872 | 7.658 | 8.443 | 9.228 | 10.014 |
| 0.813 | 3.387 | 3.780 | 4.172 | 4.565 | 4.958 | 5.350 | 5.743 | 6.136 | 6.529 | 6.921 | 7.707 | 8.492 | 9.278 | 10.063 |
| 0.875 | 3.436 | 3.829 | 4.222 | 4.614 | 5.007 | 5.400 | 5.792 | 6.185 | 6.578 | 6.970 | 7.756 | 8.541 | 9.327 | 10.112 |
| 0.938 | 3.455 | 3.878 | 4.271 | 4.663 | 5.056 | 5.449 | 5.841 | 6.234 | 6.627 | 7.019 | 7.805 | 8.590 | 9.376 | 10.161 |
| 1.000 | 3.474 | 3.927 | 4.320 | 4.712 | 5.105 | 5.498 | 5.891 | 6.283 | 6.676 | 7.069 | 7.854 | 9.639 | 9.425 | 10.210 |

# ARC LENGTH VERSUS CENTRAL ANGLE
## (Angle of Bend, Length, and Radius)

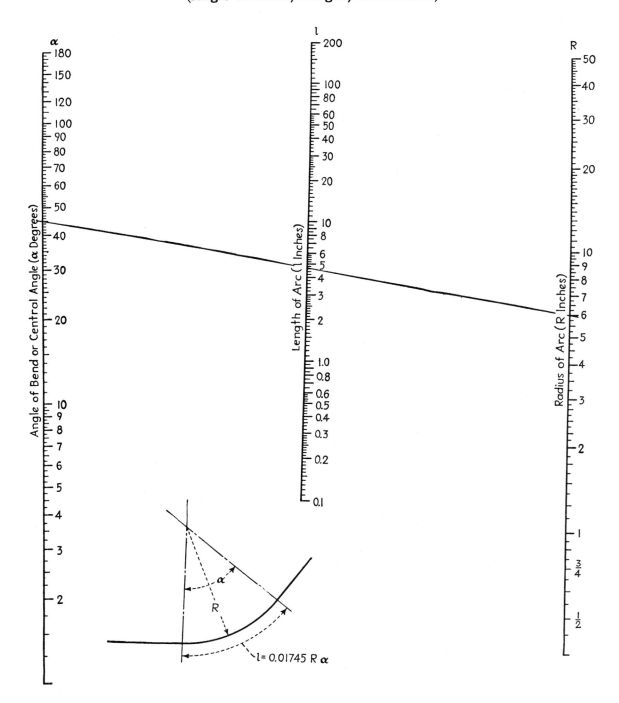

Draw a straight line through the two known points.   The answer will be found at the intersection of this line with the third scale.

*Example:* For a 6-in. radius and 45-deg. bend, length of arc is 4.7 in.

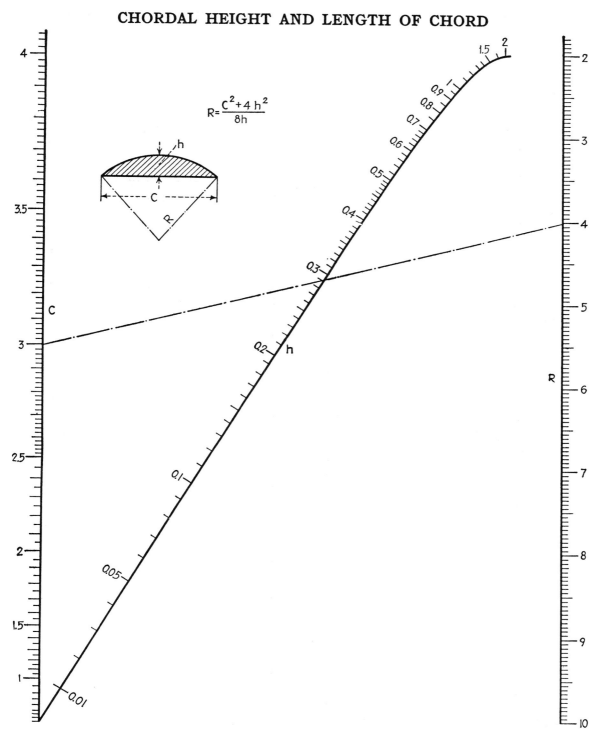

$$R = \frac{C^2 + 4h^2}{8h}$$

Draw a straight line through the two known points.  The answer will be found at the intersection of this line with the third scale.

*Example:* Length of chord is 3 in., and radius of circle is 4 in.  The height $h$ of the chord is 0.29 in.

# VOLUMES IN HORIZONTAL ROUND TANKS WITH FLAT ENDS

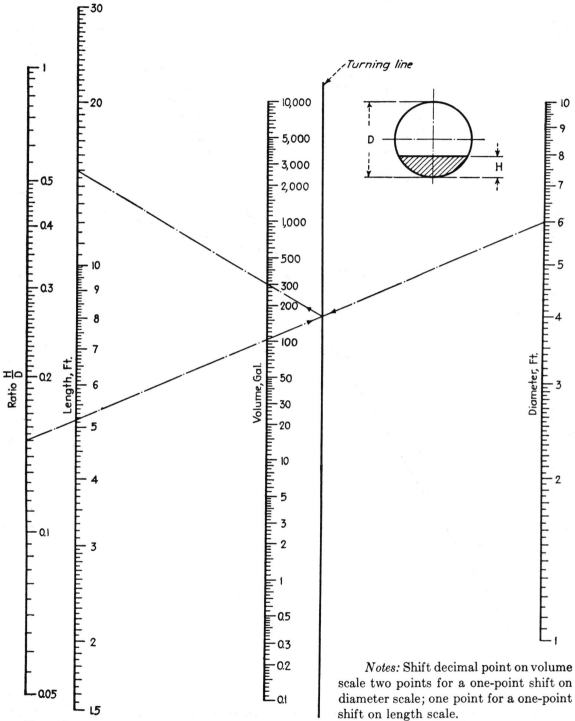

*Notes:* Shift decimal point on volume scale two points for a one-point shift on diameter scale; one point for a one-point shift on length scale.

*Example:* Tank is 6 ft. in diameter and 15 ft. long. $H = 0.9$ ft. $H/D = 0.15$. Join 0.15 on $H/D$ scale with 6 on diameter scale. From point of intersection with turning line, draw line to 15 ft. on the length scale. The volume scale shows 300 gal. If $D$ had been 0.6 ft., $H$ 0.09 ft., and length the same, the answer would be 3.00 gal.

# VOLUMES IN VERTICAL ROUND TANKS WITH FLAT BOTTOMS

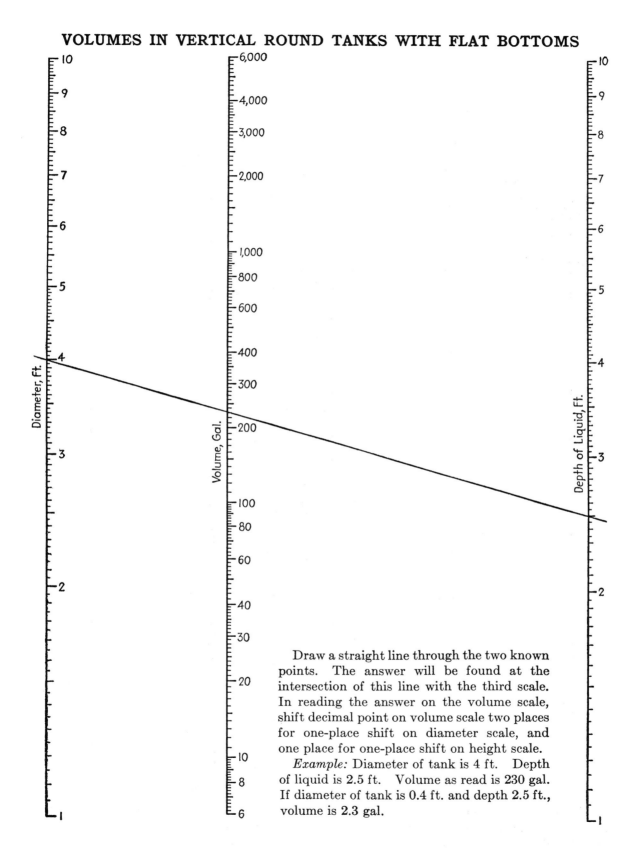

Draw a straight line through the two known points. The answer will be found at the intersection of this line with the third scale. In reading the answer on the volume scale, shift decimal point on volume scale two places for one-place shift on diameter scale, and one place for one-place shift on height scale.

*Example:* Diameter of tank is 4 ft. Depth of liquid is 2.5 ft. Volume as read is 230 gal. If diameter of tank is 0.4 ft. and depth 2.5 ft., volume is 2.3 gal.

# VOLUME, WEIGHT, AND COST CHART

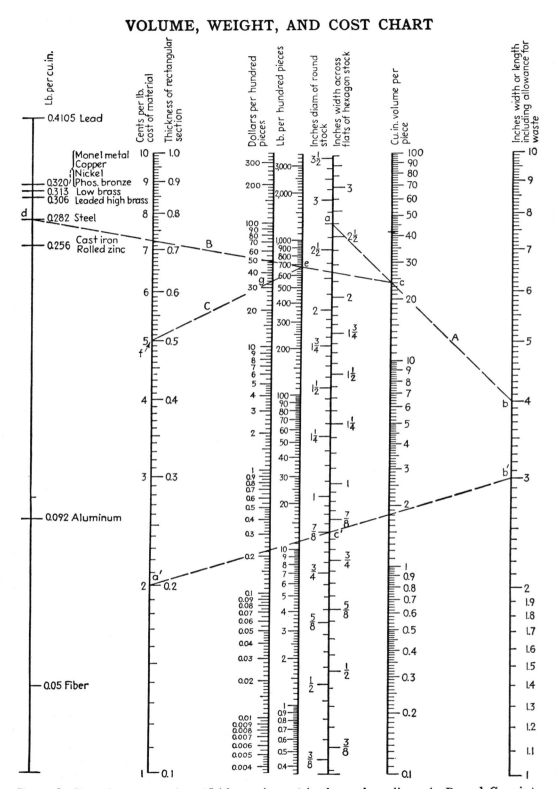

*Example:* For 2¾ in. round or 2⅝ hex, pieces 4 in. long, draw lines *A*, *B*, and *C*, points *a*, *b*, *c*, *d*, *e*, *f*, and *g* being located in alphabetical order. For a rectangular section 0.2 in. thick by 3 in. wide, line *a'b'* gives equivalent circular or hex bar at *c'*. Then proceed as with round or hex bars.

# WEIGHTS OF CYLINDRICAL PIECES

## EXAMPLE OF PROCEDURE
### CAST-IRON FLYWHEEL

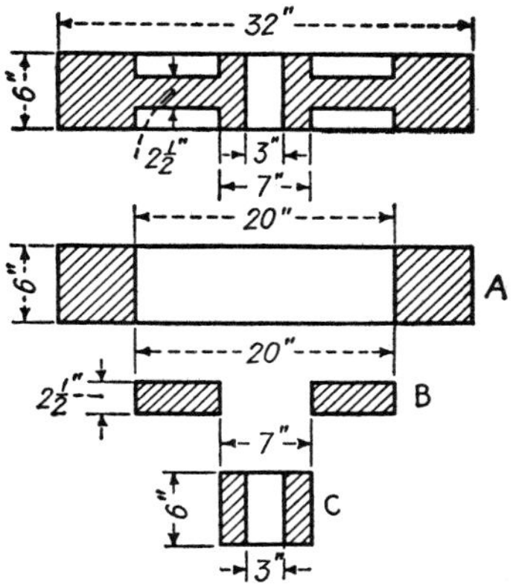

A. Weights per inch of length, from table:
32-in. diameter cylinder = 209.0 lb.
20-in. diameter cylinder = 81.5 lb.
Difference = 127.5 lb.
Weight of element $A$ = 127.5 × 6 = 765.0 lb.

B. Weights per inch of length, from table:
20-in. diameter cylinder = 81.5 lb.
7-in. diameter cylinder = 10.0 lb.
Difference = 71.5 lb.
Weight of element $B$ = 71.5 × 2½ = 178.8 lb.

C. Weights per inch of length, from table:
7-in. diameter cylinder = 10.0 lb.
3-in. diameter cylinder = 1.8 lb.
Difference = 8.2 lb.
Weight of element $C$ = 8.2 × 6 = 49.2 lb.
Total weight of flywheel = 993.0 lb.

## WEIGHTS OF CYLINDRICAL PIECES, POUNDS PER INCH OF LENGTH

| Diameter | Cast iron | Wrought iron and steel | Common yellow brass | Bronze | Aluminum | Diameter | Cast iron | Wrought iron and steel | Common yellow brass | Bronze | Aluminum |
|---|---|---|---|---|---|---|---|---|---|---|---|
| 1 | 0.204 | 0.220 | 0.237 | 0.251 | 0.072 | 11½ | 27.01 | 29.25 | 31.35 | 33.20 | 9.62 |
| 1¼ | 0.319 | 0.344 | 0.370 | 0.392 | 0.113 | 11¾ | 28.19 | 30.50 | 32.70 | 34.70 | 10.00 |
| 1½ | 0.459 | 0.497 | 0.533 | 0.565 | 0.163 | 12 | 29.41 | 31.85 | 34.15 | 36.20 | 10.47 |
| 1¾ | 0.625 | 0.677 | 0.725 | 0.768 | 0.222 | 12¼ | 30.64 | 33.15 | 35.50 | 37.70 | 10.90 |
| 2 | 0.817 | 0.885 | 0.948 | 1.005 | 0.291 | 12½ | 31.91 | 34.50 | 37.05 | 39.30 | 11.35 |
| 2¼ | 1.034 | 1.118 | 1.195 | 1.268 | 0.367 | 12¾ | 33.19 | 35.95 | 38.50 | 40.80 | 11.80 |
| 2½ | 1.276 | 1.380 | 1.480 | 1.570 | 0.454 | 13 | 34.51 | 37.35 | 40.00 | 42.45 | 12.27 |
| 2¾ | 1.544 | 1.672 | 1.790 | 1.895 | 0.550 | 13¼ | 35.85 | 38.80 | 41.60 | 44.10 | 12.75 |
| 3 | 1.837 | 1.988 | 2.130 | 2.260 | 0.654 | 13½ | 37.22 | 40.25 | 43.20 | 45.80 | 13.25 |
| 3¼ | 2.157 | 2.333 | 2.505 | 2.650 | 0.767 | 13¾ | 38.61 | 41.57 | 44.80 | 47.50 | 13.74 |
| 3½ | 2.501 | 2.701 | 2.900 | 3.075 | 0.890 | 14 | 40.02 | 43.30 | 46.40 | 49.30 | 14.23 |
| 3¾ | 2.871 | 3.105 | 3.330 | 3.530 | 1.022 | 14¼ | 41.47 | 44.80 | 48.00 | 51.00 | 14.74 |
| 4 | 3.267 | 3.548 | 3.800 | 4.020 | 1.163 | 14½ | 42.93 | 46.40 | 49.80 | 52.80 | 15.28 |
| 4¼ | 3.688 | 4.000 | 4.280 | 4.540 | 1.314 | 14¾ | 44.43 | 48.00 | 51.50 | 54.70 | 15.80 |
| 4½ | 4.135 | 4.470 | 4.790 | 5.090 | 1.471 | 15 | 45.95 | 49.70 | 53.30 | 56.50 | 16.35 |
| 4¾ | 4.607 | 4.980 | 5.350 | 5.670 | 1.640 | 15½ | 49.06 | 53.00 | 56.80 | 60.30 | 17.45 |
| 5 | 5.105 | 5.530 | 5.930 | 6.280 | 1.820 | 16 | 52.3 | 56.4 | 60.6 | 64.3 | 18.6 |
| 5¼ | 5.628 | 6.080 | 6.540 | 6.925 | 2.000 | 16½ | 55.5 | 60.0 | 64.5 | 68.3 | 19.8 |
| 5½ | 6.177 | 6.680 | 7.160 | 7.570 | 2.200 | 17 | 59.0 | 63.8 | 68.5 | 72.6 | 21.0 |
| 5¾ | 6.751 | 7.310 | 7.840 | 8.300 | 2.400 | 17½ | 62.5 | 67.6 | 72.5 | 76.9 | 22.3 |
| 6 | 7.351 | 7.960 | 8.530 | 9.040 | 2.615 | 18 | 66.2 | 71.6 | 76.8 | 81.4 | 23.6 |
| 6¼ | 7.977 | 8.640 | 9.270 | 9.820 | 2.840 | 18½ | 70.0 | 75.7 | 81.3 | 86.2 | 24.9 |
| 6½ | 8.627 | 9.340 | 10.000 | 10.611 | 3.070 | 19 | 73.6 | 79.5 | 85.5 | 90.6 | 26.2 |
| 6¾ | 9.304 | 10.067 | 10.792 | 11.444 | 3.315 | 19½ | 77.7 | 84.0 | 90.3 | 95.6 | 27.7 |
| 7 | 10.000 | 10.820 | 11.600 | 12.300 | 3.560 | 20 | 81.5 | 88.2 | 94.5 | 101.0 | 29.0 |
| 7¼ | 10.733 | 11.613 | 12.400 | 13.150 | 3.820 | 20½ | 85.7 | 92.7 | 99.6 | 106.3 | 30.5 |
| 7½ | 11.486 | 12.450 | 13.330 | 14.140 | 4.080 | 21 | 90.0 | 97.3 | 104.4 | 111.5 | 32.0 |
| 7¾ | 12.265 | 13.260 | 14.200 | 15.070 | 4.360 | 21½ | 94.3 | 102.0 | 109.4 | 117.0 | 33.5 |
| 8 | 13.069 | 14.120 | 15.150 | 16.050 | 4.650 | 22 | 98.9 | 106.7 | 114.7 | 122.5 | 35.2 |
| 8¼ | 13.898 | 15.020 | 16.130 | 17.100 | 4.950 | 22½ | 103.5 | 112.0 | 120.0 | 127.4 | 36.8 |
| 8½ | 14.754 | 15.960 | 17.130 | 18.300 | 5.250 | 23 | 108.0 | 116.7 | 125.3 | 133.0 | 38.5 |
| 8¾ | 15.634 | 16.900 | 18.100 | 19.200 | 5.570 | 23½ | 112.7 | 121.5 | 130.7 | 138.5 | 40.0 |
| 9 | 16.540 | 17.900 | 19.200 | 20.350 | 5.880 | 24 | 117.5 | 127.0 | 136.3 | 144.6 | 41.8 |
| 9¼ | 17.472 | 18.900 | 20.300 | 21.500 | 6.220 | 24½ | 122.5 | 132.4 | 142.0 | 150.7 | 43.6 |
| 9½ | 18.429 | 19.930 | 21.350 | 22.650 | 6.550 | 25 | 127.8 | 138.0 | 148.0 | 157.0 | 45.5 |
| 9¾ | 19.412 | 21.000 | 22.500 | 23.850 | 6.910 | 25½ | 132.8 | 143.5 | 154.0 | 163.0 | 47.3 |
| 10 | 20.420 | 22.100 | 23.630 | 25.100 | 7.270 | 26 | 138.0 | 149.2 | 160.0 | 170.0 | 49.2 |
| 10¼ | 21.454 | 23.250 | 24.900 | 26.400 | 7.630 | 26½ | 143.2 | 154.5 | 166.0 | 176.0 | 50.4 |
| 10½ | 22.513 | 24.350 | 26.100 | 27.700 | 8.000 | 27 | 149.0 | 161.0 | 173.0 | 183.2 | 53.0 |
| 10¾ | 23.598 | 25.550 | 27.400 | 29.000 | 8.400 | 27½ | 154.2 | 166.5 | 178.7 | 189.5 | 54.8 |
| 11 | 24.708 | 26.750 | 28.650 | 30.500 | 8.780 | 28 | 160.0 | 173.0 | 185.7 | 197.0 | 57.0 |
| 11¼ | 25.845 | 27.950 | 29.950 | 31.800 | 9.200 | 28½ | 166.0 | 179.5 | 192.5 | 204.0 | 59.2 |

## WEIGHTS OF CYLINDRICAL PIECES, POUNDS PER INCH OF LENGTH (*Continued*)

| Diameter | Cast iron | Wrought iron and steel | Common yellow brass | Bronze | Aluminum | Diameter | Cast iron | Wrought iron and steel | Common yellow brass | Bronze | Aluminum |
|---|---|---|---|---|---|---|---|---|---|---|---|
| 29 | 172 | 186 | 199 | 211 | 61 | 61 | 760 | 822 | 882 | 935 | 270 |
| 29½ | 177 | 192 | 206 | 219 | 63 | 61½ | 773 | 836 | 897 | 952 | 275 |
| 30 | 183 | 199 | 213 | 226 | 65 | 62 | 785 | 848 | 912 | 967 | 279 |
| 30½ | 190 | 205 | 221 | 234 | 67 | 62½ | 798 | 863 | 927 | 983 | 284 |
| 31 | 196 | 212 | 227 | 241 | 69 | 63 | 810 | 875 | 940 | 997 | 288 |
| 31½ | 202 | 218 | 235 | 249 | 71 | 63½ | 823 | 891 | 955 | 1,013 | 293 |
| 32 | 209 | 226 | 243 | 257 | 74 | 64 | 836 | 904 | 970 | 1,028 | 298 |
| 32½ | 216 | 231 | 251 | 266 | 77 | 64½ | 850 | 919 | 987 | 1,046 | 303 |
| 33 | 222 | 240 | 257 | 273 | 79 | 65 | 863 | 934 | 1,000 | 1,062 | 307 |
| 33½ | 229 | 247 | 265 | 282 | 81 | 65½ | 877 | 949 | 1,017 | 1,078 | 312 |
| 34 | 236 | 255 | 274 | 290 | 84 | 66 | 890 | 963 | 1,033 | 1,095 | 317 |
| 34½ | 243 | 263 | 282 | 299 | 86 | 66½ | 903 | 977 | 1,047 | 1,111 | 322 |
| 35 | 250 | 270 | 290 | 307 | 89 | 67 | 917 | 992 | 1,064 | 1,128 | 327 |
| 35½ | 257 | 278 | 299 | 317 | 91 | 67½ | 932 | 1,007 | 1,080 | 1,146 | 332 |
| 36 | 264 | 286 | 307 | 325 | 94 | 68 | 944 | 1,020 | 1,095 | 1,162 | 336 |
| 36½ | 272 | 294 | 315 | 335 | 96 | 68½ | 958 | 1,036 | 1,111 | 1,179 | 341 |
| 37 | 279 | 302 | 324 | 344 | 99 | 69 | 972 | 1,050 | 1,127 | 1,196 | 346 |
| 37½ | 287 | 310 | 333 | 354 | 102 | 69½ | 986 | 1,065 | 1,144 | 1,213 | 351 |
| 38 | 295 | 319 | 342 | 363 | 105 | 70 | 1,000 | 1,080 | 1,160 | 1,230 | 356 |
| 38½ | 303 | 328 | 352 | 373 | 108 | 70½ | 1,014 | 1,097 | 1,177 | 1,247 | 362 |
| 39 | 311 | 336 | 361 | 382 | 111 | 71 | 1,030 | 1,114 | 1,195 | 1,267 | 367 |
| 39½ | 319 | 345 | 370 | 393 | 113 | 71½ | 1,044 | 1,130 | 1,213 | 1,285 | 372 |
| 40 | 327 | 354 | 380 | 403 | 116 | 72 | 1,058 | 1,144 | 1,228 | 1,302 | 377 |
| 40½ | 335 | 362 | 389 | 412 | 119 | 72½ | 1,074 | 1,162 | 1,247 | 1,322 | 382 |
| 41 | 343 | 371 | 398 | 422 | 122 | 73 | 1,088 | 1,177 | 1,262 | 1,340 | 387 |
| 41½ | 351 | 380 | 408 | 433 | 125 | 73½ | 1,102 | 1,191 | 1,276 | 1,354 | 392 |
| 42 | 360 | 389 | 418 | 443 | 128 | 74 | 1,117 | 1,207 | 1,296 | 1,375 | 398 |
| 42½ | 386 | 398 | 428 | 453 | 131 | 74½ | 1,132 | 1,224 | 1,313 | 1,392 | 403 |
| 43 | 377 | 408 | 437 | 464 | 134 | 75 | 1,150 | 1,243 | 1,334 | 1,415 | 410 |
| 43½ | 386 | 418 | 448 | 475 | 137 | 75½ | 1,165 | 1,260 | 1,351 | 1,433 | 415 |
| 44 | 396 | 428 | 460 | 487 | 141 | 76 | 1,181 | 1,277 | 1,370 | 1,452 | 420 |
| 44½ | 405 | 438 | 470 | 498 | 144 | 76½ | 1,195 | 1,293 | 1,386 | 1,470 | 425 |
| 45 | 414 | 448 | 481 | 510 | 147 | 77 | 1,210 | 1,308 | 1,404 | 1,490 | 431 |
| 45½ | 423 | 458 | 491 | 521 | 150 | 77½ | 1,226 | 1,325 | 1,423 | 1,508 | 436 |
| 46 | 433 | 468 | 503 | 533 | 154 | 78 | 1,243 | 1,345 | 1,442 | 1,530 | 442 |
| 46½ | 442 | 477 | 513 | 544 | 157 | 78½ | 1,258 | 1,360 | 1,460 | 1,548 | 448 |
| 47 | 451 | 488 | 523 | 555 | 160 | 79 | 1,274 | 1,377 | 1,477 | 1,567 | 454 |
| 47½ | 461 | 498 | 535 | 567 | 164 | 79½ | 1,290 | 1,395 | 1,496 | 1,587 | 459 |
| 48 | 471 | 509 | 546 | 579 | 167 | 80 | 1,307 | 1,413 | 1,516 | 1,608 | 466 |
| 48½ | 481 | 520 | 558 | 592 | 171 | 80½ | 1,323 | 1,430 | 1,536 | 1,627 | 471 |
| 49 | 491 | 531 | 570 | 604 | 174 | 81 | 1,340 | 1,448 | 1,555 | 1,648 | 477 |
| 49½ | 501 | 541 | 582 | 616 | 178 | 81½ | 1,356 | 1,465 | 1,572 | 1,667 | 483 |
| 50 | 511 | 552 | 593 | 628 | 182 | 82 | 1,372 | 1,483 | 1,590 | 1,689 | 488 |
| 50½ | 521 | 563 | 605 | 641 | 185 | 82½ | 1,389 | 1,500 | 1,610 | 1,709 | 494 |
| 51 | 531 | 574 | 616 | 654 | 189 | 83 | 1,406 | 1,520 | 1,630 | 1,730 | 500 |
| 51½ | 543 | 587 | 630 | 668 | 193 | 83½ | 1,422 | 1,537 | 1,650 | 1,750 | 506 |
| 52 | 554 | 599 | 643 | 682 | 197 | 84 | 1,440 | 1,557 | 1,670 | 1,770 | 512 |
| 52½ | 564 | 610 | 655 | 694 | 201 | 84½ | 1,458 | 1,576 | 1,690 | 1,792 | 519 |
| 53 | 574 | 620 | 666 | 707 | 204 | 85 | 1,475 | 1,595 | 1,710 | 1,815 | 525 |
| 53½ | 585 | 632 | 679 | 720 | 208 | 86 | 1,510 | 1,633 | 1,750 | 1,858 | 537 |
| 54 | 596 | 644 | 692 | 733 | 212 | 87 | 1,545 | 1,670 | 1,790 | 1,900 | 550 |
| 54½ | 607 | 656 | 705 | 747 | 216 | 88 | 1,581 | 1,710 | 1,835 | 1,945 | 562 |
| 55 | 617 | 667 | 716 | 760 | 219 | 89 | 1,616 | 1,745 | 1,874 | 1,987 | 575 |
| 55½ | 630 | 681 | 732 | 775 | 224 | 90 | 1,652 | 1,783 | 1,915 | 2,003 | 588 |
| 56 | 641 | 693 | 744 | 788 | 228 | 91 | 1,691 | 1,825 | 1,960 | 2,080 | 602 |
| 56½ | 652 | 705 | 756 | 803 | 233 | 92 | 1,730 | 1,870 | 2,008 | 2,130 | 616 |
| 57 | 664 | 717 | 770 | 817 | 236 | 93 | 1,766 | 1,905 | 2,049 | 2,170 | 628 |
| 57½ | 676 | 730 | 785 | 832 | 241 | 94 | 1,805 | 1,950 | 2,092 | 2,220 | 642 |
| 58 | 688 | 743 | 798 | 847 | 245 | 95 | 1,842 | 1,968 | 2,135 | 2,265 | 655 |
| 58½ | 700 | 757 | 812 | 862 | 249 | 96 | 1,882 | 2,030 | 2,180 | 2,310 | 669 |
| 59 | 712 | 768 | 825 | 876 | 253 | 97 | 1,920 | 2,070 | 2,228 | 2,360 | 684 |
| 59½ | 723 | 782 | 838 | 890 | 257 | 98 | 1,960 | 2,115 | 2,273 | 2,410 | 697 |
| 60 | 735 | 795 | 853 | 905 | 261 | 99 | 2,000 | 2,160 | 2,320 | 2,460 | 712 |
| 60½ | 748 | 808 | 869 | 920 | 266 | 100 | 2,040 | 2,202 | 2,367 | 2,510 | 726 |

# UNIT AND TOTAL WEIGHTS

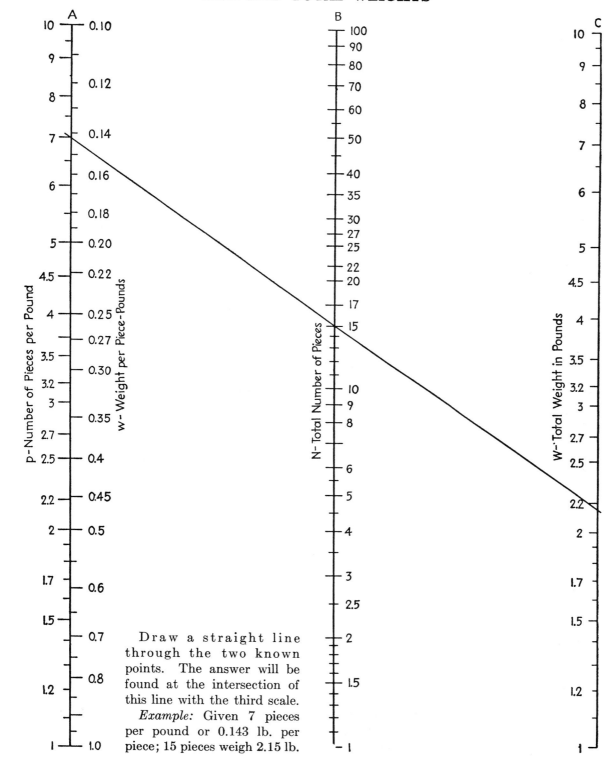

Draw a straight line through the two known points. The answer will be found at the intersection of this line with the third scale.

*Example:* Given 7 pieces per pound or 0.143 lb. per piece; 15 pieces weigh 2.15 lb.

# WEIGHT AND VOLUME

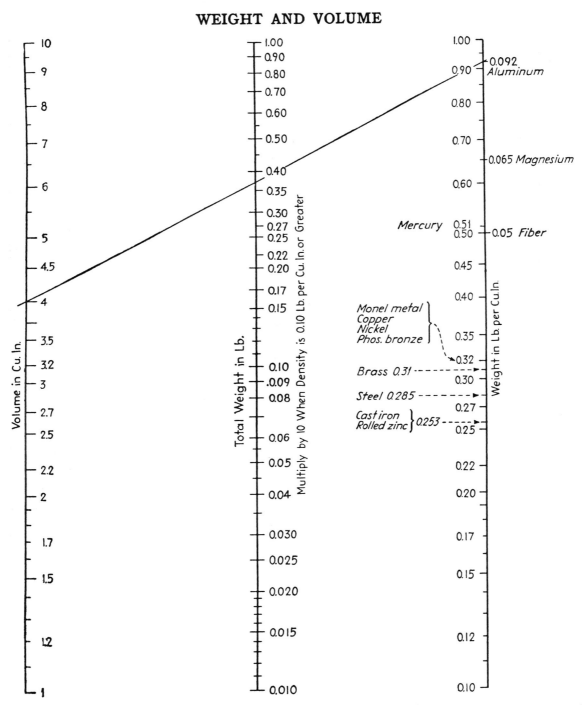

Draw a straight line through the two known points. The answer will be found at the intersection of this line with the third scale.

*Example:* 4 cu. in. of aluminum weighs 0.37 lb.

# MOMENT OF INERTIA OF A PRISM ABOUT THE AXIS *aa*

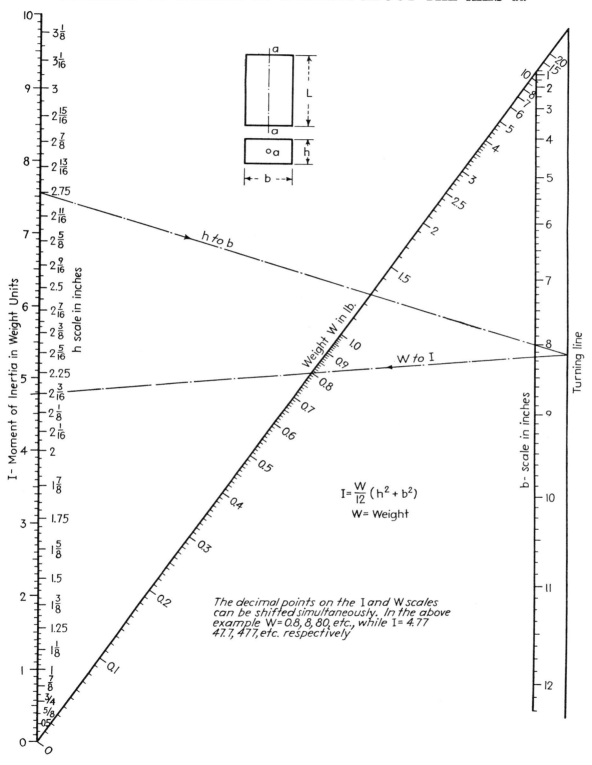

$$I = \frac{W}{12}(h^2 + b^2)$$
W = Weight

The decimal points on the I and W scales can be shifted simultaneously. In the above example W = 0.8, 8, 80, etc., while I = 4.77, 47.7, 477, etc. respectively

# CHART FOR TRANSFERRING MOMENT OF INERTIA
$$I = I_0 + WX^2$$

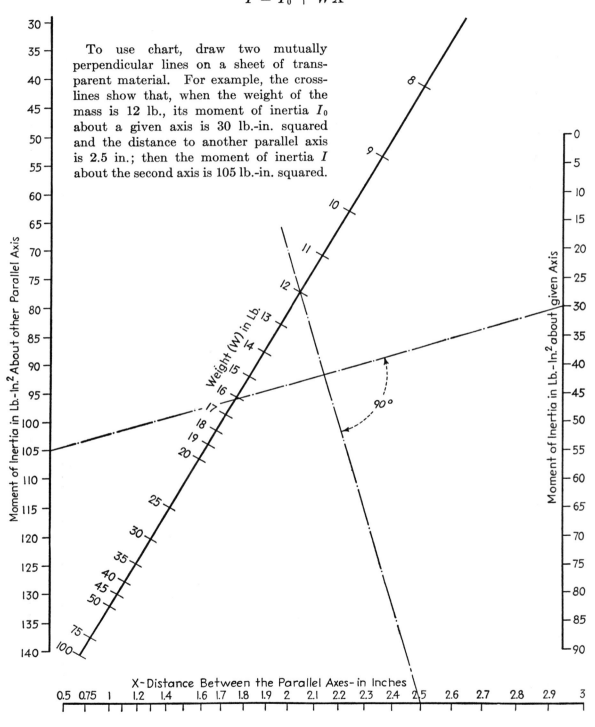

To use chart, draw two mutually perpendicular lines on a sheet of transparent material. For example, the crosslines show that, when the weight of the mass is 12 lb., its moment of inertia $I_0$ about a given axis is 30 lb.-in. squared and the distance to another parallel axis is 2.5 in.; then the moment of inertia $I$ about the second axis is 105 lb.-in. squared.

Moment of Inertia in Lb.-In.$^2$ About other Parallel Axis

Weight (W) in Lb.

Moment of Inertia in Lb.-In.$^2$ about given Axis

90°

X-Distance Between the Parallel Axes- in Inches

## RADII OF GYRATION FOR ROTATING BODIES

| | | | | | |
|---|---|---|---|---|---|
| | Solid cylinder about its own axis | $R^2 = \dfrac{r^2}{2}$ | | Cylinder about axis through center | $R^2 = \dfrac{l + 3r^2}{12}$ |
| | Hollow cylinder about its own axis | $R^2 = \dfrac{r^2_1 + r^2_2}{2}$ | | Cylinder about axis at one end | $R^2 = \dfrac{4l^2 + 3r^2}{12}$ |
| | Rectangular prism about axis through center | $R^2 = \dfrac{b^2 + c^2}{12}$ | | Cylinder about outside axis | $R^2 = \dfrac{4l^2 + 3r^2 + 12dl + 12d^2}{12}$ |
| | Rectangular prism about axis at one end | $R^2 = \dfrac{4b^2 + c^2}{12}$ | | Any body about axis outside its center of gravity | $R^2_1 = R^2_0 + d^2$ where $R_0$ = radius of gyration about axis through center of gravity; $R_1$ = radius of gyration about any other parallel axis; $d$ = distance between center of gravity and axis of rotation |
| | Rectangular prism about outside axis | $R^2 = \dfrac{4b^2 + c^2 + 12bd + 12d^2}{12}$ | | | |

## APPROXIMATIONS FOR CALCULATING MOMENTS OF INERTIA

| NAME OF PART | MOMENT OF INERTIA |
|---|---|
| Flywheels (not applicable to belt pulleys) | Moment of inertia equal to 1.08 to 1.15 times that of rim alone |
| Flywheel (based on total weight and outside diameter) | Moment of inertia equal to two-thirds of that of total weight concentrated at the outer circumference |
| Spur or helical gears (teeth alone) | Moment of inertia of teeth equal to 40 per cent of that of a hollow cylinder of the limiting dimensions |
| Spur or helical gears (rim alone) | Figured as a hollow cylinder of same limiting dimensions |
| Spur or helical gears (total moment of inertia) | Equal to 1.25 times the sum of that of teeth plus rim |
| Spur or helical gears (with only weight and pitch diameter known) | Moment of inertia considered equal to 0.60 times the moment of inertia of the total weight concentrated at the pitch circle |
| Motor armature (based on total weight and outside diameter) | Multiply outer radius of armature by following factors to obtain radius of gyration: Large slow-speed motor..................0.75–0.85 Medium speed d-c or induction motor.....0.70–0.80 Mill-type motor.......................0.60–0.65 |

# $WR^2$ OF SYMMETRICAL BODIES

For computing $WR^2$ of rotating masses of weight per unit volume $\rho$, by resolving the body into elemental shapes. See page 208 for effect of $WR^2$ on electric motor selection.

*Note:* $\rho$ in pounds per cubic inch and dimensions in inches give $WR^2$ in lb.-in. squared.

### 1. Weights per Unit Volume of Materials.

| MATERIAL | WEIGHT, LB. PER CU. IN. |
|---|---|
| Cast iron | 0.260 |
| Cast-iron castings of heavy section *i.e.*, flywheel rims | 0.250 |
| Steel | 0.283 |
| Bronze | 0.319 |
| Lead | 0.410 |
| Copper | 0.318 |

### 2. Cylinder, about Axis Lengthwise through the Center of Gravity.

$$\text{Volume} = \frac{\pi}{4} L(D^2_1 - D^2_2)$$

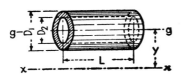

(a) For any material:

$$WR^2 = \frac{\pi}{32} \rho L(D^4_1 - D^4_2)$$

where $\rho$ is the weight per unit volume.

(b) For cast iron:

$$WR^2 = \frac{L(D^4_1 - D^4_2)}{39.2}$$

(c) For cast iron (heavy sections):

$$WR^2 = \frac{L(D^4_1 - D^4_2)}{40.75}$$

(d) For steel:

$$WR^2 = \frac{L(D^4_1 - D^4_2)}{36.0}$$

### 3. Cylinder, about an Axis Parallel to the Axis through Center of Gravity.

$$\text{Volume} = \frac{\pi}{4} L(D^2_1 - D^2_2)$$

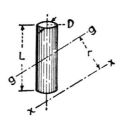

(a) For any material:

$$WR^2_{x-x} = \frac{\pi}{4} \rho L(D^2_1 - D^2_2)\left(\frac{D^2_1 + D^2_2}{8} + y^2\right)$$

(b) For steel:

$$WR^2_{x-x} = \frac{(D^2_1 - D^2_2)L}{4.50}\left(\frac{D^2_1 + D^2_2}{8} + y^2\right)$$

### 4. Solid Cylinder, Rotated about an Axis Parallel to a Line that Passes through the Center of Gravity and Is Perpendicular to the Center Line.

$$\text{Volume} = \frac{\pi}{4} D^2 L$$

(a) For any material:

$$WR^2_{x-x} = \frac{\pi}{4} D^2 L \rho \left(\frac{L^2}{12} + \frac{D^2}{16} + r^2\right)$$

(b) For steel:

$$WR^2_{x-x} = \frac{D^2 L}{4.50}\left(\frac{L^2}{12} + \frac{D^2}{16} + r^2\right)$$

## 5. Rod of Rectangular or Elliptical Section, Rotated about an Axis Perpendicular to and Passing through the Center Line.

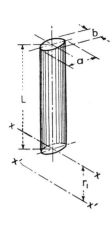

For rectangular cross sections:

$$K_1 = \tfrac{1}{12}; \qquad K_2 = 1$$

For elliptical cross sections:

$$K_1 = \frac{\pi}{64}; \qquad K_2 = \frac{\pi}{4}$$

$$\text{Volume} = K_2 abL$$

(a) For any material:

$$WR^2_{x'-x'} = \rho abL \left\{ K_2 \left[ \frac{L^2}{3} + r_1(r_1 + L) \right] + K_1 a^2 \right\}$$

(b) For a cast-iron rod of elliptical section ($\rho = 0.260$):

$$WR^2_{x'-x'} = \frac{abL}{4.90} \left[ \frac{L^2}{3} + r_1(r_1 + L) + \frac{a^2}{16} \right]$$

## 6. Elliptical Cylinder, about an Axis Parallel to the Axis through the Center of Gravity.

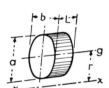

$$\text{Volume} = \frac{\pi}{4} abL$$

(a) For any material:

$$WR^2_{x-x} = \rho \frac{\pi}{4} abL \left( \frac{a^2 + b^2}{16} + r^2 \right)$$

(b) For steel:

$$WR^2_{x-x} = \frac{abL}{4.50} \left( \frac{a^2 + b^2}{16} + r^2 \right)$$

## 7. Cylinder with Frustum of a Cone Removed.

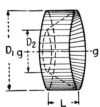

$$\text{Volume} = \frac{\pi L}{2(D_1 - D_2)} \left[ \frac{1}{3} (D^3_1 - D^3_2) - \frac{D^2}{2} (D^2_1 - D^2_2) \right]$$

$$WR^2_{g-g} = \frac{\pi \rho L}{8(D_1 - D_2)} \left[ \frac{1}{5} (D^5_1 - D^5_2) - \frac{D_2}{4} (D^4_1 - D^4_2) \right]$$

## 8. Frustum of a Cone with a Cylinder Removed.

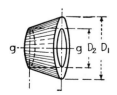

$$\text{Volume} = \frac{\pi L}{2(D_1 - D_2)} \left[ \frac{D_1}{2} (D^2_1 - D^2_2) - \frac{1}{3} (D^3_1 - D^3_2) \right]$$

$$WR^2_{g-g} = \frac{\pi \rho L}{8(D_1 - D_2)} \left[ \frac{D_1}{4} (D^4_1 - D^4_2) - \frac{1}{5} (D^5_1 - D^5_2) \right]$$

### 9. Solid Frustum of a Cone.

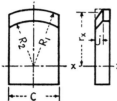

$$\text{Volume} = \frac{\pi L}{12} \frac{(D^3{}_1 - D^3{}_2)}{(D_1 - D_2)}$$

$$WR^2{}_{g-g} = \frac{\pi\rho L}{160} \frac{(D^5{}_1 - D^5{}_2)}{(D_1 - D_2)}$$

### 10. Chamfer Cut from Rectangular Prism Having One End Turned about a Center.

Distance to center of gravity, where $A = R_2/R_1$ and $B = C/2R_1$

$$r_x = \frac{jR^3{}_1 B}{\text{volume} \times (1 - A)}\Bigg[\frac{1}{3}(A^3 - 3A + 2)$$
$$+ \frac{B^2}{3}\Big(1 - A - A\log_e\frac{1}{A}\Big) + \frac{3}{40}\frac{B^4}{A}(A^2 - 2A + 1)$$
$$+ \frac{5}{672}\frac{B^6}{A^3}(3A^4{}_1 - 4A^3 + 1)\cdots\Bigg]$$

$$\text{Volume} = \frac{jR^2{}_1 B}{(1 - A)}\Bigg\{(A^2 - 2A + 1) + \frac{B^2}{3}\Big[\log_e\frac{1}{A} - (1 - A)\Big]$$
$$+ \frac{1}{40}\frac{B^4}{A^2}(2A^3 - 3A + 1) + \frac{1}{224}\frac{B^6}{A^4}(4A^5 - 5A^4 + 1) + \cdots\Bigg\}$$

$$WR^2{}_{x-x} = -\frac{\rho jR^4{}_1 B}{6(1 - A)}\Bigg\{(A^4 - 4A + 3) + B^2(A^2 - 2A + 1)$$
$$+ \frac{9}{10}B^4\Big[\log_e\frac{1}{A} - (1 - A)\Big] + \frac{5}{56}\frac{B^6}{A^2}(2A^3 - 3A^2 + 1) + \cdots\Bigg\}$$

### 11. Complete Torus.

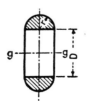

$$\text{Volume} = \pi^2 D r^2$$

$$WR^2{}_{g-g} = \frac{\pi^2 \rho D r^2}{4}(D^2 + 3r^2)$$

### 12. Outside Part of a Torus.

$$\text{Volume} = 2\pi r^2\Big(\frac{\pi D}{4} + \frac{2}{3}r\Big)$$

$$WR^2{}_{g-g} = \pi\rho r^2\Big[\frac{D^2}{4}\Big(\frac{\pi D}{2} + 4r\Big) + r^2\Big(\frac{3\pi}{8}D + \frac{8}{15}r\Big)\Big]$$

## 13. Inside Part of a Torus.

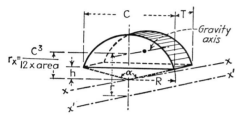

$$\text{Volume} = 2\pi r^2 \left( \frac{\pi D}{4} - \frac{2}{3} r \right)$$

$$WR^2{}_{g-g} = \pi \rho r^2 \left[ \frac{D^2}{4} \left( \frac{\pi D}{2} - 4r \right) + r^2 \left( \frac{3\pi}{8} D - \frac{8}{15} r \right) \right]$$

## 14. Circular Segment about an Axis through Center of Circle.

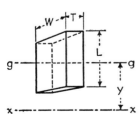

$$\alpha = 2 \sin^{-1} \frac{C}{2R} \text{ deg.}$$

$$\text{Area} = \frac{R^2 \alpha}{114.59} - \frac{C}{2} \sqrt{R^2 - \frac{C^2}{4}}$$

(*a*) Any material:

$$WR^2{}_{x-x} = \rho T \left[ \frac{R^4 \alpha}{229.2} - \frac{1}{6} \left( 3R^2 - \frac{C^2}{2} \right) \frac{C}{2} \sqrt{R^2 - \frac{C^2}{4}} \right]$$

(*b*) For steel:

$$WR^2{}_{x-x} = \frac{T}{3.534} \left[ \frac{R^4 \alpha}{229.2} - \frac{1}{6} \left( 3R^2 - \frac{C^2}{2} \right) \frac{C}{2} \sqrt{R^2 - \frac{C^2}{4}} \right]$$

## 15. Circular Segment about Any Axis Parallel to an Axis through the Center of the Circles.   (Refer to 14 for Figure.)

$$WR^2{}_{x'-x'} = WR^2{}_{x-x} + \text{weight} \,(r^2 - r^2{}_x)$$

## 16. Rectangular Prism about an Axis Parallel to the Axis through the Center of Gravity.

$$\text{Volume} = WLT$$

(*a*) For any material:

$$WR^2{}_{x-x} = \rho WLT \left( \frac{W^2 + L^2}{12} + y^2 \right)$$

(*b*) For steel:

$$WR^2{}_{x-x} = \frac{WLT}{3.534} \left( \frac{W^2 + L^2}{12} + y^2 \right)$$

### 17. Isosceles Triangular Prism, Rotated about an Axis through Its Vertex.

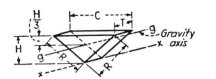

$$\text{Volume} = \frac{CHT}{2}$$

$$WR^2_{x-x} = \frac{\rho CHT}{2}\left(\frac{R^2}{2} - \frac{C^2}{12}\right)$$

### 18. Isosceles Triangular Prism, Rotated about Any Axis Parallel to an Axis through the Vertex.

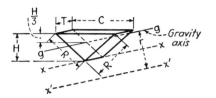

$$\text{Volume} = \frac{CHT}{2}$$

$$WR^2_{x'-x'} = \frac{\rho CHT}{2}\left(\frac{R^2}{2} - \frac{C^2}{12} - \frac{4}{9}H^2 + r^2\right)$$

### 19. Prism with Square Cross Section and Cylinder Removed, along Axis through Center of Gravity of Square.

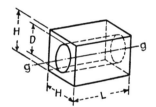

$$\text{Volume} = L\left(H^2 - \frac{\pi D^2}{4}\right)$$

$$WR^2_{g-g} = \frac{\pi \rho L}{32}(1.697H^4 - D^4)$$

### 20. Any Body about an Axis Parallel to the Gravity Axis, When $WR^2$ about the Gravity Axis Is Known.

$$WR^2_{x-x} = WR^2_{g-g} + \text{weight} \times r^2$$

### 21. $WR^2$ of a Piston, Effective at the Cylinder Center Line, about the Crankshaft Center Line.

$$WR^2 = r^2 W_p\left(\frac{1}{2} + \frac{r^2}{8L^2}\right)$$

where $r$ = crank radius

$L$ = center-to-center length of connecting rod

$W_p$ = weight of complete piston, rings, and pin

**22.** $WR^2$ **of a Connecting Rod, Effective at the Cylinder Center Line, about the Crankshaft Center Line.**

$$WR^2 = r^2 \left[ W_1 + W_2 \left( \frac{1}{2} + \frac{r^2}{8L^2} \right) \right]$$

where $r$ = crank radius

$L$ = center-to-center length of connecting rod

$W_1$ = weight of the lower or rotating part of the rod = $[W_R(L - L_1)]/L$

$W_2$ = weight of the upper or reciprocating part of the rod = $W_R L_1/L$

$W_R = W_1 + W_2$, the weight of the complete rod

$L_1$ = distance from the center line of the crankpin to the center of gravity of the connecting rod

**23. Mass Geared to a Shaft.**—The equivalent flywheel effect at the shaft in question is

$$WR^2 = h^2 (WR^2)'$$

where $h$ = gear ratio

$\quad = \dfrac{\text{r.p.m. of mass geared to shaft}}{\text{r.p.m. of shaft}}$

$(WR^2)'$ = flywheel effect of the body in question about its own axis of rotation

**24. Mass Geared to Main Shaft and Connected by a Flexible Shaft.**—The effect of the mass $(WR^2)'$ at the position of the driving gear on the main shaft is

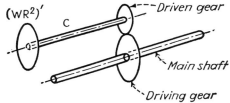

$$WR^2 = \frac{h^2 (WR^2)'}{1 - \dfrac{(WR^2)' f^2}{9.775C}}$$

where $h$ = gear ratio

$\quad = \dfrac{\text{r.p.m. of driven gear}}{\text{r.p.m. of driving gear}}$

$(WR^2)'$ = flywheel effect of geared-on mass

$f$ = natural torsional frequency of the shafting system, in vibrations per sec.

$C$ = torsional rigidity of flexible connecting shaft, in pound-inches per radian

**25. Belted Drives.**—The equivalent flywheel effect of the driven mass at the driving shaft is

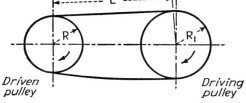

$$WR^2 = \frac{h^2 (WR^2)'}{1 - \dfrac{(WR^2)' f^2}{9.775C}}$$

where $h = R_1/R$

$\quad = \dfrac{\text{r.p.m. of pulley belted to shaft}}{\text{r.p.m. of shaft}}$

$(WR^2)'$ = flywheel effect of the driven body about its own axis of rotation

$f$ = natural torsional frequency of the system, in vibrations per sec.

$C = R^2 A E/L$

$A$ = cross-sectional area of belt, in sq. in.

$E$ = modulus of elasticity of belt material in tension, in lb. per sq. in.

$R$ = radius of driven pulley, in in.

$L$ = length of tight part of belt which is clear of the pulley, in in.

**26. Effect of the Flexibility of Flywheel Spokes on $WR^2$ of Rim.**—The effective $WR^2$ of the rim is

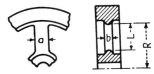

$$WR^2 = \frac{(WR^2)'}{1 - \dfrac{(WR^2)'f^2}{9.775C}}$$

where $(WR^2)'$ = flywheel effect of the rim

$f$ = natural torsional frequency of the system of which the flywheel is a member, in vibrations per sec.

$C$ = torque required to move the rim through one radian relative to the hub

$$C = \frac{12_g E k a^3 b R}{L^2}\left(\frac{L}{3R} + \frac{R}{L} - 1\right)$$

where $g$ = number of spokes

$E$ = bending modulus of elasticity of the spoke material

$k = \pi/64$ for elliptical, and $k = \frac{1}{12}$ for rectangular section spokes

All dimensions are in inches.

For cast-iron spokes of elliptical section:

$$E = 15 \times 10^6 \text{ lb. per sq. in.}$$

$$C = \frac{g a^3 b R \times 10^6}{0.1132 L^2}\left(\frac{L}{3R} + \frac{R}{L} - 1\right)\frac{\text{lb.-in.}}{\text{radians}}.$$

*Note:* It is found by comparative calculations that with spokes of moderate taper very little error is involved in assuming the spoke to be straight and using cross section at mid-point for area calculation.

**TYPICAL EXAMPLE**

The flywheel shown below is used in a Diesel engine installation. It is required to determine effective $WR^2$ for calculation of one of the natural frequencies of torsional vibration. The anticipated natural frequency of the system is 56.4 vibrations per sec.

| Part of fly wheel | Formula | $WR^2$ |
|---|---|---|
| (a) | 2c | $\dfrac{10[(52)^4 - (43)^4]}{40.75} = 955{,}300$ |
| (b) | 2b | $\dfrac{2.375[(43)^4 - (39)^4]}{39.2} = 67{,}000$ |
| (c) | 16a neglecting $\left(\dfrac{W^2 + L^2}{12}\right)$ | $-0.250 \times 1.75 \times 2$ $\times 1.375(25)^2 \times 8 = -6{,}000$ |
| | | Total for rim = 1,016,300 lb.-in. squared |
| (d) | 5b | $6 \times \dfrac{5.25 \times 2.5 \times 11}{4.90}\left[\dfrac{(11)^2}{3}\right.$ $\left. + 8.5(8.5+11) + \dfrac{(5.25)^2}{16}\right] = 36{,}800$ |
| (e) | 2b | $\dfrac{2.625[(17)^4 - (13)^4]}{39.2} = 3{,}700$ |
| (f) | 19 | $\dfrac{\pi \times 0.250 \times 12}{32}$ $[1.697 \times (13)^4 - (6)^4] = 13{,}900$ |
| | | Total for remainder of flywheel = 54,400 lb.-in. squared |

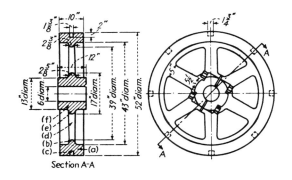

Section A-A

*Note:* Since the beads at the ends of the spokes comprise but a small part of the flywheel $WR^2$, very little error will result in assuming them to be of rectangular cross section. Also, because of the effect of the clamping bolts, the outer hub will be considered a square equal to the diameter. The spokes will be assumed straight and of mid-point cross section.

From formula (26)

$$C = \frac{6 \times (5.25)^3 \times 2.5 \times 19.5 \times 10^6}{0.1132 \times (11)^2}$$

$$\left(\frac{11}{3 \times 19.5} + \frac{19.5}{11} - 1\right) = 2{,}970 \times 10^6 \frac{\text{lb.-in.}}{\text{radians}}$$

and $$WR^2 = \frac{1{,}016{,}300}{1 - \dfrac{1{,}016{,}300 \times (56.4)^2}{9.775 \times 2{,}970 \times 10^6}} + 54{,}400$$

$$= 1{,}197{,}000 \text{ lb.-in. squared}$$

# Rules for Calculating Spur Gears

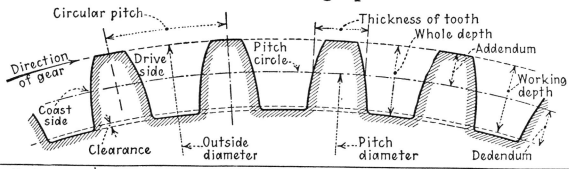

| Having | To Get | Rule | Formula |
|---|---|---|---|
| Diametral Pitch | Circular Pitch | Divide 3.1416 by the Diametral Pitch | $P' = \dfrac{3.1416}{P}$ |
| Outside Diameter and the Number of Teeth | Circular Pitch | Divide Outside Diameter by the Product of .3183 and Number of Teeth plus 2 | $P' \dfrac{D}{.3183\ N + 2}$ |
| Number of Teeth and the Circular Pitch | Pitch Diameter | Continued Product of the Number of Teeth, the Circular Pitch and .3183 | $D' = NP'\ .3183$ |
| Number of Teeth and the Outside Diameter | Pitch Diameter | Divide the Product of Number of Teeth and Outside Diameter by Number of Teeth plus 2 | $D' = \dfrac{ND}{N + 2}$ |
| Number of Teeth and the Circular Pitch | Outside Diameter | Continued Product of the Number of Teeth plus 2, the Circular Pitch and .3183 | $D = (N + 2)\ P'\ .3183$ |
| Circular Pitch | Thickness of Tooth | One-half the Circular Pitch | $t = \dfrac{P'}{2}$ |
| Circular Pitch | Addendum | Multiply the Circular Pitch by .3183 or $s = \dfrac{D'}{N}$ | $s = P'\ .3183$ |
| Circular Pitch | Working Depth | Multiply the Circular Pitch by .6366 | $D'' = P'\ .6366$ |
| Thickness of Tooth | Clearance | One-tenth the Thickness of Tooth at Pitch Line | $f = \dfrac{t}{10}$ |
| Circular Pitch | Diametral Pitch | Divide 3.1416 by the Circular Pitch | $P = \dfrac{3.1416}{P'}$ |
| Outside Diameter and the Number of Teeth | Diametral Pitch | Divide Number of Teeth plus 2 by Outside Diameter | $P = \dfrac{N + 2}{D}$ |
| Number of Teeth and the Outside Diameter | Pitch Diameter | Divide the Product of Outside Diameter and Number of Teeth by Number of Teeth plus 2 | $D' = \dfrac{DN}{N + 2}$ |
| Outside Diameter and the Diametral Pitch | Pitch Diameter | Subtract from the Outside Diameter the Quotient of 2 Divided by the Diametral Pitch | $D' = D - \dfrac{2}{P}$ |
| Number of Teeth and the Diametral Pitch | Outside Diameter | Divide Number of Teeth plus 2 by the Diametral Pitch | $D = \dfrac{N + 2}{P}$ |
| Pitch Diameter and the Number of Teeth | Outside Diameter | Divide the Number of Teeth plus 2 by the Quotient of Number of Teeth divided by the Pitch Diameter | $D = \dfrac{N + 2}{\dfrac{N}{D'}}$ |
| Pitch Diameter and the Diametral Pitch | Number of Teeth | Multiply Pitch Diameter by the Diametral Pitch | $N = D'P$ |
| Outside Diameter and the Diametral Pitch | Number of Teeth | Multiply Outside Diameter by the Diametral Pitch and subtract 2 | $N = DP - 2$ |
| Diametral Pitch | Thickness of Tooth | Divide 1.5708 by the Diametral Pitch | $t = \dfrac{1.5708}{P}$ |
| Diametral Pitch | Working Depth | Divide 2 by the Diametral Pitch | $D'' = \dfrac{2}{P}$ |
| Diametral Pitch | Whole Depth | Divide 2.157 by the Diametral Pitch | $D'' + f = \dfrac{2.157}{P}$ |
| Diametral Pitch | Clearance | Divide .157 by the Diametral Pitch | $f = \dfrac{.157}{P}$ |

The stub form of tooth is designated by two figures, such as 4/5, which represents that the tooth is 4 pitch but cut to a depth of a 5-pitch tooth. These gear calculations are figured accordingly.

# CHART FOR DETERMINING CENTRIFUGAL FORCE

$$F = 0.000341 WRn^2$$

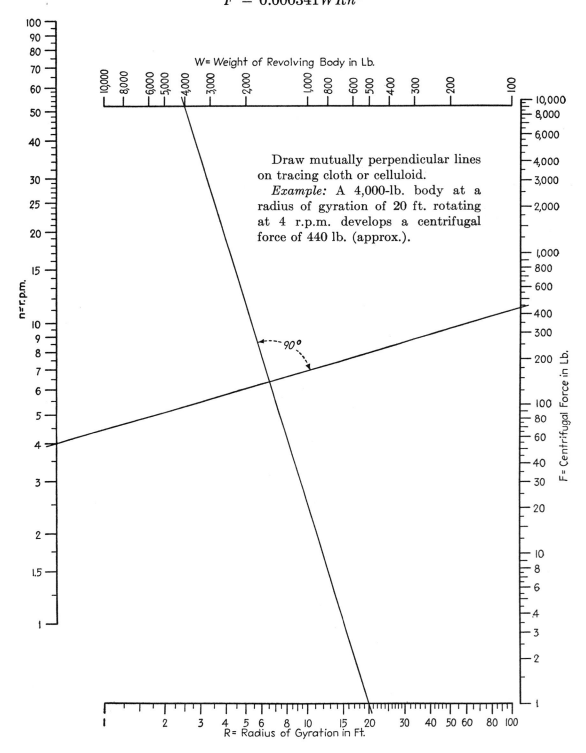

W= Weight of Revolving Body in Lb.

Draw mutually perpendicular lines on tracing cloth or celluloid.

*Example:* A 4,000-lb. body at a radius of gyration of 20 ft. rotating at 4 r.p.m. develops a centrifugal force of 440 lb. (approx.).

n=r.p.m.

F= Centrifugal Force in Lb.

R= Radius of Gyration in Ft.

# FORCES IN TOGGLE JOINT WITH EQUAL ARMS

$$\frac{P}{F} = \frac{S}{4h}$$

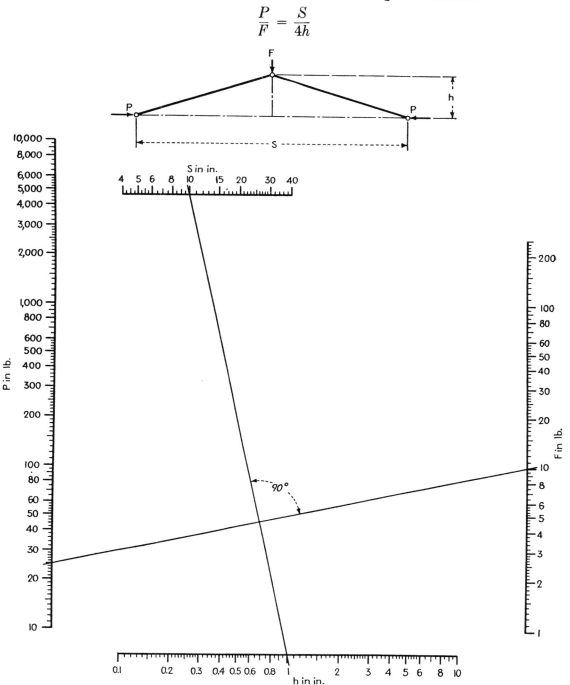

*Example:* Use mutually perpendicular lines drawn on tracing cloth or celluloid. In the example given for $S = 10$ in. and $h = 1$ in., a force $F$ of 10 lb. exerts pressures $P$ of 25 lb. each.

# ACCELERATED LINEAR MOTION

$$\frac{2S}{T^2} = \frac{V}{2S} = \frac{V}{T} = \frac{32.16F}{W} = G$$

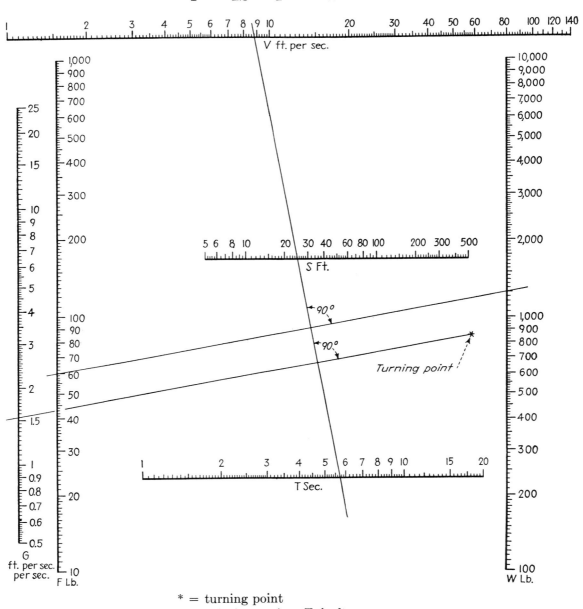

* = turning point
$V$ = velocity at time $T$, in ft. per sec.
$S$ = distance passed through, in ft.
$T$ = time during which force acts, in sec.
$F$ = accelerating force, in lb.
$W$ = weight of moving body, in lb.
$G$ = constant acceleration, in ft. per sec.

# ROTARY MOTION

$$V = \frac{P}{F} = \frac{S}{T} = \frac{2\pi R n}{12 \times 60}$$

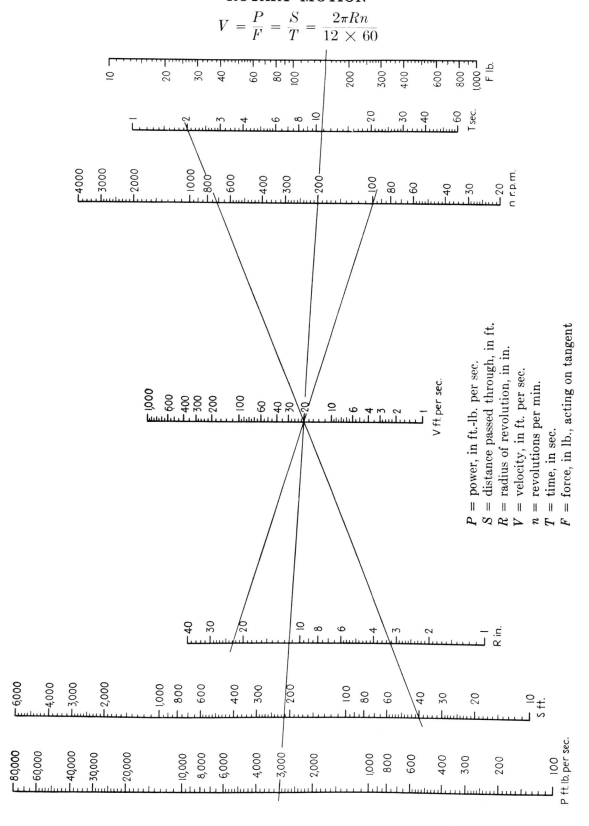

$P$ = power, in ft.-lb. per sec.
$S$ = distance passed through, in ft.
$R$ = radius of revolution, in in.
$V$ = velocity, in ft. per sec.
$n$ = revolutions per min.
$T$ = time, in sec.
$F$ = force, in lb., acting on tangent

# Chart for Determining Bending Moments

A CHART for obtaining the maximum bending moment for various types of beams with different loadings and span lengths is shown on the following page. On this page are given section moduli and moments of inertia for typical sections.

In the chart on the next page, the two left-hand scales give total load in pounds, and also various conditions of loading as listed diagrammatically under $C$. In all cases, the total load, be it uniform or distributed, must be used. The charts under $C$ designate concentrated loads as $P$. These loads are to be used in the $W$ scale, as noted on the chart. The center line, marked "Turning Scale," is where the index lines cross, as shown in the example. The scales on the right, labeled $L$ and $M$, are the length $L$ in inches between supports or support and load, and the maximum bending moment $M$ expressed in pound-inch units.

When using the chart, two known variables, such as $C$ to $L$ or $W$ to $M$, should be connected in the manner shown by the chart key. The turning scale will be cut. At this intersection the point of a sharp instrument is placed and the straight edge swung until the other known variable is reached. Then the opposite end of the straight edge will cut the scale of the unknown variable, giving the answer. A large variety of problems can be solved merely by moving the straight edge.

*Example 1*—A cantilever beam is 4 ft. long and has a load of 800 lb. concentrated at its free end. This might also be a shaft with an overhanging fly-wheel. Neglecting the weight of the beam, find the maximum bending moment in lb.-in.

Place a straight edge on scale $C$ at 1, and set the other end at 48 in. on scale $L$. Place a pointed instrument on the turning scale, guided by the straight edge. Swing it around the point until 800 lb. is reached on scale $W$. The answer will be seen on scale $M$ to be 38,000 lb.-in. The correct answer as computed is 38,400 lb.-in.

*Example 2*—Should the weight of the beam or shaft of Example 1 be given as 3.03 lb. per in., the problem would be solved as follows. Lay the straight edge on line $C$ at 2 and cut line $L$ at 48 in. Swing straight edge around marked point, on turning scale, to 146 lb. (3.03 lb. per in. $\times$ 48 in.) on scale $W$. Then scale $M$ will show the answer to be 3,500 lb.-in. The computed figure is 3,504. Considering this bending moment to have a positive sign, this figure should be added to the bending moment previously found for the concentrated load, which is also positive. The total maximum bending moment will be 38,000 lb.-in. plus 3,500 lb.-in., or 41,500 lb.-in. Computations would show the exact figure to be 41,904.

Two or more loading combinations may be solved. It must be remembered when dealing with problems involving more than one loading that the bending moments must be added algebraically. Those with like signs should be added; those with opposite should be subtracted.

| Shape of Section A=Area | Moment of Inertia | Section Modulus |
|---|---|---|
| Solid Rectangle | $\dfrac{bh^3}{12}$ | $\dfrac{bh^2}{6}$ |
| Hollow Rectangle | $\dfrac{bh^3-b_1h_1^3}{12}$ | $\dfrac{bh^3-b_1h_1^3}{6h}$ |
| Solid Circle | $\dfrac{1}{64}\pi D^4$ $=0.0491 D^4$ | $\dfrac{1}{32}\pi D^3$ $=0.0982 D^3$ |
| Hollow Circle A, Area of large section; a, Area of small section | $\dfrac{AD^2-ad^2}{16}$ | $\dfrac{AD^2-ad^2}{8D}$ |
| Solid triangle | $\dfrac{bh^3}{36}$ | $\dfrac{bh^2}{24}$ |
| Even angle | $\dfrac{Ah^2}{10.2}$ | $\dfrac{Ah}{7.2}$ |
| Uneven angle | $\dfrac{Ah^2}{9.5}$ | $\dfrac{Ah}{6.5}$ |
| Even cross | $\dfrac{Ah^2}{19}$ | $\dfrac{Ah}{9.5}$ |
| Even tee | $\dfrac{Ah^2}{11.1}$ | $\dfrac{Ah}{8}$ |
| I-beam | $\dfrac{Ah^2}{6.66}$ | $\dfrac{Ah}{3.2}$ |
| Channel | $\dfrac{Ah^2}{7.34}$ | $\dfrac{Ah}{3.67}$ |

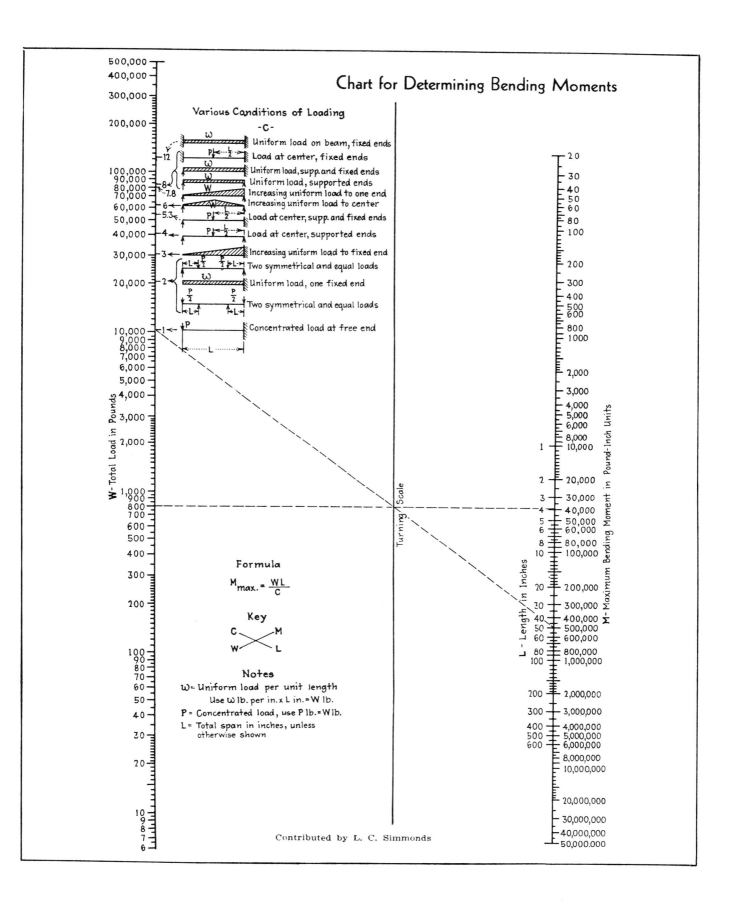

# Chart for Determining Bending Moments

**Various Conditions of Loading**

-C-

Uniform load on beam, fixed ends

Load at center, fixed ends

Uniform load, supp. and fixed ends

Uniform load, supported ends

Increasing uniform load to one end

Increasing uniform load to center

Load at center, supp. and fixed ends

Load at center, supported ends

Increasing uniform load to fixed end

Two symmetrical and equal loads

Uniform load, one fixed end

Two symmetrical and equal loads

Concentrated load at free end

Turning Scale

**W** - Total Load in Pounds

**L** - Length in Inches

**M** - Maximum Bending Moment in Pound-Inch Units

### Formula

$$M_{max.} = \frac{WL}{C}$$

### Key

C    M

W    L

### Notes

ω = Uniform load per unit length
    Use ω lb. per in. x L in. = W lb.

P = Concentrated load, use P lb. = W lb.

L = Total span in inches, unless
    otherwise shown

Contributed by L. C. Simmonds

# MEAN COOLING TEMPERATURE

Where $Y_A$ and $Y_B$ are any two ordinates to the curve $Y=ae^{-bx}$ the usual form of cooling curve, the mean value $Y_M$ of all the ordinates between $Y_A$ and $Y_B$ is given by the relation

$$\text{Log mean } Y_M = \frac{Y_A - Y_B}{\text{Log } Y_A - \text{Log } Y_B}$$

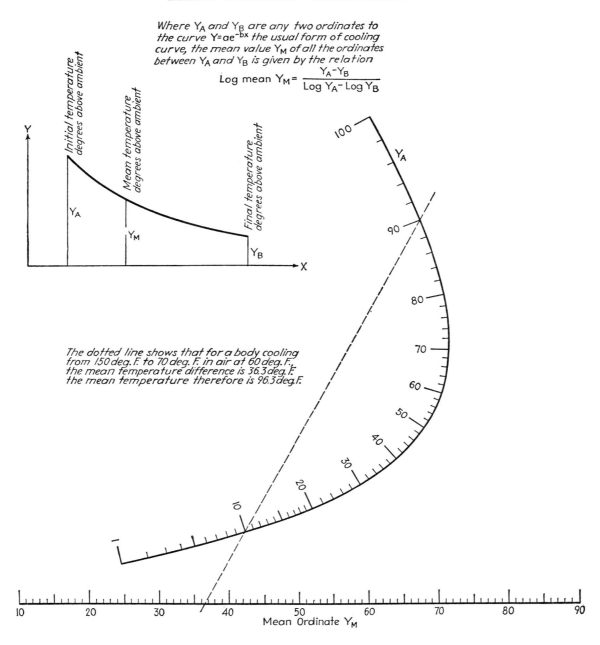

The dotted line shows that for a body cooling from 150 deg. F. to 70 deg. F. in air at 60 deg. F., the mean temperature difference is 36.3 deg. F. the mean temperature therefore is 96.3 deg. F.

Mean Ordinate $Y_M$

*Chapter 2*

# ACCESSORIES

# CLAMPING DEVICES FOR ACCURATELY

Methods of clamping parts which must be readily movable are as numerous and as varied as the requirements. In many instances, a clamp of any design is satisfactory, provided it has sufficient strength to hold the parts immovable when tightened. However, it is sometimes necessary that the movable part be clamped to maintain accurate alignment with some fixed part. Examples of this latter-type are described and illustrated.

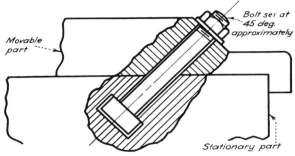

**LOUIS KASPER**

FIG. 2—Lower edge of the bolt head contacts the angular side of locating groove, causing the keys to be held tightly against the opposite side of the groove. This design permits easy removal of the clamped part, but is effective only if the working pressure is directly downward or in a direction against the perpendicular side of the slot.

FIG. 1—When nut is tightened, the flange on the edge of the movable part is drawn against the machined edge of the stationary part. This method is effective, but removal of the clamped part may be difficult if it is heavy or unbalanced.

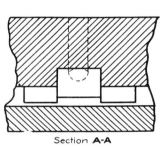

Section A-A

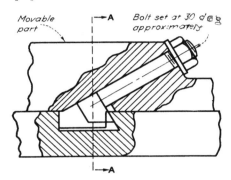

FIG. 3—The movable part is held against one side of the groove while the T-nut is forced against the other side. Removal of the screw permits easy removal of the clamped part. Heavy pressure toward the side of the key out of contact with the slot may permit slight movement due to the springing of the screw.

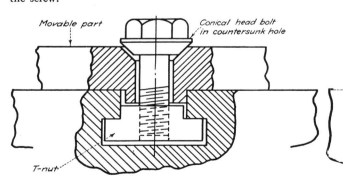

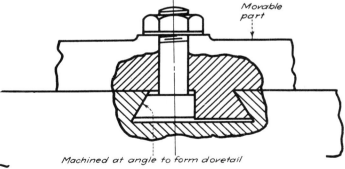

FIG. 4—One side of the bolt is machined at an angle to form a side of the dovetail, which tightens in the groove as the nut is drawn tight. Part must be slid entire length of slot for removal.

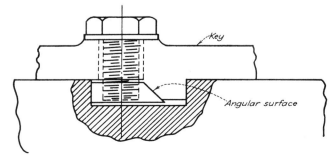

FIG. 5—The angular surface of the nut contacts the angular side of the key, and causes it to move outward against the side of the groove. This exerts a downward pull on the clamped part due to friction of nut against side of groove as nut is drawn upward by the screw.

# ALIGNING ADJUSTABLE PARTS

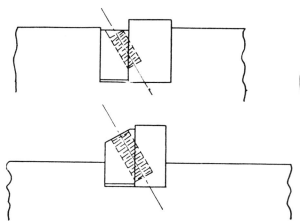

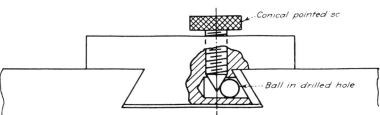

**FIG. 8**—Screw contact causes the ball to exert an outward pressure against the gib. The gib is loosely pinned to the movable part. This slide can be applied to broad surfaces where it would be impractical to apply adjusting screws through the stationary part.

**FIGS. 6 and 7**—These designs differ only in depth of the grooves. They cannot withstand heavy pressure in an upward direction but possess the advantage of being applicable to narrow grooves.

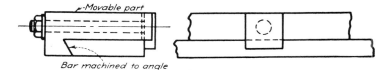

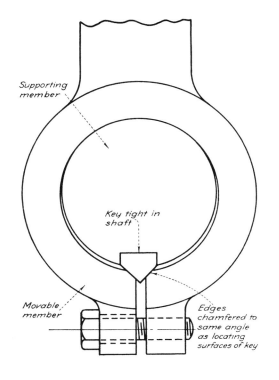

**FIG. 10**—One edge of a bar is machined at an angle which fits into mating surfaces on the movable part. When the bolt, which passes through the movable part, is drawn tight, the two parts are clamped firmly together.

**FIG. 9**—The movable member is flanged on one side and carries a conical pointed screw on the other side. A short shaft passes through both members and carries a detent slightly out of alignment with the point of the screw. This shaft is flattened on opposite sides where it passes through the stationary member, to prevent its turning when the movable member is removed. A heavy washer is screwed to the under side of the shaft. When the knurled screw is turned inward, the shaft is drawn upward while the movable member is drawn downward and backward against the flange. The shaft is forced forward against the edge of the slot. The upper member may thus be moved and locked in any position. Withdrawing the point of the screw from the detent in the shaft permits removal of the upper member.

**FIG. 11**—As the screw is tightened, the chamfered edges of the cut tend to ride outward on the angular surfaces of the key. This draws the movable member tightly against the opposite side of the shaft.

**FIG. 12**—As the screw is turned, it causes the movable side, which forms one side of the dovetail groove, to move until it clamps tightly on the movable member. The movable side should be as narrow as possible, because there is a tendency for this part to ride up on the angular surface of the clamped part.

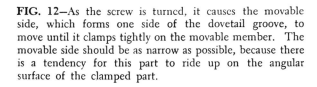

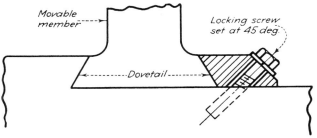

# FRICTION CLAMPING DEVICES

BERNARD J. WOLFE

ALL TYPES of mechanisms used for gaining mechanical advantage have probably been used in the design of friction clamps. This type of clamp can hold moderately large loads by friction grip on smooth surfaces even of comparatively small area and, in some designs, tightened or released with little effort and movement of the control. In the clamps illustrated here the mechanical advantage is gained by the use of the common devices: lever, toggle, screw, wedge, and combinations of these means.

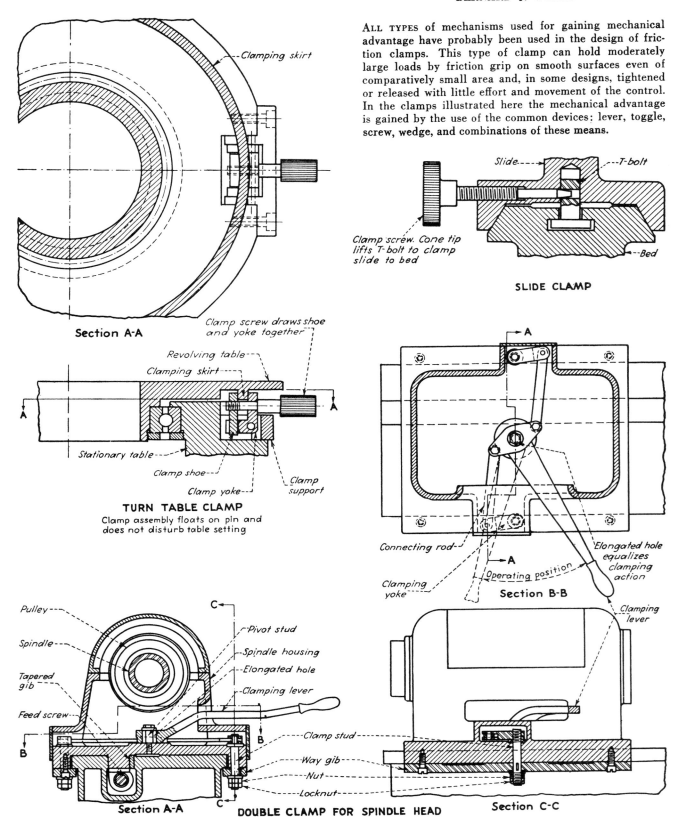

Section A-A

**TURN TABLE CLAMP**
Clamp assembly floats on pin and does not disturb table setting

**SLIDE CLAMP**

Clamp screw. Cone tip lifts T-bolt to clamp slide to bed

Section B-B

**DOUBLE CLAMP FOR SPINDLE HEAD**

Section A-A          Section C-C

# AND PRINCIPLES OF DESIGN

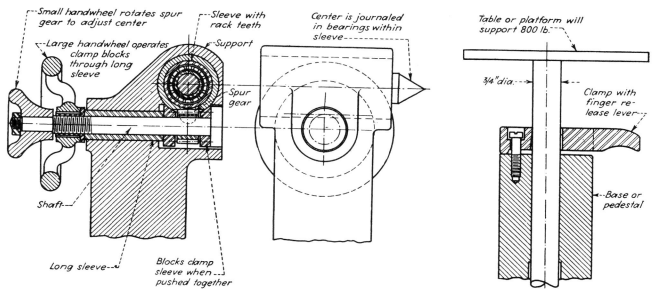

**CENTER SUPPORT CLAMP**

Small handwheel rotates spur gear to adjust center

Large handwheel operates clamp blocks through long sleeve

Sleeve with rack teeth

Support

Center is journaled in bearings within sleeve

Spur gear

Shaft

Long sleeve

Blocks clamp sleeve when pushed together

**PEDESTAL CLAMP**

Table or platform will support 800 lb.

3/4"dia.

Clamp with finger release lever

Base or pedestal

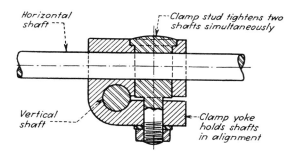

**RIGHT ANGLE CLAMP**

Horizontal shaft

Clamp stud tightens two shafts simultaneously

Vertical shaft

Clamp yoke holds shafts in alignment

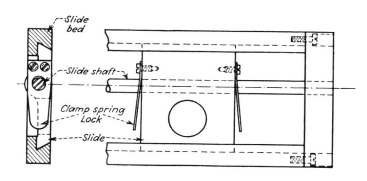

**SLIDE CLAMP**

Slide bed

Slide shaft

Clamp spring Lock

Slide

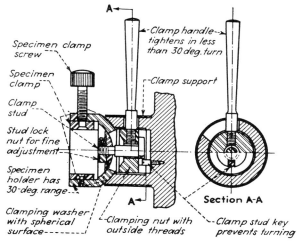

**SPECIMEN HOLDER CLAMP**

Specimen clamp screw

Specimen clamp

Clamp stud

Stud lock nut for fine adjustment

Specimen holder has 30-deg. range

Clamping washer with spherical surface

A

Clamp handle tightens in less than 30 deg. turn

Clamp support

A

Clamping nut with outside threads

Section A-A

Clamp stud key prevents turning

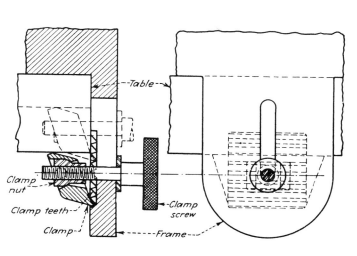

**TABLE CLAMP**

Table

Clamp nut

Clamp teeth

Clamp

Clamp screw

Frame

# —Manual and Automatic Latching Devices

Methods of door and cover latching range from simple gravity catches to elaborate cam and roller mechanisms. The principle of operation of many latches is fundamentally the same, regardless of whether the latch is designed as a finished hardware fitting or as a unit for industrial applications. Various latches are designed for one type of application and their characteristics prohibit interchanging from one type of application to another. Some latches classified as multiple, friction, and hook types are illustrated. Each classification is sub-divided according to methods of mounting, actuation, operation, and use.

**MULTIPLE LATCHES** are used to fasten a door or cover at two or more points and are controlled with one handle. Springs are rarely used, the cam effect of the actuating rods providing a positive bearing pressure between the door and jamb. This pressure can be increased by a sealing gasket around the jamb, giving a water and dust-tight inclosure in certain applications.

Rods engage edge of door jamb at top and bottom and draw door closed

--Roller

-Sealing strip

Cam operates latching rods when handle is lifted from cup and turned

Handle recesses into cup

Hooks at top and bottom engage vertical pins as rod is turned

Handle actuated cam causes arms to extend Rollers at ends of arms engage surface of cabinet, at top and bottom drawing door inward against sealing strip

This device applies leverage to draw door into shape if warped or if closing against a door seat

American Hardware Co.

Length of rods adjustable

Handle is lifted and turned to turn vertical rod

Bolts act vertically to engage strikers at top and bottom when handle is turned

Cam engages striker or bearing plate on door jamb and draws door closed

Provision for padlock or pin

Square D Co

The Stanley Works

American Hardware Co.

40

# For Doors, Covers and Lids—I

**FRICTION LATCHES** utilize spring pressure in their actuation. The springs can be of helical, clip, or cantilever design and their resiliency controls the effectiveness of the latch. Friction latches are either mortised or surface-mounted, depending upon the particular application and in either instance are generally invisible when the door or cover is closed.

## MORTISED FRICTION TYPES

Mortised housing

Striker mounted on door jamb

Spring loaded bullet in door engages striker detent

*National Brass Co.*

Striker mortised in door jamb

Mortised housing

Spring loaded bullet in door engages striker detent

*National Brass Co.*

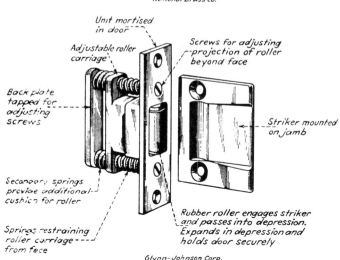

Unit mortised in door

Adjustable roller carriage

Screws for adjusting projection of roller beyond face

Back plate tapped for adjusting screws

Striker mounted on jamb

Secondary springs provide additional cushion for roller

Springs restraining roller carriage from face

Rubber roller engages striker and passes into depression. Expands in depression and holds door securely

*Glynn-Johnson Corp.*

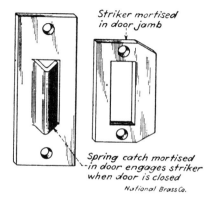

Striker mortised in door jamb

Spring catch mortised in door engages striker when door is closed

*National Brass Co.*

## SURFACE FRICTION TYPES

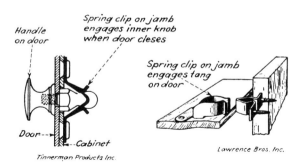

Handle on door

Spring clip on jamb engages inner knob when door closes

Door

Cabinet

*Tinnerman Products Inc.*

Spring clip on jamb engages tang on door

*Lawrence Bros. Inc.*

Hole in cover acts as detent for raised boss on spring clip. Clip must be sprung and unsprung manually

*Tinnerman Products Inc.*

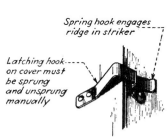

Spring hook engages ridge in striker

Latching hook on cover must be sprung and unsprung manually

*Tinnerman Products Inc.*

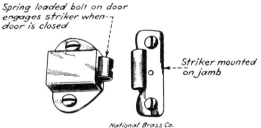

Spring loaded bolt on door engages striker when door is closed

Striker mounted on jamb

*National Brass Co.*

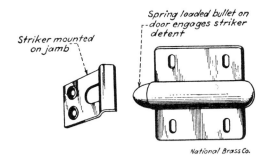

Spring loaded bullet on door engages striker detent

Striker mounted on jamb

*National Brass Co.*

Spring loaded arm engages striker on door jamb

*H. B. Ives Co.*

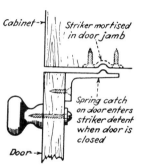

Cabinet

Striker mortised in door jamb

Spring catch on door enters striker detent when door is closed

Door

**HOOK LATCHES** for doors or covers are of either the gravity or spring type, both of which usually require manual latching and unlatching. In the gravity type, the hook falls into place when aligned with its mating element. In the spring type the hooking action is controlled and under pressure from the actuating spring until manually unlatched.

## SPRING HOOK TYPES

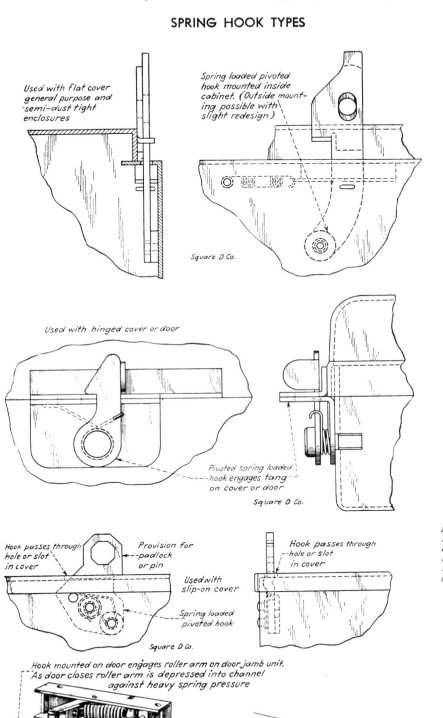

Used with flat cover general purpose and semi-dust tight enclosures

Spring loaded pivoted hook mounted inside cabinet. (Outside mounting possible with slight redesign)

Square D Co.

Used with hinged cover or door

Pivoted spring loaded hook engages tang on cover or door

Square D Co.

Hook passes through hole or slot in cover

Provision for padlock or pin

Used with slip-on cover

Spring loaded pivoted hook

Square D Co.

Hook passes through hole or slot in cover

Hook mounted on door engages roller arm on door jamb unit. As door closes roller arm is depressed into channel against heavy spring pressure

Spring tension adjustable

Tension adjusting screw

H. B. Ives Co.

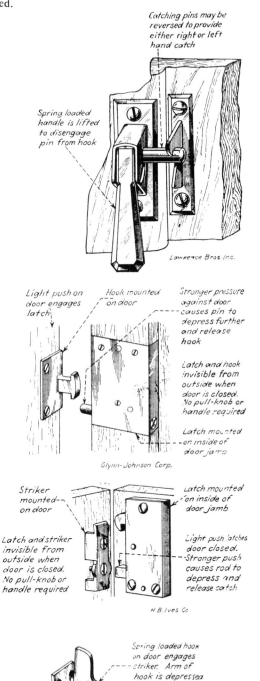

Catching pins may be reversed to provide either right or left hand catch

Spring loaded handle is lifted to disengage pin from hook

Lawrence Bros. Inc.

Light push on door engages latch

Hook mounted on door

Stronger pressure against door causes pin to depress further and release hook

Latch and hook invisible from outside when door is closed. No pull-knob or handle required

Latch mounted on inside of door jamb

Glynn-Johnson Corp.

Striker mounted on door

Latch mounted on inside of door jamb

Latch and striker invisible from outside when door is closed. No pull-knob or handle required

Light push latches door closed. Stronger push causes rod to depress and release catch

H. B. Ives Co.

Spring loaded hook on door engages striker. Arm of hook is depressed to release

Lawrence Bros. Inc.

Striker mounted on jamb

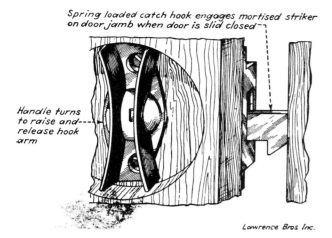

Spring loaded catch hook engages mortised striker on door jamb when door is slid closed

Handle turns to raise and release hook arm

Lawrence Bros Inc.

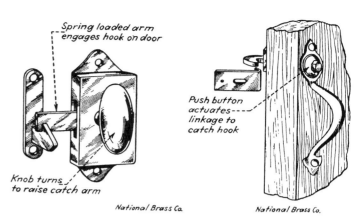

Spring loaded arm engages hook on door

Knob turns to raise catch arm

National Brass Co.

Push button actuates linkage to catch hook

National Brass Co.

## GRAVITY HOOK TYPES

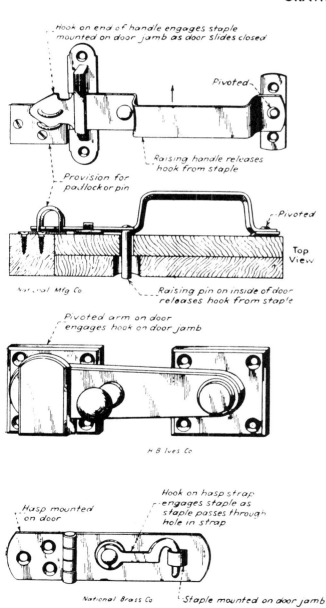

Hook on end of handle engages staple mounted on door jamb as door slides closed

Pivoted

Raising handle releases hook from staple

Provision for padlock or pin

Pivoted

Top View

National Mfg Co

Raising pin on inside of door releases hook from staple

Pivoted arm on door engages hook on door jamb

H B Ives Co

Hasp mounted on door

Hook on hasp strap engages staple as staple passes through hole in strap

National Brass Co

Staple mounted on door jamb

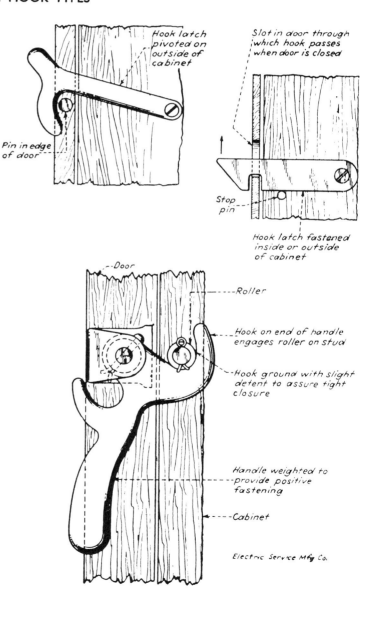

Hook latch pivoted on outside of cabinet

Pin in edge of door

Slot in door through which hook passes when door is closed

Stop pin

Hook latch fastened inside or outside of cabinet

Door

Roller

Hook on end of handle engages roller on stud

Hook ground with slight detent to assure tight closure

Handle weighted to provide positive fastening

Cabinet

Electric Service Mfg Co.

# Manual and Automatic Latching Devices

In addition to the types of latches presented in the August issue, others, classified as the bolt and draw-tight types, utilize cams, levers, and springs in their operation. Some of these are described and illustrated, each classification being subdivided according to methods of mounting, actuation, operation, and use.

**LATCHES OF THE BOLT TYPE** require either manual or spring pressure for their actuation. The manual type of bolt cannot be fastened or unfastened without hand control. The spring type of bolt can generally be fastened automatically by slamming the door or cover shut, but manual effort is required to release the bolt from the striker plate.

## BOLT TYPE

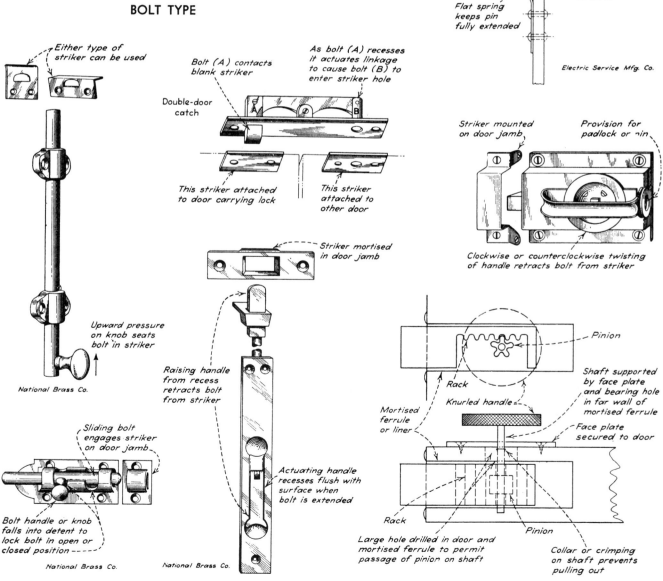

Outward pull on knurled handle releases pin from hole in cover bracket

Cover

Pin enters hole in bracket mounted on cover

Flat spring keeps pin fully extended

Electric Service Mfg. Co.

Either type of striker can be used

Bolt (A) contacts blank striker

As bolt (A) recesses it actuates linkage to cause bolt (B) to enter striker hole

Double-door catch

This striker attached to door carrying lock

This striker attached to other door

Striker mounted on door jamb

Provision for padlock or pin

Clockwise or counterclockwise twisting of handle retracts bolt from striker

Upward pressure on knob seats bolt in striker

Striker mortised in door jamb

National Brass Co.

Raising handle from recess retracts bolt from striker

Pinion

Rack

Shaft supported by face plate and bearing hole in far wall of mortised ferrule

Knurled handle

Face plate secured to door

Mortised ferrule or liner

Sliding bolt engages striker on door jamb

Actuating handle recesses flush with surface when bolt is extended

Rack

Pinion

Bolt handle or knob falls into detent to lock bolt in open or closed position

Large hole drilled in door and mortised ferrule to permit passage of pinion on shaft

Collar or crimping on shaft prevents pulling out

National Brass Co.

National Brass Co.

# For Doors, Covers and Lids—II

### SPRING BOLT TYPE

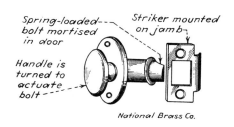

Spring-loaded bolt mortised in door

Striker mounted on jamb

Handle is turned to actuate bolt

National Brass Co.

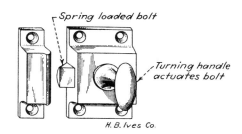

Spring loaded bolt

Turning handle actuates bolt

H. B. Ives Co.

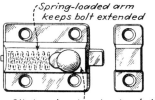

Spring-loaded arm keeps bolt extended

Sliding knot actuates bolt

Lawrence Bros. Inc.

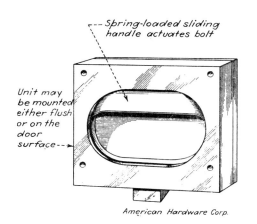

Spring-loaded sliding handle actuates bolt

Unit may be mounted either flush or on the door surface

American Hardware Corp.

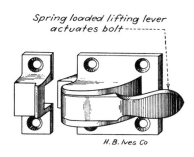

Spring loaded lifting lever actuates bolt

H. B. Ives Co

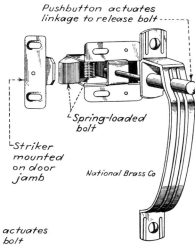

Pushbutton actuates linkage to release bolt

Striker mounted on door jamb

Spring-loaded bolt

National Brass Co

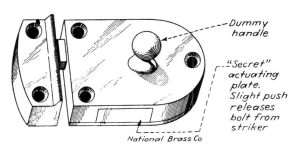

Dummy handle

"Secret" actuating plate. Slight push releases bolt from striker

National Brass Co

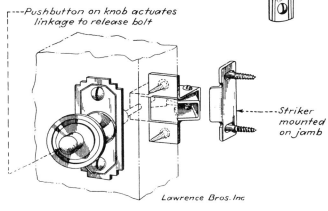

Pushbutton on knob actuates linkage to release bolt

Striker mounted on jamb

Lawrence Bros. Inc

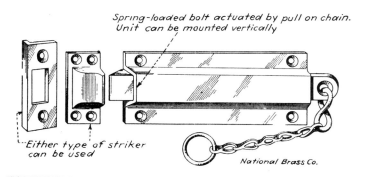

Spring-loaded bolt actuated by pull on chain. Unit can be mounted vertically

Either type of striker can be used

National Brass Co.

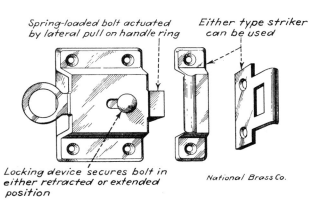

Spring-loaded bolt actuated by lateral pull on handle ring

Either type striker can be used

Locking device secures bolt in either retracted or extended position

National Brass Co.

# LATCHING DEVICES (continued)

**LATCHES OPERATING ON THE DRAW-TIGHT PRIN-CIPLE** are manually operated. These latches draw the cover or door tightly against the jamb. The pressure of the door against the jamb can be increased by use of gasket material around the door or cover making the closure air, dust of water tight. The lever linkage type of latch multi-plies the manual effort expended in closing the latch. The screw type of closure requires tools for latching and unlatching, but provides the tightest closure available. The cam type draws the cover or door closed with an ever increasing pressure as the latching arm follows the cam striker. The spring type draw-tight latch holds the door or cover closed.

## CAM TYPE DRAW TIGHT

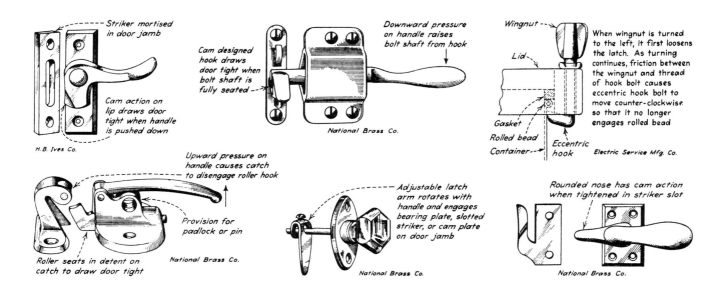

Striker mortised in door jamb

Cam action on lip draws door tight when handle is pushed down

H. B. Ives Co.

Cam designed hook draws door tight when bolt shaft is fully seated

Downward pressure on handle raises bolt shaft from hook

National Brass Co.

Wingnut

Lid

Gasket

Rolled bead

Container

Eccentric hook

When wingnut is turned to the left, it first loosens the latch. As turning continues, friction between the wingnut and thread of hook bolt causes eccentric hook bolt to move counter-clockwise so that it no longer engages rolled bead

Electric Service Mfg. Co.

Upward pressure on handle causes catch to disengage roller hook

Provision for padlock or pin

Roller seats in detent on catch to draw door tight

National Brass Co.

Adjustable latch arm rotates with handle and engages bearing plate, slotted striker, or cam plate on door jamb

National Brass Co.

Rounded nose has cam action when tightened in striker slot

National Brass Co.

## LEVER LINKAGE DRAW TIGHT TYPE

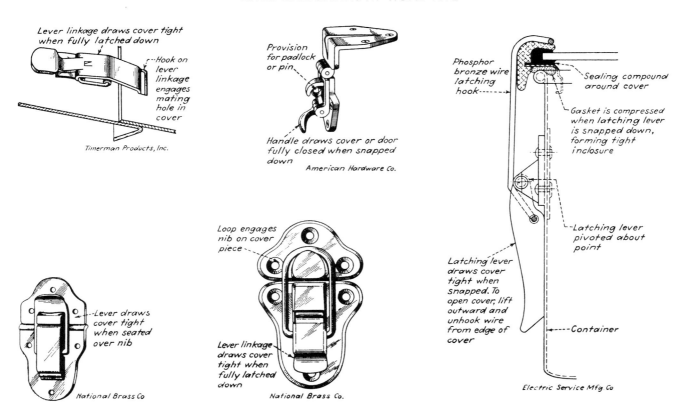

Lever linkage draws cover tight when fully latched down

Hook on lever linkage engages mating hole in cover

Timerman Products, Inc.

Provision for padlock or pin

Handle draws cover or door fully closed when snapped down

American Hardware Co.

Phosphor bronze wire latching hook

Sealing compound around cover

Gasket is compressed when latching lever is snapped down, forming tight inclosure

Latching lever pivoted about point

Latching lever draws cover tight when snapped. To open cover, lift outward and unhook wire from edge of cover

Container

Electric Service Mfg. Co.

Lever draws cover tight when seated over nib

National Brass Co

Loop engages nib on cover piece

Lever linkage draws cover tight when fully latched down

National Brass Co.

## SCREW TYPE DRAW TIGHT

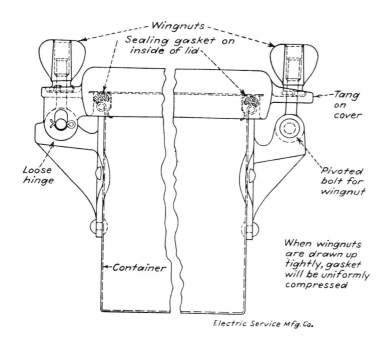

Wingnuts

Sealing gasket on inside of lid

Tang on cover

Loose hinge

Pivoted bolt for wingnut

Container

When wingnuts are drawn up tightly, gasket will be uniformly compressed

*Electric Service Mfg. Co.*

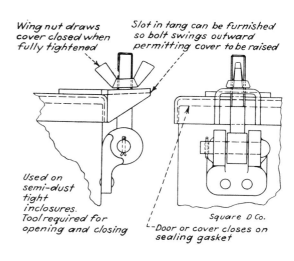

Wing nut draws cover closed when fully tightened

Slot in tang can be furnished so bolt swings outward permitting cover to be raised

Used on semi-dust tight inclosures. Tool required for opening and closing

Square D Co.

Door or cover closes on sealing gasket

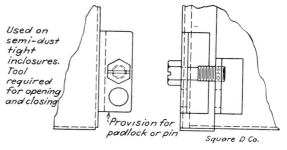

Used on semi-dust tight inclosures. Tool required for opening and closing

Provision for padlock or pin

Square D Co.

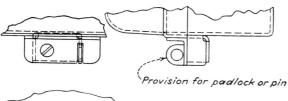

Provision for padlock or pin

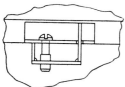

Used on general purpose inclosures having slip-on covers. Tool required for opening or closing

Square D Co.

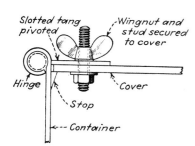

Slotted tang pivoted

Wingnut and stud secured to cover

Hinge

Cover

Stop

Container

Wingnut must be removed from stud for tang to be raised and cover opened

## SPRING TYPE DRAW TIGHT

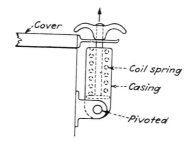

Upward pressure on knob compresses internal coil spring allowing knob to be swung outward and to disengage slotted tang on cover

Cover

Coil spring

Casing

Pivoted

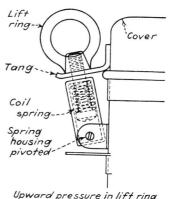

Lift ring

Cover

Tang

Coil spring

Spring housing pivoted

Upward pressure in lift ring compresses internal coil spring allowing lift ring to swing outward and to disengage slotted tang on cover

*Electric Service Mfg. Co.*

# Low-cost latches give

These latches cut costs where appearance
is a secondary consideration.

*L KASPER, design consultant, Phila*

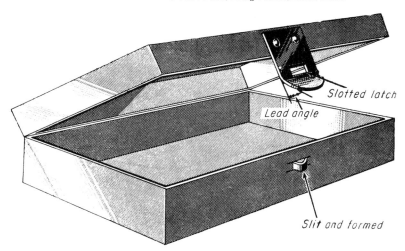

Slotted latch

Lead angle

Slit and formed

**SLIT AND FORMED** box side depends upon spring action of box metal and latch plate for engagement in latch-plate hole. A box that is too stiff will require a relatively flexible latch plate for ease of operation.

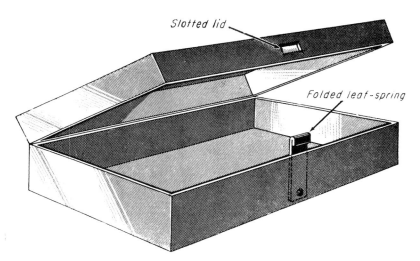

Slotted lid

Folded leaf-spring

**FOLDED LEAF-SPRING** end is another positive, spring-action latch. Here, however, the leaf spring itself provides spring action — box can be as heavy as desired without interfering with opening or closing. Careful alignment of spring and notch is necessary.

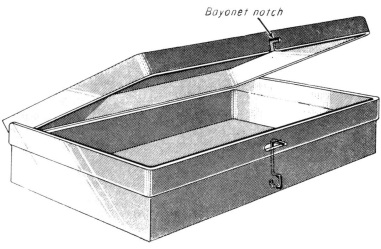

Bayonet notch

**BAYONET ACTION** of formed-wire spring in lid is again automatic upon closing. Spring must be manipulated for opening unless a lead is deliberately designed into the lid notch so that opening force can overcome holding-force.

# high-class results

**SPIRAL SPRING** holds the lid in a manner similar to the previous latch arrangement. Spring action comes from tension windup rather than cantilever and so design is suitable for boxes where a long latch spring is not possible.

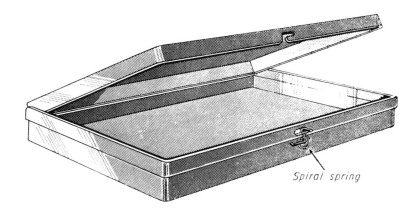

Spiral spring

**FINGER RING** is here provided by forming the spring to do double duty — it not only performs as the latch spring but provides finger hold for withdrawing the box from a narrow shelf or desk drawer. Disadvantage is that protruding spring takes extra space.

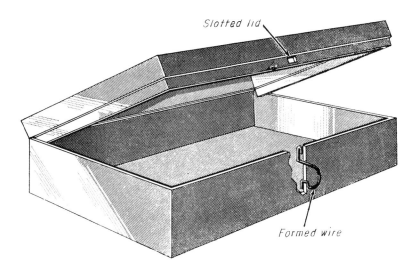

Slotted lid

Formed wire

**LATCH SPRINGS** projecting through the box top provide for stacking by engaging a slot in the bottom of the box above. Several boxes can thus be carried without risk of sliding. The lid can be hinged or completely removable.

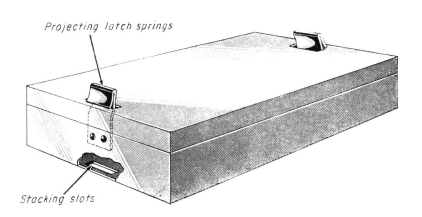

Projecting latch springs

Stacking slots

# 6 More low-cost latches

This is the second part of a review of some cost-cutting latch-designs.

*L. KASPER, design consultant, Philadelphia, Pa.*

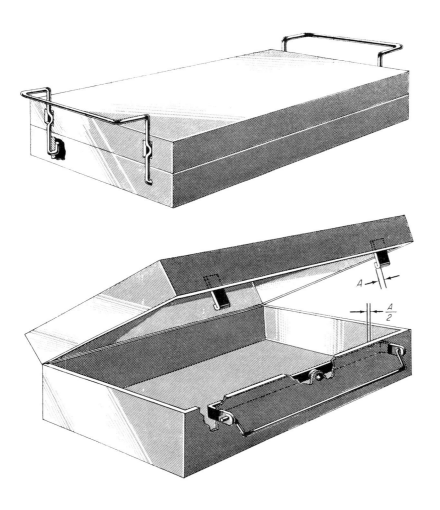

**1**

**LATCH SPRING** formed into shape of a handle is suitable for long, narrow boxes. The shape of the handle section permits several boxes to be stacked and carried safely.

**2**

**CARRYING-HANDLE** is attached to the latch spring, which is attached to its center with a spacer between. Press the handle to release the catch.

**3**

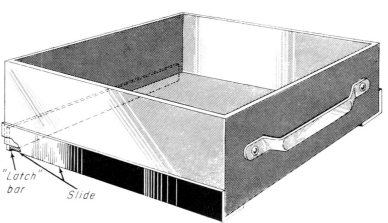

"Latch" bar

Slide

**LATCH BAR** at rear falls into slot when drawer is slid fully in. To withdraw, the box must be raised at the rear by tilting on the front edge. Effect is a self-locking, secret-opening drawer.

# for top performance

**SWIVEL HANDLE** is attached by shoulder screw at pivot point. To withdraw the drawer, tilt the handle about the pivot point until the latch is disengaged from slot in runner.

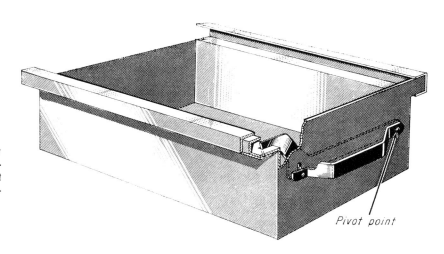

Pivot point

**DOUBLE-BAYONET** notch in one lid snaps over V-spring in other lid to hold box closed. Press spring to open. This type of latch is very suitable for long, narrow boxes.

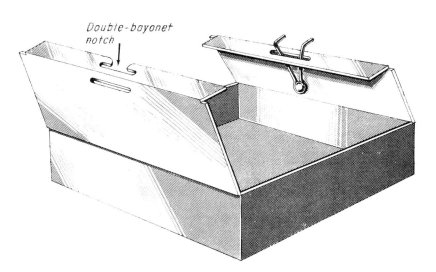

Double-bayonet notch

**NOTCHES** are specially shaped to hold cover over instrument housing. Simply lift cover and slide out support legs to remove cover. If fit of legs and slides is made fairly tight, accidental removal or tampering is improbable.

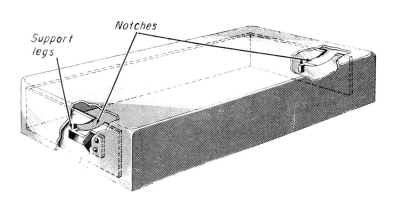

Support legs

Notches

# 6 INGENIOUS JOBS for ROLLER CHAIN

How this low-cost industrial workhorse can be harnessed in a variety of ways to perform tasks other than simply transmitting power. More examples will be presented in a coming issue.

**PETER C NOY,** *manufacturing engineer*
*Canadian General Electric Co Ltd, Barrie, Ont*

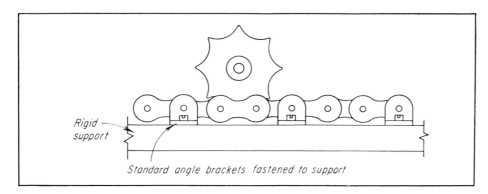

**1 LOW-COST RACK-AND-PINION** device is easily assembled from standard parts.

**2 AN EXTENSION OF RACK-AND-PINION PRINCIPLE—** soldering fixture for noncircular shells. Positive-action cams can be similarly designed. Standard angle brackets attach chain to cam or fixture plate.

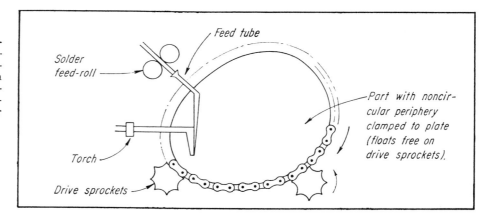

**3 CONTROL-CABLE DIRECTION-CHANGER** extensively used in aircraft.

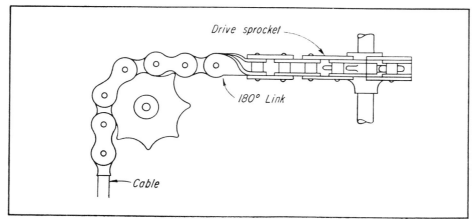

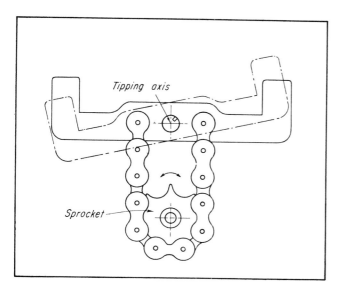

**4** **TRANSMISSION OF TIPPING OR ROCKING MOTION.** Can be combined with previous example (3) to transmit this type of motion to a remote location and around obstructions. Tipping angle should not exceed 40° approx.

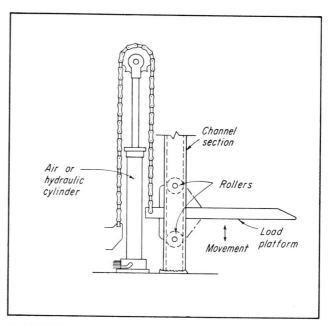

**5** **LIFTING DEVICE** is simplified by roller chain.

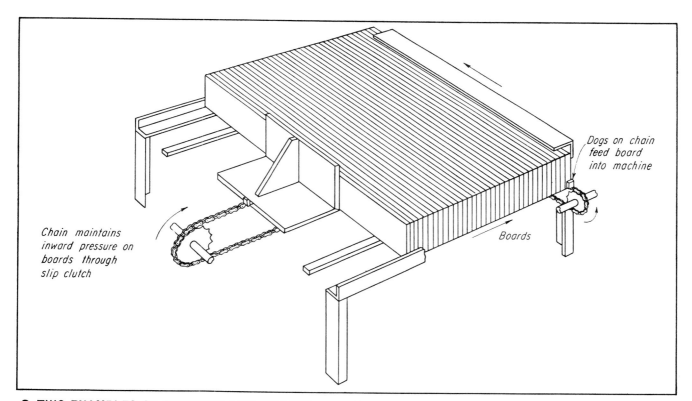

**6** **TWO EXAMPLES OF INDEXING AND FEEDING** uses of roller chain are shown here in a setup that feeds plywood strips into a brush-making machine. Advantages of roller chain as used here are flexibility and long feed.

# 6 MORE JOBS for ROLLER CHAIN

Some further examples of how this low-cost but precision-made product can be arranged to do tasks other than transmit power. Other examples were given in the May 2 issue.

**PETER C NOY,** *manufacturing engineer*
*Canadian General Electric Co Ltd, Barrie, Ont*

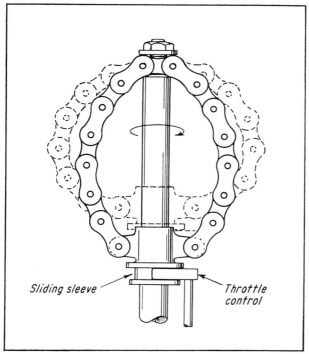

**1** SIMPLE GOVERNOR—weights can be attached by means of standard brackets to increase response force when rotation speed is slow.

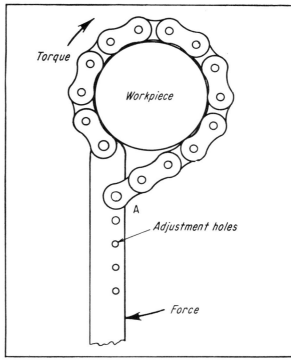

**2** WRENCH—pivot **A** can be adjusted to grip a variety of regularly or irregularly shaped objects.

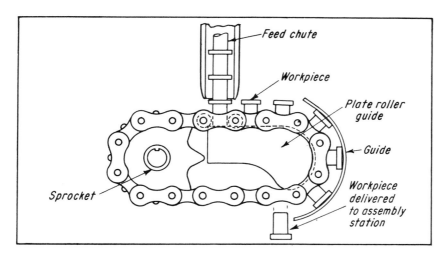

**3** SMALL PARTS CAN BE CONVEYED, fed, or oriented between spaces of roller chain.

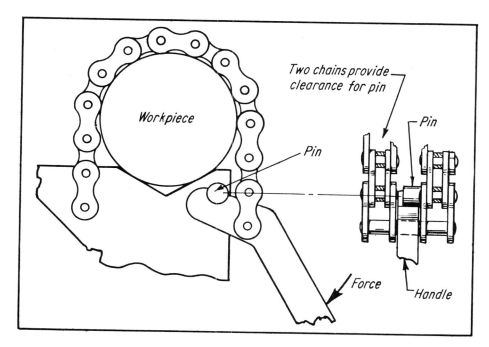

*Two chains provide clearance for pin*

*Workpiece*

*Pin*

*Pin*

*Force*

*Handle*

**4** CLAMP—toggle action is supplied by two chains, thus clearing pin at fulcrum.

**5** LIGHT-DUTY TROLLEY CONVEYORS can be made by combining standard roller-chain components with standard curtain-track components. Small gearmotors are used to drive the conveyor.

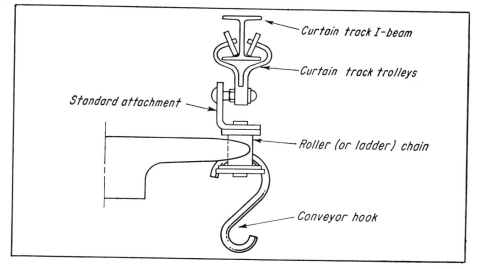

*Curtain track I-beam*

*Curtain track trolleys*

*Standard attachment*

*Roller (or ladder) chain*

*Conveyor hook*

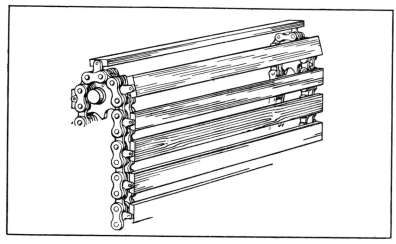

**6** SLATTED BELT, made by attaching wood, plastic or metal slats, can serve as adjustable safety guard, conveyor belt, fast-acting security-wicket window.

## Common Types of Bellows and Methods of Attaching End Fittings

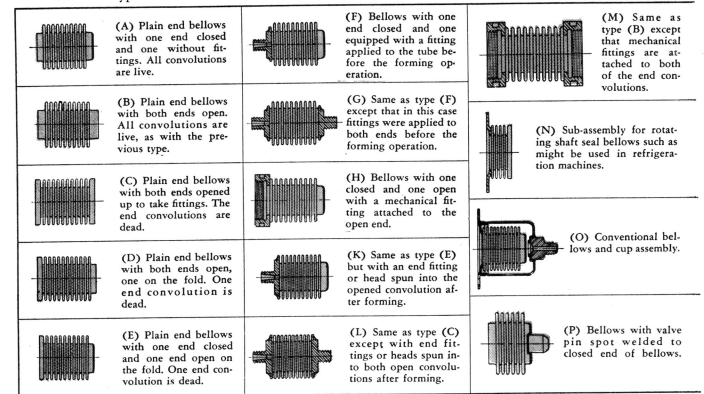

(A) Plain end bellows with one end closed and one without fittings. All convolutions are live.

(B) Plain end bellows with both ends open. All convolutions are live, as with the previous type.

(C) Plain end bellows with both ends opened up to take fittings. The end convolutions are dead.

(D) Plain end bellows with both ends open, one on the fold. One end convolution is dead.

(E) Plain end bellows with one end closed and one end open on the fold. One end convolution is dead.

(F) Bellows with one end closed and one equipped with a fitting applied to the tube before the forming operation.

(G) Same as type (F) except that in this case fittings were applied to both ends before the forming operation.

(H) Bellows with one closed and one open with a mechanical fitting attached to the open end.

(K) Same as type (E) but with an end fitting or head spun into the opened convolution after forming.

(L) Same as type (C) except with end fittings or heads spun into both open convolutions after forming.

(M) Same as type (B) except that mechanical fittings are attached to both of the end convolutions.

(N) Sub-assembly for rotating shaft seal bellows such as might be used in refrigeration machines.

(O) Conventional bellows and cup assembly.

(P) Bellows with valve pin spot welded to closed end of bellows.

# What to Consider
# When Selecting A

### 1. CONSTRUCTION

Open ends
Closed ends
Soldered fitting
Mechanical fitting
Special assembly

### 2. MATERIALS

Brass
Bronze
Monel
Stainless Steel
Others

### 3. FLEXIBILITY

Diameter
Wall thickness
Number of folds
Length

### 4. FILLING MEDIUM

Gas
Vapor
Liquid

THE BASIC CHARACTERISTIC of a metallic bellows is that it is axially flexible. This flexibility may be great or small, depending on such factors as the material of which the bellows is made, the wall thickness, the ratio of bellows length to diameter, and others. But if properly selected and applied, the bellows can be made to linearly or differentially respond to changes in temperature or pressure. In this respect, it is somewhat similar to a metallic diaphragm.

In so far as control of temperature or pressure is concerned, an electric strain gage might also be used. The difference between such devices and a bellows assembly is largely one of refinement and cost. The strain gage is highly sensitive and can be used under a wider range of operating conditions, but the bellows is less costly and does not require separate control devices or extensive instrumentation. As a matter of fact, most applications do not require any auxiliary actuating equipment, the movement of the bel-

## Life Prediction Chart for Metallic Bellows

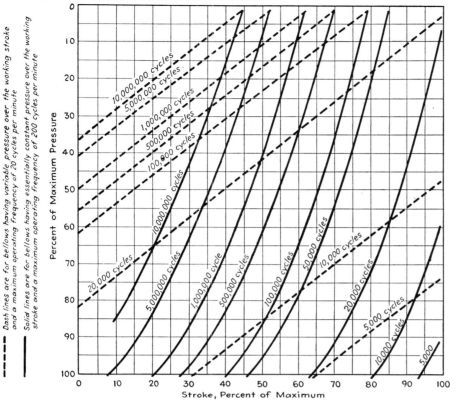

*Dash lines are for bellows having variable pressure over the working stroke and a maximum operating frequency of 20 cycles per minute*

*Solid lines are for bellows having essentially constant pressure over the working stroke and a maximum operating frequency of 200 cycles per minute*

*Percent of Maximum Pressure*

*Stroke, Percent of Maximum*

**A. H. ELLIS and J. H. HOWARD**
Clifford Manufacturing Company

# Metallic Bellows

## 5. LIFE

Stroke
Pressure
Temperature
Operating frequency

## 6. APPLICATION

Temperature control
Pressure control
Shaft seal

Expansion joint
Coupling
Liquid transmission

lows being depended upon to move the controlled device and thus regulate the desired quantity.

## CONSTRUCTION OF BELLOWS

A bellows usually is formed in one continuous operation from a thin seamless tube into the finished form, but the final construction may be varied

considerably. Both ends may be opened or closed. If open, they may be open on the folds or between the folds. The ends may be fitted with different attachments: An internal or external screw head attachment; a special fitting having a valve pin on the end; a special shaft seal fitting; or an enclosing envelope. These modifications are

shown in the accompanying table. The reasons for these various constructions is to facilitate assembly or to improve adaptation of the bellows to a particular control device, as will be discussed.

## MATERIALS

Bellows can be made of any one of several metals. Brass, of an 80-20 composition, is by far the most common. Bronze, phosphor bronze (95 copper-5 tin), cupro-nickel alloys, Everdur, nickel, Monel, stainless steel, and silver clad brass also are used. The type of material selected depends primarily on the atmospheric conditions encountered in service, the operating temperature, and on the gas or liquid with which the bellows comes in contact. It does not depend on the amount of expansion or travel required per increment change in pressure, as this usually is taken care of by varying the wall thickness.

## FLEXIBILITY

The flexibility of a bellows is directly proportional to number of convolutions in a given length, materials and wall thickness remaining the same. Doubling the number of convolutions doubles the flexibility and halves the spring rate. While this may be done when space is limited, the simpler procedure is to use a longer bellows. However, the length to diameter ratio should not be much greater than 1 to 1 to avoid buckling in service. This tendency can be alleviated to some extent by using an internal or external guide.

The smaller the diameter, the less the flexibility and the smaller the deflection with a given load. Flexibility in terms of stroke per unit load varies directly as the square of the outside diameter of the bellows. The stiffness of a small bellows therefore may require that the length be increased to $1\frac{1}{2}$ or even twice the diameter to obtain the desired length of travel.

## FILLING MEDIUM

A bellows may be a thermostatic assembly, in which case it is operated by the fluid with which it is filled. This fluid may be a liquid, gas or vapor.

Bellows that depend on gaseous expansion are filled with an inert gas. Changes in temperature cause corresponding changes in volume. This type of control requires a bulb sub-assembly whose volume is many times greater than that of the bellows. Even with such an arrangement, however, the movement of the bellows per unit change in temperature is small, and the switch or valve to be operated must be capable of functioning with a bellows movement of 0.006 to 0.007 in.

57

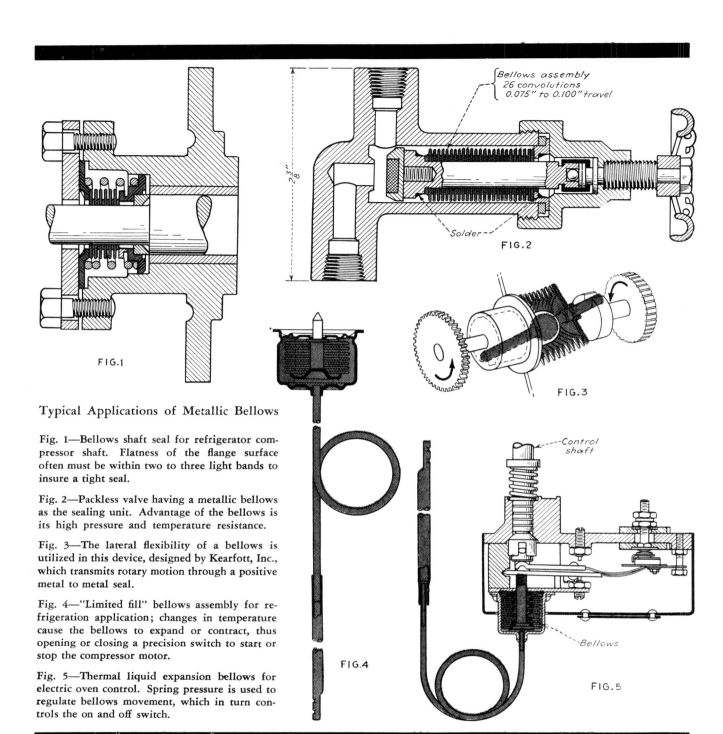

Bellows assembly
26 convolutions
0.075" to 0.100" travel

Solder

FIG.2

FIG.1

FIG.3

Control shaft

Bellows

FIG.4

FIG.5

## Typical Applications of Metallic Bellows

Fig. 1—Bellows shaft seal for refrigerator compressor shaft. Flatness of the flange surface often must be within two to three light bands to insure a tight seal.

Fig. 2—Packless valve having a metallic bellows as the sealing unit. Advantage of the bellows is its high pressure and temperature resistance.

Fig. 3—The lateral flexibility of a bellows is utilized in this device, designed by Kearfott, Inc., which transmits rotary motion through a positive metal to metal seal.

Fig. 4—"Limited fill" bellows assembly for refrigeration application; changes in temperature cause the bellows to expand or contract, thus opening or closing a precision switch to start or stop the compressor motor.

Fig. 5—Thermal liquid expansion bellows for electric oven control. Spring pressure is used to regulate bellows movement, which in turn controls the on and off switch.

5, the bellows expands and opens the contact above a certain temperature; when used in a gas range, expansion of the bellows acuates a control valve and throttles down the gas flow. The bellows is filled with a chemically stable liquid for operation up to 650 F.

When used as an overload protective device for electric motors, the supply lines to the motor may be wrapped around the bulb or else the bellows may be put directly in the motor circuit. A bulb also could be placed in the motor winding. Over

loads heat up the bellows, which then expands and breaks supply contacts.

PRESSURE CONTROL. Since even those bellows that are used for temperature control are actuated by pressure, it is a simple matter to apply the units directly in pressure indicating and recording instruments or control devices. The hook-up is similar to those already shown except that one end of the bellows usually is equipped with a fitting for the pressure supply line. This is not always necessary if barometric

pressure is relied on to actuate the bellows as is the case with evacuated bellows used in aircraft.

In both pressure and temperature applications, two or more bellows can be directly connected together, or connected through suitable levers, so that motion of one affects the motion of the other. The motion relationship is dependent on the method of connection and on flexibility and size of the units. Thus the type of application governs not only the type of bellows, but its physical construction as well.

# Chapter 3

# BASIC AND GENERAL DESIGN

# Here's your compilation of
# Volume and CG equations

The list covers 55 shapes, many of which are the result of drilled holes, bosses, and fillets in machined and cast parts.

E. W. JENKINS, *Knolls Atomic Power Laboratory, General Electric Co, Schenectady, NY*

## CYLINDERS

**1 . . Cylinder**

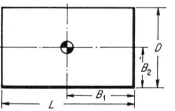

$$V = \frac{\pi}{4} D^2 L = 0.7854 D^2 L$$

$$B_1 = L/2$$
$$B_2 = R$$

**2 . . Half cylinder**

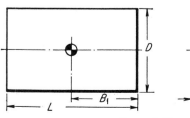

$$V = \frac{\pi}{8} D^2 L = 0.3927 D^2 L$$

$$B_1 = L/2$$
$$B_2 = \frac{4R}{3\pi} = 0.4244R$$

**3 . . Sector of cylinder**

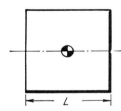 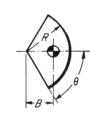

$$V = \theta R^2 L$$

$$B = \frac{2R \sin \theta}{3\theta}$$

**4 . . Segment of cylinder**

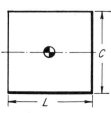 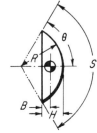

$$V = LR^2 \left(\theta - \frac{1}{2} \sin 2\theta\right)$$

$$V = 0.5L\,[RS - C(R - H)]$$

$$B = \frac{4R \sin^3 \theta}{6\theta - 3 \sin 2\theta}$$

$$S = 2R\theta$$
$$H = R(1 - \cos \theta)$$
$$C = 2R \sin \theta$$

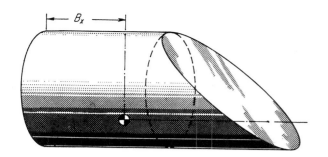

VOLUME equations are included for all cases. Where the equation for the CG (center of gravity) is not given, you can easily obtain it by looking up the volume and CG equations for portions of the shape and then combining values. For example, for the shape above, use the equations for a cylinder, Fig 1, and a truncated cylinder, Fig 10 (subscripts $C$ and $T$, respectively, in the equations below). Hence taking moments

$$B_x = \frac{V_c B_c + V_T(B_T + L_c)}{V_c + V_T}$$

or

$$B_x = \frac{\left(\frac{\pi}{4} D^2 L_c\right)\left(\frac{L_c}{2}\right) + \frac{\pi}{8} D^2 L_T\left(\frac{5}{16} L_T + L_c\right)}{\frac{\pi}{4} D^2 L_c + \frac{\pi}{8} D^2 L_T}$$

$$B_x = \frac{L_c^2 + L_T\left(\frac{5}{16} L_T + L_c\right)}{2L_c + L_T}$$

In the equations to follow, angle $\theta$ can be either in degrees or in radians. Thus $\theta$ (rad) $= \pi\theta/180$ (deg) $= 0.01745\,\theta$ (deg). For example, if $\theta = 30$ deg in Case 3, then $\sin \theta = 0.5$ and

$$B = \frac{2R\,(0.5)}{3\,(30)\,(0.01745)} = 0.637R$$

Symbols used are: $B$ = distance from CG to reference plane, $V$ = volume, $D$ and $d$ = diameter, $R$ and $r$ = radius, $H$ = height, $L$ = length.—*Nicholas P. Chironis*

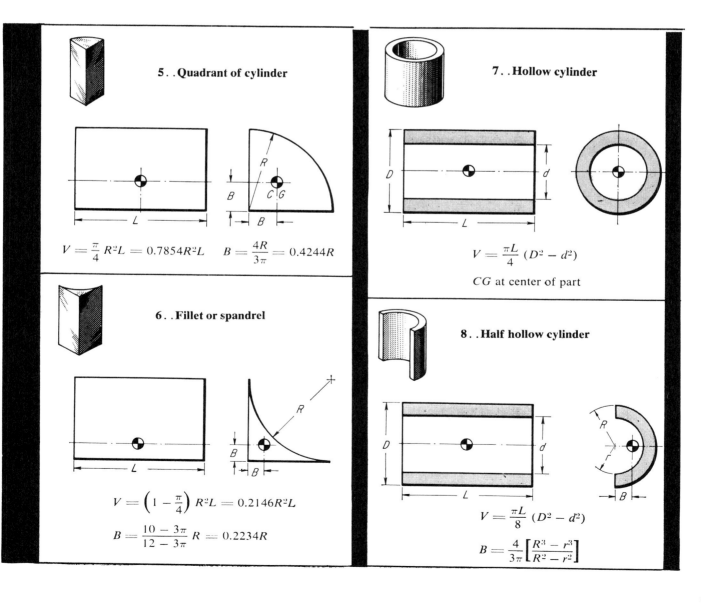

**5..Quadrant of cylinder**

$$V = \frac{\pi}{4} R^2 L = 0.7854R^2L \qquad B = \frac{4R}{3\pi} = 0.4244R$$

**6..Fillet or spandrel**

$$V = \left(1 - \frac{\pi}{4}\right) R^2 L = 0.2146R^2L$$

$$B = \frac{10 - 3\pi}{12 - 3\pi} R = 0.2234R$$

**7..Hollow cylinder**

$$V = \frac{\pi L}{4} (D^2 - d^2)$$

*CG* at center of part

**8..Half hollow cylinder**

$$V = \frac{\pi L}{8} (D^2 - d^2)$$

$$B = \frac{4}{3\pi}\left[\frac{R^3 - r^3}{R^2 - r^2}\right]$$

### 9 . . Sector of hollow cylinder

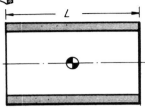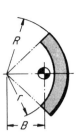

$$V = 0.01745\,(R^2 - r^2)\,\theta L$$

$$B = \frac{38.1972\,(R^3 - r^3)\,\sin\theta}{(R^2 - r^2)\,\theta}$$

### 10 . . Truncated cylinder (with full circle base)

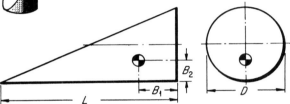

$$V = \frac{\pi}{8}\,D^2 L = 0.3927 D^2 L$$

$$B_1 = 0.3125L$$
$$B_2 = 0.375D$$

### 11 . . Truncated cylinder
### (with partial circle base)

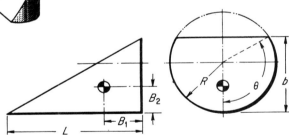

$$b = R\,(1 - \cos\theta)$$

$$V = \frac{R^3 L}{b}\left[\sin\theta - \frac{\sin^3\theta}{3} - \theta\cos\theta\right]$$

$$B_1 = \frac{L\left[\dfrac{\theta\cos^2\theta}{2} - \dfrac{5\sin\theta\cos\theta}{8} + \dfrac{\sin^3\theta\cos\theta}{12} + \dfrac{\theta}{8}\right]}{\left[1 - \cos\theta\right]\left[\sin\theta - \dfrac{\sin^3\theta}{3} - \theta\cos\theta\right]}$$

$$B_2 = \frac{2R\left[-\dfrac{\theta\cos\theta}{2} + \dfrac{\sin\theta}{2} - \dfrac{\theta}{8} + \dfrac{\sin\theta\cos\theta}{8} - N\right]}{\left[\sin\theta - \dfrac{\sin^3\theta}{3} - \theta\cos\theta\right]}$$

$$\text{where}\quad N = \frac{5\sin^3\theta}{6} - \frac{\sin^3\theta\cos\theta}{12}$$

### 12 . . Oblique cylinder
### (or circular hole at oblique angle)

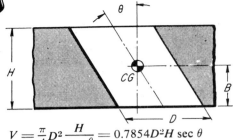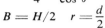

$$V = \frac{\pi}{4}D^2\,\frac{H}{\cos\theta} = 0.7854 D^2 H \sec\theta$$

$$B = H/2 \qquad r = \frac{d}{2}$$

### 13 . . Bend in cylinder

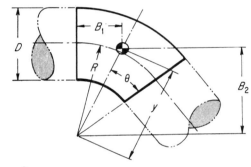

$$V = \frac{\pi^2}{360}\,D^2 R\theta = 0.0274 D^2 R\theta$$

$$y = R\left[1 + \frac{r^2}{4R^2}\right]$$

$$B_1 = y\tan\theta$$
$$B_2 = y\cot\theta$$

### 14 . . Curved groove in cylinder

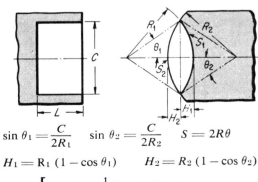

$$\sin\theta_1 = \frac{C}{2R_1} \qquad \sin\theta_2 = \frac{C}{2R_2} \qquad S = 2R\theta$$

$$H_1 = R_1\,(1 - \cos\theta_1) \qquad H_2 = R_2\,(1 - \cos\theta_2)$$

$$V = L\left[R_1^2\left(\theta_1 - \frac{1}{2}\,\theta_1\sin 2\theta_1\right) + R_2^2\left(\theta_2 - \frac{1}{2}\,\theta_2\sin 2\theta_2\right)\right]$$

Compute $CG$ of each part separately

## 15..Slot in cylinder

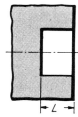

$$H = R(1 - \cos \theta) \qquad \sin \theta = \frac{C}{2R} \qquad S = 2R\theta$$

$$V = L\left[CN + R^2\left(\theta - \frac{1}{2}\sin 2\theta\right)\right]$$

## 16..Slot in hollow cylinder

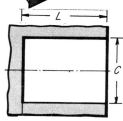
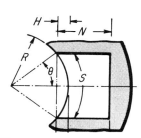

$$S = 2R\theta \qquad \sin \theta = \frac{C}{2R} \qquad H = R(1 - \cos \theta)$$

$$V = L\left[CN - R^2\left(\theta - \frac{1}{2}\sin 2\theta\right)\right]$$

$$V = L\left(CN - 0.5\left[RS - C(R - H)\right]\right)$$

## 17..Curved groove in hollow cylinder

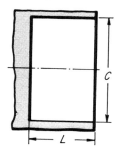
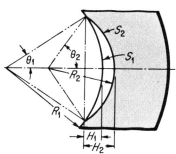

$$\sin \theta_1 = \frac{C}{2R_1} \qquad \sin \theta_2 = \frac{C}{2R_2} \qquad S = 2R\theta$$

$$H_1 = R_1(1 - \cos \theta_1) \qquad H_2 = R_2(1 - \cos \theta_2)$$

$$V = L\left(\left[R_2^2\left(\theta_2 - \frac{1}{2}\sin 2\theta_2\right)\right] - \left[R_1^2\left(\theta_1 - \frac{1}{2}\sin 2\theta_1\right)\right]\right)$$

$$V = \frac{L}{2}\left(\left[R_2S_2 - C(R_2 - H_2)\right] - \left[R_1S_1 - C(R_1 - H_1)\right]\right)$$

## 18..Slot through hollow cylinder

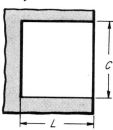
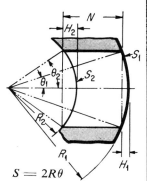

$$\sin \theta_1 = \frac{C}{R_1} \qquad \sin \theta_2 = \frac{C}{R_2} \qquad S = 2R\theta$$

$$H_1 = R_1(1 - \cos \theta_1) \qquad H_2 = R_2(1 - \cos \theta_2)$$

$$V = L\left(CN + \left[R_1^2\left(\theta_1 - \frac{1}{2}\sin 2\theta_1\right)\right] - \left[R_2\left(\theta_2 - \frac{1}{2}\sin \theta_2\right)\right]\right)$$

$$V = L\left(CN + 0.5\left[R_1S_1 - C(R_1 - H_1)\right] - 0.5\left[R_2S_2 - C(R_2 - H_2)\right]\right)$$

## 19..Intersecting cylinder
### (volume of junction box)

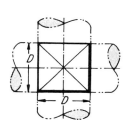

$$V = D^3\left(\frac{\pi}{2} - \frac{2}{3}\right) = 0.9041D^3$$

## 20..Intersecting hollow cylinders
### (volume of junction box)

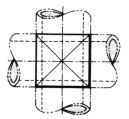

$$V = \left(\frac{\pi}{2} - \frac{2}{3}\right)(D^3 - d^3) - \frac{\pi}{2}d^2(D - d)$$

$$V = 0.9041(D^3 - d^3) - 1.5708\,d^2(D - d)$$

### 21..Intersecting parallel cylinders
$$(M < R_1)$$

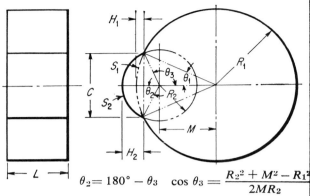

$$\theta_2 = 180° - \theta_3 \qquad \cos \theta_3 = \frac{R_2{}^2 + M^2 - R_1{}^2}{2MR_2}$$

$$\cos \theta_1 = \frac{R_1{}^2 + M^2 - R_2{}^2}{2MR_1} \qquad \begin{array}{l} H_1 = R_1\,(1 - \cos \theta_1) \\ S_1 = 2R_1\theta_1 \end{array}$$

$$V = L\left(\pi R_1{}^2 + \left[R_2{}^2\left(\theta_2 - \frac{1}{2}\sin 2\theta_2\right) - \left[R_1{}^2\left(\theta_1 - \frac{1}{2}\sin 2\theta_1\right)\right]\right)\right.$$

### 22..Intersecting parallel cylinders
$$(M > R_1)$$

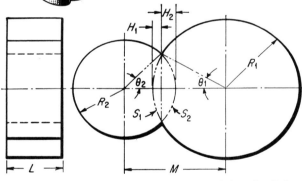

$$\begin{array}{l} H_1 = R_1\,(1 - \cos \theta_1) \\ S_1 = 2R_1\theta_1 \end{array} \qquad \cos \theta_1 = \frac{R_1{}^2 + M^2 - R_2{}^2}{2MR_1}$$

$$V = L\left(\left[\pi\,(R_1{}^2 + R_2{}^2)\right] - \left[R_1{}^2\left(\theta_1 - \frac{1}{2}\sin 2\theta_1\right)\right]\right.$$
$$\left. - \left[R_2{}^2\left(\theta_2 - \frac{1}{2}\sin 2\theta_2\right)\right]\right)$$

## SPHERES

### 23..Sphere

 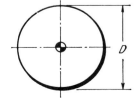

$$V = \frac{\pi D^3}{6} = 0.5236D^3$$

### 24..Hemisphere

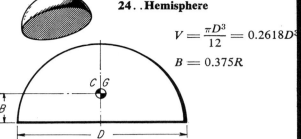

$$V = \frac{\pi D^3}{12} = 0.2618D^3$$

$$B = 0.375R$$

### 25..Spherical segment

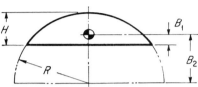

$$V = \pi H^2\left(R - \frac{H}{3}\right)$$

$$B_1 = \frac{H\,(4R - H)}{4\,(3R - H)}$$

$$B_2 = \frac{3\,(2R - H)^2}{4\,(3R - H)}$$

### 26..Spherical sector

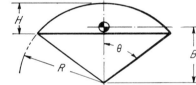

$$V = \frac{2\pi}{3}R^2H = 2.0944R^2H$$

$$B = 0.375\,(1 + \cos \theta)\,R = 0.375\,(2R - H)$$

### 27..Shell of hollow hemisphere

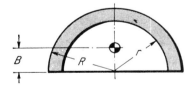

$$V = \frac{2\pi}{3}\,(R^3 - r^3) \qquad B = 0.375\left(\frac{R^4 - r^4}{R^3 - r^3}\right)$$

### 28..Hollow sphere

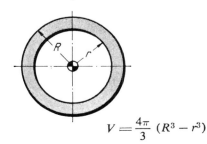

$$V = \frac{4\pi}{3}\,(R^3 - r^3)$$

64

### 29 . . Shell of spherical sector

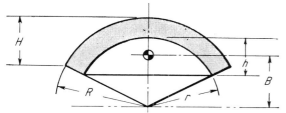

$$V = \frac{2\pi}{3} \, (R^2 H - r^2 h)$$

$$B = 0.375 \left\{ \frac{[R^2 H \, (2R - H)] - [r^2 h \, (2r - h)]}{R^2 H - r^2 h} \right\}$$

### 30 . . Shell of spherical segment

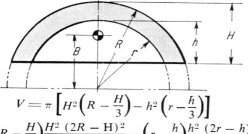

$$V = \pi \left[ H^2 \left( R - \frac{H}{3} \right) - h^2 \left( r - \frac{h}{3} \right) \right]$$

$$B = \frac{3}{4} \left[ \frac{\left( R - \dfrac{H}{3} \right) \dfrac{H^2 \, (2R - H)^2}{3R - H} - \left( r - \dfrac{h}{3} \right) \dfrac{h^2 \, (2r - h)^2}{3r - h}}{H^2 \left( R - \dfrac{H}{3} \right) - h^2 \left( r - \dfrac{h}{3} \right)} \right]$$

### 31 . . Circular hole through sphere

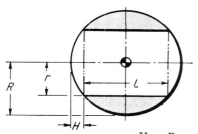

$$V = \pi \left[ r^2 L + 2H^2 \left( R - \frac{H}{3} \right) \right] \qquad H = R - \sqrt{R^2 - r^2}$$

$$L = 2(R - H)$$

### 32 . . Circular hole through hollow sphere

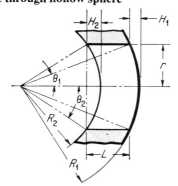

$$V = \pi \left\{ r^2 L + H_1 \left( R_1 - \frac{H_1}{3} \right) - H_2^2 \left( R_2 - \frac{H_2}{3} \right) \right\}$$

$$\sin \theta_1 = r/R_1 \qquad \sin \theta_2 = r/R_2 \qquad H = R \, (1 - \cos \theta)$$

### 33 . . Spherical zone

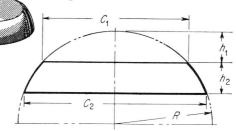

$$V = \pi \left\{ \left[ H^2 \left( R - \frac{H}{3} \right) \right] - \left[ h_1^2 \left( R - \frac{h}{3} \right) \right] \right\}$$

$$V = \frac{\pi h_2}{6} \left[ \frac{3}{4} \, C_1^2 + \frac{3}{4} \, C_2^2 + h_2^2 \right]$$

### 34 . . Conical hole through spherical shell

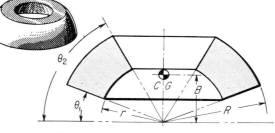

$$V = \frac{2\pi}{3} \, (R^3 - r^3) \, (\sin \theta_2 - \sin \theta_1)$$

$$B = \frac{0.375 \, (R^4 - r^4) \, (\sin \theta_2 + \sin \theta_1)}{R^3 - r^3}$$

## RINGS

### 35 . . Torus         36 . . Hollow torus

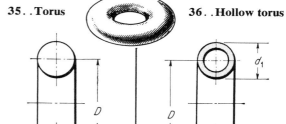

$$V = \frac{1}{4} \, \pi^2 d^2 D = 2.467 d^2 D \qquad V = \frac{1}{4} \, \pi^2 D \, (d_1^2 - d_2^2)$$

### 37 . . Bevel ring

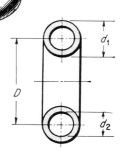
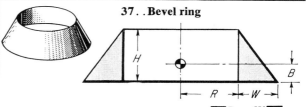

$$V = \pi \left( R + \frac{1}{3} \, W \right) WH \qquad B = H \left[ \frac{\dfrac{R}{3} + \dfrac{W}{12}}{R + \dfrac{W}{3}} \right]$$

### 38 . . Bevel ring

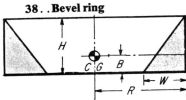

$$B > \frac{H}{3}$$

$$V = \pi \left( R - \frac{1}{3} W \right) WH$$

$$B = H \left[ \frac{\dfrac{R}{3} - \dfrac{W}{12}}{R - \dfrac{W}{3}} \right]$$

### 39 . . Quarter torus

$$B < 0.4244R$$

$$V = \frac{\pi^2 R^2}{2} \left( r + \frac{4R}{3\pi} \right) = 4.9348R^2 \, (r + 0.4244R)$$

$$B = \frac{4R}{3\pi} \left[ \frac{r + \dfrac{3R}{8}}{r + \dfrac{4R}{3\pi}} \right] = \frac{0.4244Rr + 0.1592R^2}{r + 0.4244R}$$

### 40 . . Quarter torus

$$V = \frac{\pi^2 R^2}{2} \left[ r - \frac{4R}{3\pi} \right] \qquad B = \frac{4R}{3\pi} \left[ \frac{r - \dfrac{3R}{8}}{r - \dfrac{4R}{3\pi}} \right]$$

### 41 . . Curved shell ring

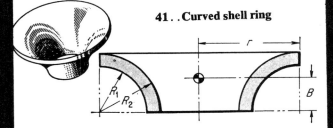

$$V = 2\pi \left\{ r - \frac{4}{3\pi} \left[ \frac{R_2{}^3 - R_1{}^3}{R_2{}^2 - R_1{}^2} \right] \right\} \frac{\pi}{4} \, (R_2{}^2 - R_1{}^2)$$

$$B = \frac{4}{3\pi} \left[ \frac{R_2{}^3 \left( r - \dfrac{3}{8} R_2 \right) - R_1{}^3 \left( r - \dfrac{3}{8} R_1 \right)}{(R_2{}^2 - R_1{}^2) \left\{ r - \dfrac{4}{3\pi} \left[ \dfrac{R_2{}^3 - R_1{}^3}{R_2{}^2 - R_1{}^2} \right] \right\}} \right]$$

### 42 . . Curved shell ring

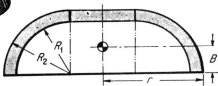

$$V = \frac{\pi^2}{2} \left[ r(R_2{}^2 - R_1{}^2) + \frac{4}{3\pi} \, (R_2{}^3 - R_1{}^3) \right]$$

$$B = \frac{2}{\pi} \left[ \frac{\dfrac{2r}{3} \, (R_2{}^3 - R_1{}^3) + \dfrac{1}{4} \, (R_2{}^4 - R_1{}^4)}{r(R_2{}^2 - R_1{}^2) + \dfrac{4}{3\pi} \, (R_2{}^3 - R_1{}^3)} \right]$$

### 43 . . Fillet ring

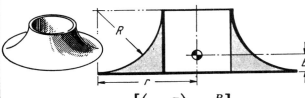

$$V = 2\pi R^2 \left[ \left( 1 - \frac{\pi}{4} \right) r - \frac{R}{6} \right]$$

$$B = R \left[ \frac{\left( \dfrac{5}{6} - \dfrac{\pi}{4} \right) r - \dfrac{R}{24}}{\left( 1 - \dfrac{\pi}{4} \right) r - \dfrac{R}{6}} \right]$$

### 44 . . Fillet ring

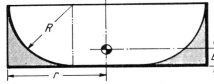

$$V = 2\pi R^2 \left[ \left( 1 - \frac{\pi}{4} \right) r - \left( \frac{5}{6} - \frac{\pi}{4} \right) R \right]$$

$$B = R \left[ \frac{\left( \dfrac{5}{6} - \dfrac{\pi}{4} \right) r - \left( \dfrac{19}{24} - \dfrac{\pi}{4} \right) R}{\left( 1 - \dfrac{\pi}{4} \right) r - \left( \dfrac{5}{6} - \dfrac{\pi}{4} \right) R} \right]$$

### 45 . . Curved-sector ring

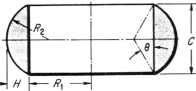

$$V = 2\pi R_2{}^2 \; \times$$

$$\left[ R_1 + \left( \frac{4 \sin 3\theta}{6\theta - 3 \sin 2\theta} - \cos \theta \right) R_2 \right] \left[ \theta - 0.5 \sin 2\theta \right]$$

# MISCELLANEOUS

### 46..Ellipsoidal cylinder

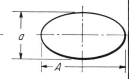

$$V = \frac{\pi}{4} AaL$$

### 47..Ellipsoid

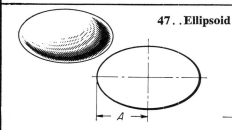
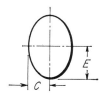

$$V = \frac{4}{3} \pi ACE$$

### 48..Paraboloid

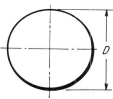

$$V = \frac{\pi}{8} HD^2 \qquad B = \frac{1}{3} H$$

### 49..Pyramid (with base of any shape)

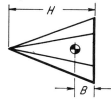

$A = Area\ of\ base$

$$V = \frac{1}{3} AH \qquad B = \frac{1}{4} H$$

### 50..Frustum of pyramid (with base of any shape)

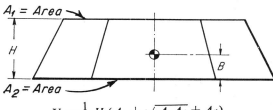

$A_1 = Area$

$A_2 = Area$

$$V = \frac{1}{3} H (A_1 + \sqrt{A_1 A_2} + A_2)$$

$$B = \frac{H (A_1 + 2\sqrt{A_1 A_2} + 3A_2)}{4 (A_1 + \sqrt{A_1 A_2} + A_2)}$$

### 51..Cone

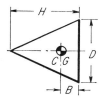

$$V = \frac{\pi}{12} D^2 H$$

$$B = \frac{1}{4} H$$

### 52..Frustum of cone

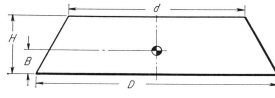

$$V = \frac{\pi}{12} H (D^2 + Dd + d^2)$$

$$B = \frac{H (D^2 + 2Dd + 3d^2)}{4 (D^2 + Dd + d^2)}$$

### 53..Frustum of hollow cone

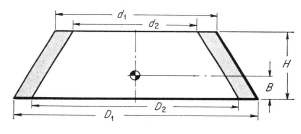

$$V = 0.2618H [(D_1{}^2 + D_1 d_1 + d_1{}^2) - (D_2{}^2 + D_2 d_2 + d_2{}^2)]$$

### 54..Hexagon

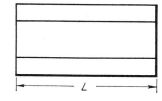

$$V = \frac{\sqrt{3}}{2} d^2 L$$

$$V = 0.866 d^2 L$$

### 55..Closely packed helical springs

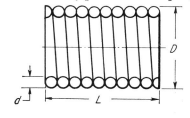

$$V = \frac{\pi^2 dL}{4} (D - d)$$

$$V = 2.4674 (D - d)$$

# How Design Is Affected By Foundry Practice

**10** BASIC RULES which the designer should follow to facilitate production of sand cast metal parts. Although these rules should not be applied mechanically, their judicious use will lead to a sounder and more economical product. In addition to specific rules relating to shape and size of a part, reasons for the influence of casting problems on product design—such as shrinkage allowance—are explained in detail.

**OLIVER SMALLEY**, Meehanite Metal Corporation

## RULE 1— Design for Sound Castings

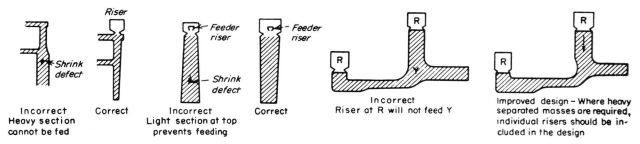

Incorrect
Heavy section cannot be fed

Correct

Incorrect
Light section at top prevents feeding

Correct

Incorrect
Riser at R will not feed Y

Improved design – Where heavy separated masses are required, individual risers should be included in the design

To offset liquid shrinkage, design so that all members of the parts increase progressively in thickness to one or more suitable locations where risers (feeder heads) can be placed to supply the metal required. These are illustrations of correct and incorrect methods of designing to assure soundness of section.

## RULE 2— Design Sections as Uniform in Thickness as Possible

All heavy sections should be accessible for feeding — see Rule 1.

Uniform section saves weight, material, machining costs and results in stronger casting ---

Incorrect

Correct

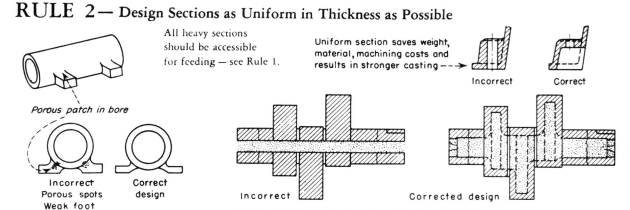

Porous patch in bore

Incorrect
Porous spots
Weak foot
Cylinder with lugs

Correct
design

Incorrect

Corrected design

Hydraulic Pump—Designed originally with 2 in. core through center. This gave excessive metal and porous patches on machined casting.

# RULE 3 — At Adjoining Sections Avoid Sharp Angles And Abrupt Section Changes

**Metal Structure is Affected by Shape of Casting Section.** Solidification of molten metal always proceeds from the mold face, forming unbalanced crystal grains that penetrate into the mass at right angles to the plane of cooling surface. A simple section presents uniform cooling conditions and greatest freedom from mechanical weakness. When two or more sections conjoin, mechanical weakness is induced at the junction and free cooling is interrupted, creating a "hot spot."

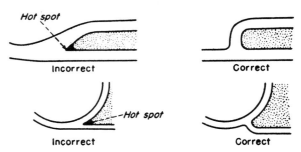

Cylinder castings (marine cylinder port core.) Avoid core design that does not present a cooling surface.

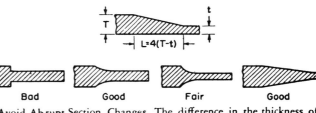

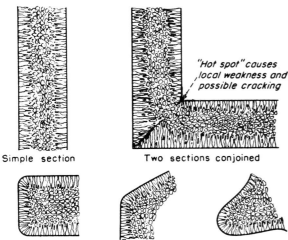

Simple section    Two sections conjoined

"Hot spot" causes local weakness and possible cracking

Crystal structure of various casting forms shows advantages of rounded corners. The extent of formation of columnar crystals is primarily a function of the metal used, the rate of solidification and the shape of the casting.

**Avoid Abrupt Section Changes.** The difference in the thickness of adjoining sections should be a minimum and not exceed a ratio of 2:1. Where a greater difference is unavoidable, consider design with detachable parts—ways of machine tool beds can be bolted. When a change of thickness is less than 2:1, it may take the form of a fillet; where the difference is greater, the recommended form is a wedge. Wedge-shaped changes in wall thickness should be designed with a taper not exceeding 1:4. Where light and heavy sections are unavoidable, use proper fillets or tapering sections or both. If blending of sections is not possible, use fillets of fairly large size at junctions.

Avoid stress concentration at adjoining sections. Replace all sharp corners with radii and avoid heat and stress concentration. When the thickness of flanges differ from that of the body of the casting, the change in thickness should be gradual and tapered 1:4.5.

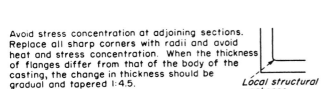

Local structural weakness    Local shrink weakness    Too large fillet causes weak metal structure or shrinkage defect    Improved design

Poor design

# RULE 4 — Fillet All Sharp Angles

Fillets have two functional purposes: (1) To reduce stress-concentration in the casting in service; and (2) to prevent cracks, tears and draws at re-entry angles; to make corners more moldable.

To fulfill engineering stress requirements and reduce stress concentration relatively large fillets should be used:

$$R = T \text{ to } 2T$$

where $R =$ radius of fillet
$T =$ thickness of casting

However, where this dimension fillet is used, casting thickness is increased at the joint and tends to cause structural weakness in casting. Casting design should preferably take the form shown as "improved" design of L section. Where this is not possible, it should be decided whether the engineering design or the foundry casting problem is most vital. From the foundryman's viewpoint, too large fillets are undesirable and the radius of the fillet should approximate one-third the thickness of the section joined.

$R = \dfrac{T}{3}$ or $\dfrac{T}{2}$

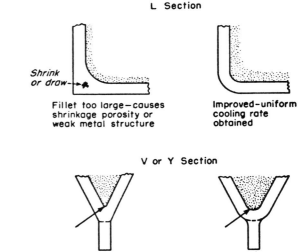

L Section

Shrink or draw

Fillet too large—causes shrinkage porosity or weak metal structure

Improved—uniform cooling rate obtained

V or Y Section

Poor—"hot spot" causes structural weakness

Improved—less localization of heat effect

# RULE 5 — Bring Minimum Number of Adjoining Sections Together

In a well designed casting, sections are no thicker than is essential to the desired unit of strength and are evenly proportioned to avoid local slow cooling.

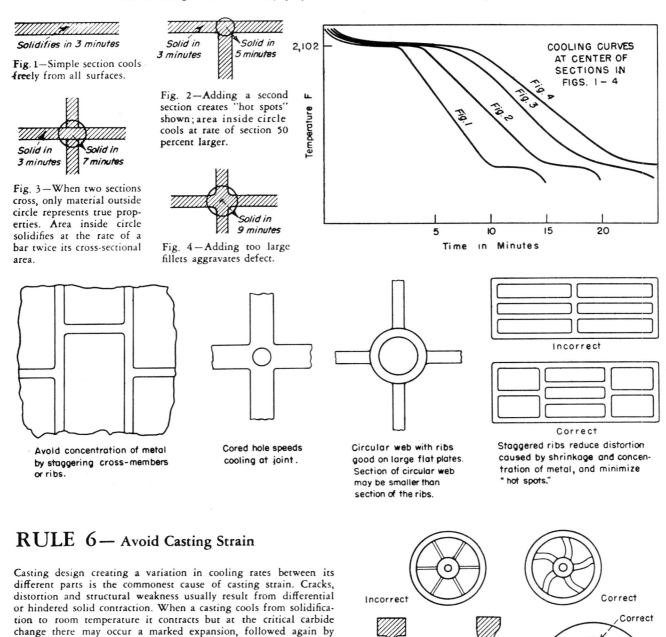

**Solidifies in 3 minutes**

**Fig. 1**—Simple section cools freely from all surfaces.

**Solid in 3 minutes**    **Solid in 5 minutes**

**Fig. 2**—Adding a second section creates "hot spots" shown; area inside circle cools at rate of section 50 percent larger.

**Solid in 3 minutes**    **Solid in 7 minutes**

**Fig. 3**—When two sections cross, only material outside circle represents true properties. Area inside circle solidifies at the rate of a bar twice its cross-sectional area.

**Solid in 9 minutes**

**Fig. 4**—Adding too large fillets aggravates defect.

COOLING CURVES AT CENTER OF SECTIONS IN FIGS. 1 – 4

2,102 — Temperature F — Time in Minutes

Avoid concentration of metal by staggering cross-members or ribs.

Cored hole speeds cooling at joint.

Circular web with ribs good on large flat plates. Section of circular web may be smaller than section of the ribs.

Incorrect

Correct

Staggered ribs reduce distortion caused by shrinkage and concentration of metal, and minimize "hot spots."

# RULE 6 — Avoid Casting Strain

Casting design creating a variation in cooling rates between its different parts is the commonest cause of casting strain. Cracks, distortion and structural weakness usually result from differential or hindered solid contraction. When a casting cools from solidification to room temperature it contracts but at the critical carbide change there may occur a marked expansion, followed again by normal contraction. To reduce or prevent casting strain:

1. Avoid sudden changes of form producing a corresponding change in the direction of shrinkage.
2. Avoid re-entrant angles.
3. Avoid multiplicity of cores—these expand under influence of heat and offer resistance to free shrinkage.
4. Avoid widely differing section sizes—especially those in close juxtaposition—which might give rise to different rates of cooling.
5. Where internal casting strain must be a minimum or where complete stability is vital, provide for a stress relief anneal.

When designing gears, flywheels and spoked wheels:
1. Use odd number and curved spokes.
2. Provide for all cross-sections to cool as evenly as possible by avoiding excessive sectional variation.
3. Blend sections of varying sizes carefully.

Incorrect    Correct

Correct

Incorrect    (A)    Correct    Incorrect

The rim of the flywheel (A) is designed heavier than the spokes, and when poured solidifies last. Due to restrained contraction and cooling of the uneven sections, the rim will be left with tension strains, with corresponding compression forces in the spokes and hub Arms of sufficient section, having a cooling rate more nearly that of the hub and rim, represents good design.

# RULE 7 — Bosses, Lugs and Pads Should Not Be Used Unless Absolutely Necessary

Bosses and pads increase metal thickness, create hot spots and cause open grain or shrinks. Blend into casting by tapering or flattening the fillets. Bosses should not be included in casting design when support for bolts can be obtained by milling or countersinking.

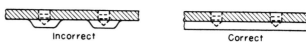

Continuous rib instead of a series of bosses permits shifting hole location.

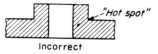 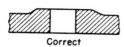

Thickness of bosses and pads should preferably be less than the thickness of the casting section they adjoin, but thick enough to permit machining without touching the casting wall. Where the casting section is light and does not permit use of this rule, then the following minimum recommended heights can serve as a guide:

| Approximate Casting Length, ft | Height of Boss, in |
|---|---|
| Up to 1½ | 0.25 |
| 1½-6 | 0.75 |
| Over 6 | 1.0 |

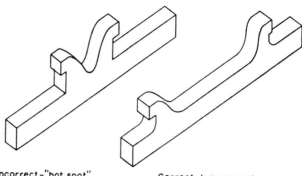

Incorrect—"hot spot" at center.

Correct—lugs spread out promotes uniform solidification.

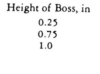

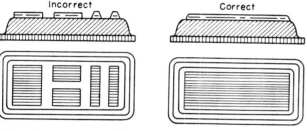

When there are several lugs and bosses on one surface they should be joined if possible, to facilitate machining. A panel of uniform thickness instead of many pads of varying height simplifies machining.

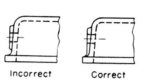

Undercuts should be eliminated wherever possible.

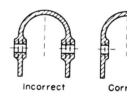

Omit outside bosses to obtain straight draft.

# RULE 8 — Proportion Dimensions of Inner Walls Correctly

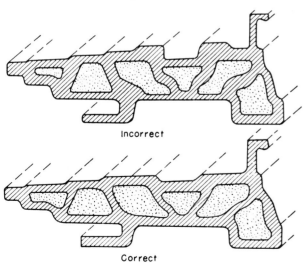

Inner sections of castings resulting from complex cores cool much slower than outer sections, therefore reduce inner sections to 0.7 to 0.9 of the outer wall, depending on intricacy and shape of design. Avoid sharp angles.

Cylinders and Bushings

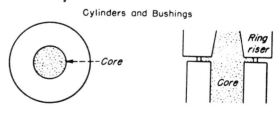

When diameter of core equals thickness of casting, danger point of casting soundness and risering is being reached and core begins to slow cooling of center—making feeding difficult unless chillers are used in core.

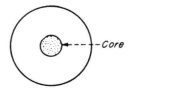 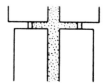

When diameter of core is one-third of casting section or less, feeding is difficult if ordinary sand is used. Steel tube core filled with lead or sand, or a graphite, steel or cast iron rod is preferred. In such bushings, do not use cores, and cast solid.

# RULE 9—Design Ribs and Brackets for Maximum Effectiveness

Ribs have two functions: (a) To improve stiffness; and (b) to reduce weight. Correct rib depth and spacing depends on the overall engineering design.

Stiffness of structures may be improved by selection of type of cast metal used. A plate or wall in an iron with high modulus of elasticity may not require to be ribbed, but ribbing would be necessary with a lower modulus material.

Ribs and brackets can create molding problems, "shrinks" and local casting weakness if incorrectly designed and applied. If too shallow in depth or too widely spaced, they are ineffectual.

Thickness of Ribs. Uniformity of casting section and freedom from "hot spots" is essential. Ribs tend to increase metal section.

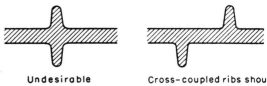

**Undesirable**      **Cross-coupled ribs should preferably be designed as doubled T forms.**

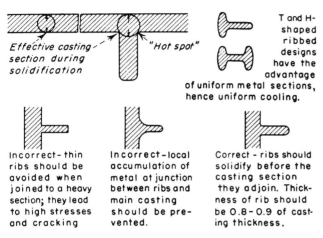

Effective casting section during solidification    "Hot spot"

T and H-shaped ribbed designs have the advantage of uniform metal sections, hence uniform cooling.

**Incorrect-thin ribs should be avoided when joined to a heavy section; they lead to high stresses and cracking**

**Incorrect-local accumulation of metal at junction between ribs and main casting should be prevented.**

**Correct - ribs should solidify before the casting section they adjoin. Thickness of rib should be 0.8-0.9 of casting thickness.**

DEPTH OF RIBS. Preference is for ribs having depth appreciably greater than thickness. Ribs in compression offer a greater factor of safety than ribs in tension. However, castings having thin ribs or webs in compression may require design changes to give necessary stiffening to avoid buckling.

Cross ribbing or ribbing on both sides of a casting is undesirable from the foundry viewpoint, increasing casting defectives and total cost to user. Cross ribbing creates local "hot spots," renders feeding solid difficult, causes local weakness and porosity. In flexure, ribbing on both sides of the plate results in inefficient use of metal and local casting weakness. Avoiding complex ribbing simplifies molding procedure and assures more uniform solidification conditions. Casting stresses and stress distribution favor omission of ribbing if the casting wall itself can be made of ample strength and stiffness.

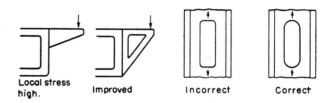

**Local stress high.**    **Improved**    **Incorrect**    **Correct**

BRACKETS. Brackets carrying offset loads introduce bending moments both local and in the body of the casting. Contact with main casting should be as long as possible. Brackets can be detached from the main casting (cast separately) and attached to the main structure. Simplifies molding—reduces cost of manufacture.

Avoid rectangular shaped cored holes in ribs or webs. Use oval shaped cored holes with the longest dimension in the direction of the stresses.

# RULE 10 — Allow for Shrinkage and Machine Finish in Dimensional Tolerances

A rule sometimes applied is that dimensional tolerances should be approximately half the maximum shrinkage allowable for the particular type of metal. This rule does not hold in extremely large and complex castings, and in castings made with such accuracy that no machining or finishing outside the foundry is required.

CAST METAL SHRINKAGE ALLOWANCES
(Contraction in. per ft )

| | |
|---|---|
| Gray Cast Iron | 1/10-5/32 |
| White Cast Iron | 1/4 |
| Malleable Cast Iron | 1/8-3/32 |
| Meehanite Metals | 1/8-1/10 |
| Aluminum Alloys | 5/32 |
| Magnesium Alloys | 5/32 |
| Yellow Brass | 5/32-3/16 |
| Gun Metal Bronze | 1/8-3/16 |
| Phosphor Bronze | 1/8-3/16 |
| Aluminum Bronze | 1/4 |
| Manganese Bronze | 1/4 |
| Open Hearth Steel | 3/16 |
| Electric Steel | 1/4 |
| High Manganese Steel | 5/16 |

These figures are to be used with caution because most castings have several different shrinkage allowances according to their size, design complexity, relative mass of core vs metal, varying metal thickness, nature of metal, temperature of pouring and mold material.

MACHINE FINISH ALLOWANCE. The allowance for machine finish depends on: (a) Type of metal used; (b) design of the casting; (c) size; (d) tendency to warp; and (e) machining method.

TYPICAL MACHINE FINISH ALLOWANCES
(in addition to shrinkage allowance)

| Dimension of Casting, in | Expected Tolerances for "As Cast" Dimension, in. |
|---|---|
| up to 8 | ± 1/16 |
| up to 14 | ± 3/32 |
| up to 18 | ± 1/8 |
| up to 24 | ± 5/32 |
| up to 30 | ± 3/16 |
| up to 36 | ± 1/4 |

Machining allowances for cylinder bores are difficult to specify in a general way. Often a plain cylinder, such as is cast for piston ring stock or for a cylinder liner, will contract a normal amount lengthwise but there may be no contraction in the inside bore. The accompanying allowances are given as a guide.

ALLOWANCES FOR MACHINING CYLINDERS OF SINGLE BORE

| Diameter, in. | Allowances, in. |
|---|---|
| 4 | 0.12-0.2 |
| 4-8 | 0.12-0.24 |
| 8-12 | 0.2 -0.32 |
| 12-20 | 0.25-0.40 |

CYLINDERS OF MORE THAN ONE BORE

| Diameter, in. | Allowance on Wall Thickness, in. |
|---|---|
| 8 | 0.16-0.24 |
| 8-12 | 0.2 -0.28 |
| 12-20 | 0.24-0.32 |
| 20-32 | 0.24-0.40 |
| 32-48 | 0.32-0.47 |
| 48-71 | 0.40-0.55 |
| 71-102 | 0.4 -0.65 |
| 102-150 | 0.55-0.65 |
| 150-215 | 0.7 -0.8 |
| over 215 | 0.8 -0.9 |

Casting section dimensions should not be reduced by drilled holes or machining. An inserted stud cannot restore the effectiveness of the original metal sections; therefore, the wall section adjacent to drilled holes should be equivalent to the main body of the casting.

Wherever two dissimilar metals touch in the presence of moisture, there is chance that one of them will corrode. Here are five steps that will help

# STOP GALVANIC CORROSION

Galvanic corrosion gives you an electrical cell you don't want (A). Like the galvanic cell in an auto battery the requirements are: two dissimilar metals, an electrolyte and a complete circuit. Corrosion is stopped by choosing similar metals; protecting parts from water, the usual electrolyte; or breaking the circuit. Here are five protective steps based on these principles.

**FEDERICO STRASSER**
*Mankowitz & Strasser Ltd*
*Santiago, Chile*

### Choosing "nearby" materials

The more anodic the metal, the more readily it dissolves in an electrolyte. The galvanic series, shown in the table, ranks metals by their tendency to dissolve. The farther apart two metals are in the series, the stronger the

| GALVANIC SERIES | |
|---|---|
| (in order of decreasing anodic value) | |
| Magnesium | Brass |
| Magnesium alloys | Copper |
| Zinc | Stainless steel |
| Chromium | Bronzes |
| Aluminum | Monel |
| Cadmium | Silver |
| Mild steel, cast | Nickel |
| and wrought iron | Inconel |
| Lead-tin solders | Gold |
| Lead | Platinum |
| Tin | Titanium |

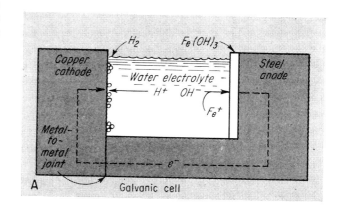

A    Galvanic cell

cell and the more the anode corrrodes. To reduce corrosion, use metals which are near each other in the galvanic series.

### Waterproofing

Keeping the electrolyte out of contact with the metals stops operation of the cell. Waterproofers include: waterproof paint with zinc chromate primer, varnish, lacquer, porcelain enamel and anodizing. To insulate electrical connections, use grease or tape.

Poor waterproofing can be worse than none at all. Small bare spots on the anode concentrate corrosion. For the same reason small anodic fasteners are especially vulnerable.

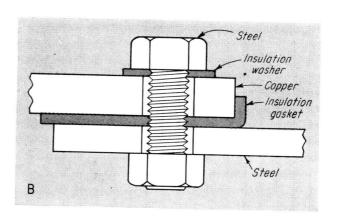

### Insulating

An insulator at the metal-to-metal joint breaks the galvanic circuit. In the example (B), the bolt and the lower plate are both of steel, so the bolt has to have an insulating washer only under the head.

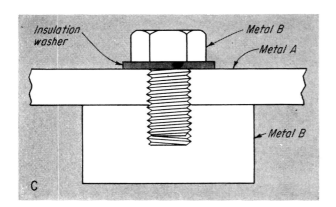

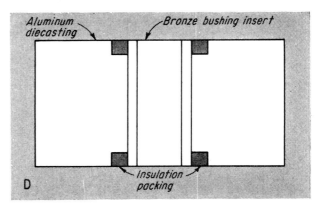

Some insulators are more like moisture hurdles because they insulate only the metal-to-metal joint exposed to moisture. As shown (C) they make it more difficult for moisture to bridge the gap between the metals. This washer also keeps moisture away from the threads.

Instead of a gasket or washer, the insulator can be packing or cement pressed into a groove at the joint as with the diecasting insert (D).

Insulating gaskets between lengths of pipe of different metals (E) is not enough. Dissolved and abraded cathodic metal in the liquid will set up galvanic cells as it passes through the anodic section. With flow from anodic to cathodic sections, only the suspended particles corrode.

### Dividing potential difference

This method separates two metals that are far apart in the galvanic series with a metal that falls between them in the series. The result: two weak cells are substituted for one strong one. In the example (F) the zinc plating falls between steel and magnesium in the galvanic series. Cadmium is a suitable plating for steel inserts in aluminum diecastings.

### Protecting with sacrificers

Sacrificial protectors are purposely allowed to corrode so that important parts won't. More anodic than either of the two protected metals, they waste away, requiring periodic replacement. Pumps and condensers use sacrificers because parts are completely immersed in water and metal-to-metal contact is unavoidable. Under such conditions zinc plates or pencils are the only workable solution. Zinc is a good sacrificial protector because it is near the top of the galvanic series and is cheap.

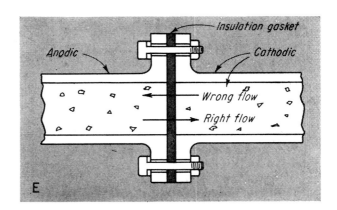

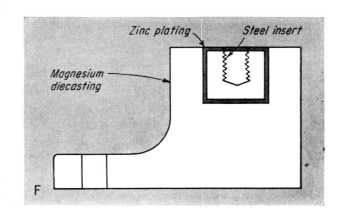

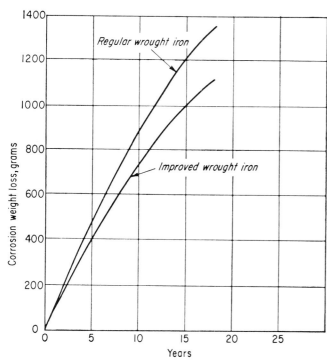

Fig. 1—Corrosion weight loss vs time in severe industrial atmosphere. One ft sq by 1/4 in. thick specimens were exposed to dirt and fumes from 1939 to 1957. Periodic inspection of the plates were made. After cleaning, the specimens were reweighed. Weight loss data: improved iron about 20% more resistant than regular wrought iron to industrial atmosphere.

*From:* Byers Technical Bulletin

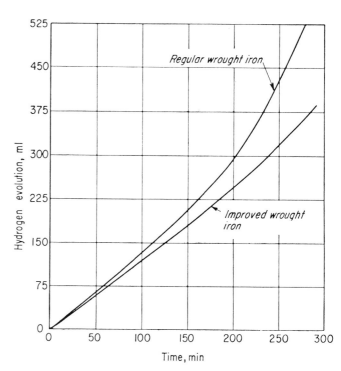

Fig. 2—Corrosion rate measured as hydrogen evolution vs time. Two irons measured in 2% hydrochloric acid by collecting and measuring the amount of hydrogen evolved during the acid attack—the more hydrogen, the more corrosion. Improved wrought iron dissolves 25% more slowly than regular iron in dilute acid. Test using 5% acid showed similar results.

# Corrosion rate of wrought iron

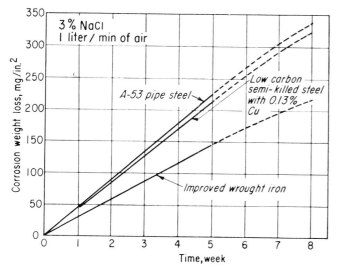

Fig. 3—Corrosion losses in aerated salt water. Data for wrought iron and the steels plot as virtually straight lines, with wrought iron having a lower slope—rate of attack. Curves will flatten with time (projected dotted line) and from these data it would appear that the wrought iron curve will flatten at a lower rate than either of the steel curves.

**W**ROUGHT iron, with its unusual two component composition as contrasted to the chemicals or alloy relationship that generally exists between the constituents of other metals, is finding new uses where corrosion is a problem. The recent development of a wrought iron having increased amounts of deoxidizer and phosphorus as well as more siliceous slag is further extending the use of wrought in the corrosion resistance field.

The major reasons for the superior corrosion resistance are: (1) the iron silicate fibers—one of the two component composition—halt and spread the corrosive attack and discourages pitting; and (2) the protective scale developed by the metal acts as a shield against direct attack.

The fibers of iron silicate help to halt the concentrated or localized attack and spread it over a greater area. Hence, any reduction in wall thickness takes place slowly and uniformly, with the least amount of pitting.

When corrosion starts, the oxide scale formed on the surface is anchored by the network of fibers, and adheres more tightly than similar scale on ordinary materials. This scale is almost immune to corrosion and it shields the underlying metal.

The improved wrought iron shows even better values than regular wrought material when subjected to atmospheric corrosion, acid corrosion and salt water corrosion. Figs. 1, 2 and 3 show the results of these tests.

REFERENCE:
Technical Bulletins from A.M. Byers Company

# Design hints for mechanical

How to avoid close tolerances,
and otherwise improve parts, where
accurate assembly is necessary.

*FEDERICO STRASSER, Mankowitz and Strasser, Santiago, Chile*

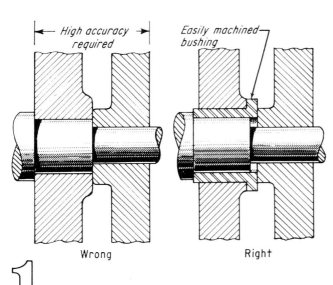

**1** **BUSHING FACE** is much easier to machine than the hub of a large part such as a flywheel or heavy gear.

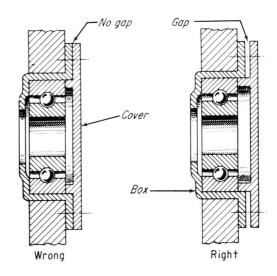

**2** **HOLD-DOWN COVER** for bearing should have a take-up gap between the cover flange and the bearing box.

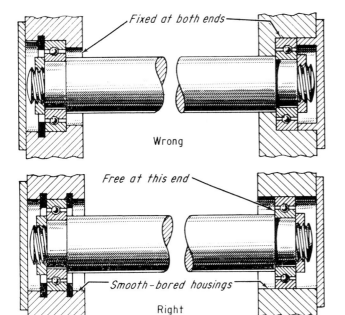

**5** **SMOOTH-BORED HOUSINGS** shown on right let one bearing move when shaft length changes because of expansion.

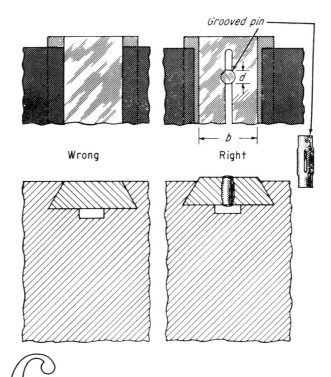

**6** **DOVETAILED** parts that are to be a tight fit are best provided with a slot and grooved pin where $d$ equals $b/3$ to $b/4$.

# parts

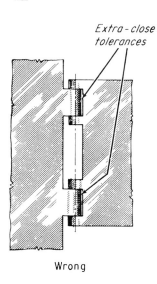

Extra-close tolerances

Wrong

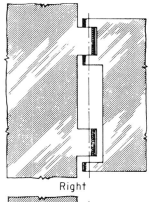

Right

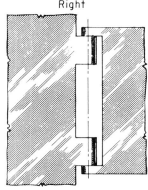

Right

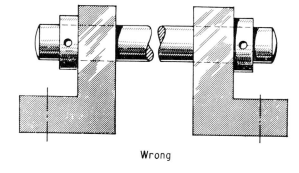

Wrong

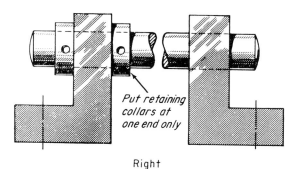

Put retaining collars at one end only

Right

 **HINGE MOUNTINGS** of the design shown on the left will entail extremely close tolerances. Let one end float.

**COLLARS** that retain the axial position of journal bearings should be placed at one end only to accommodate expansion.

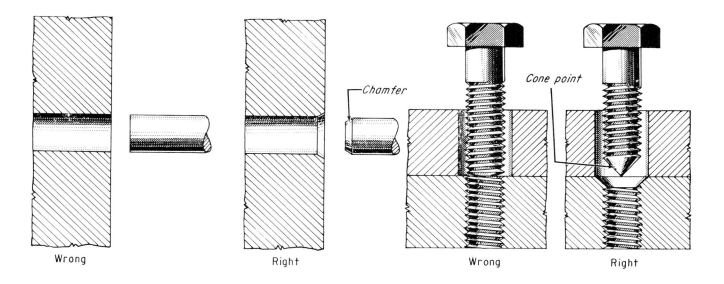

Wrong

Chamfer

Right

Cone point

Wrong

Right

**CHAMFER** on pins and shafts that must be driven into holes is advisable if entry is to be clean and easy.

 **CONE POINT** on screw and corresponding chamfer on internal thread ensures quick engagement in blind thread.

# Designing for easier

Flat working surfaces, bushings, single fits and other features simplify setups, speed machining, reduce tool replacement, and save material.

*FEDERICO STRASSER, Mankowitz & Strasser, Santiago, Chile*

**FLATS PROVIDE DRILLING SURFACES.**

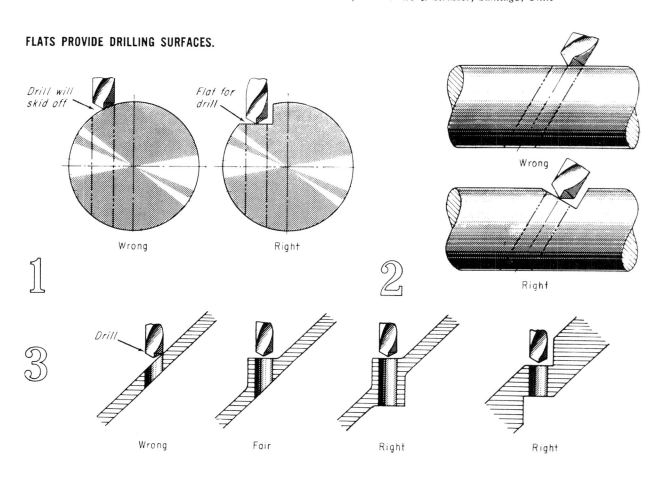

1    Drill will skid off — Wrong    Flat for drill — Right

2    Wrong    Right

3    Drill — Wrong    Fair    Right    Right

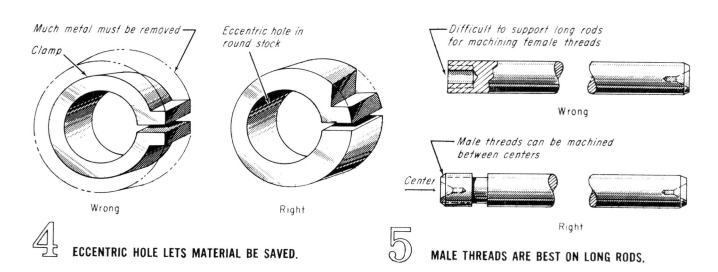

Much metal must be removed — Clamp — Wrong

Eccentric hole in round stock — Right

4    **ECCENTRIC HOLE LETS MATERIAL BE SAVED.**

Difficult to support long rods for machining female threads — Wrong

Male threads can be machined between centers — Center — Right

5    **MALE THREADS ARE BEST ON LONG RODS.**

# machining

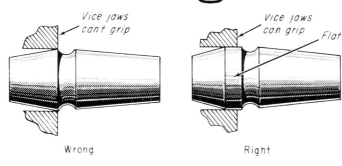

Vice jaws can't grip

Wrong

Vice jaws can grip — Flat

Right

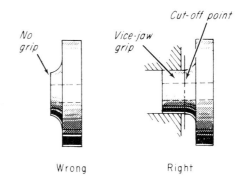

No grip

Wrong

Cut-off point

Vice-jaw grip

Right

**6** PROVIDE GRIPPING SURFACES WHEN MACHINING IS TO BE DONE.

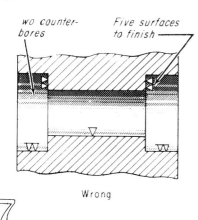

wo counterbores

Five surfaces to finish

Wrong

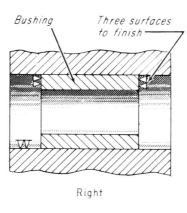

Bushing

Three surfaces to finish

Right

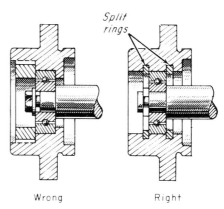

Split rings

Wrong

Right

**7** BUSHINGS REDUCE MACHINING COSTS AND AID STANDARDIZATION . . . SPLIT RINGS ALSO GIVE GOOD RESULTS.

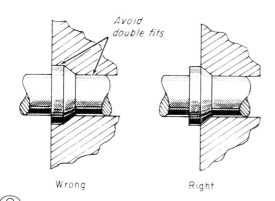

Avoid double fits

Wrong

Right

**8** SINGLE FITS ALLOW TIGHTER TOLERANCES.

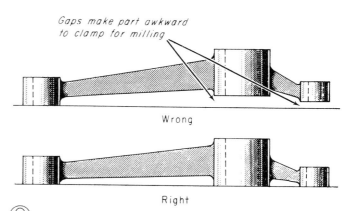

Gaps make part awkward to clamp for milling

Wrong

Right

**9** KEEP SURFACES ON SAME PLANE FOR BETTER CLAMPING.

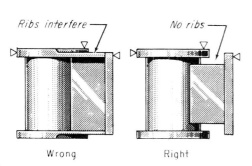

Ribs interfere

No ribs

Wrong

Right

**10** DON'T LET RIBS INTERFERE WITH MACHINING.

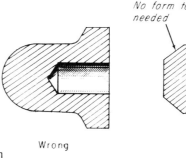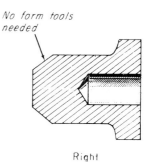

No form tools needed

Wrong

Right

**11**  DON'T CALL FOR CONTOURS THAT NEED SPECIAL FORM CUTTERS.

# How to design for

To prevent cracking and warping in heat treated parts, avoid abrupt changes of workpiece contours.

*FEDERICO STRASSER, Mankowitz & Strasser, Santiago, Chile*

The ideal shape for a part that is to be heat treated is a shape in which every point of any section or surface receives and gives back the same amount of heat with the same speed. Such a shape, of course, does not exist, but it is the designer's task to come as near to it as possible. To do this, keep the workpiece body simple, uniform, and symmetrical. For example, the first figures below show how changes in cross section must be made gradually to minimize stress concentrations during heat treatment. The other figures show further specific ways to keep out of trouble when subjecting parts to heat treatment. Holes, for example, should be correctly located.

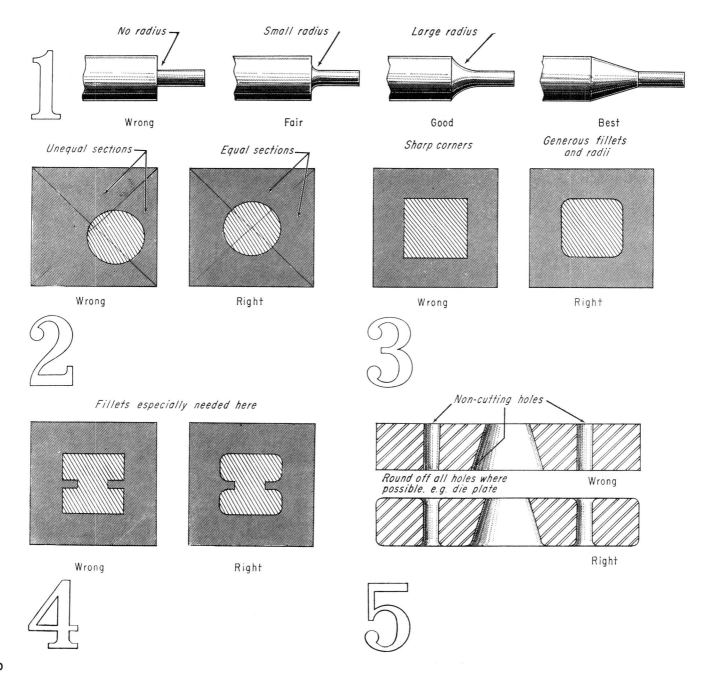

**1**

No radius — Wrong

Small radius — Fair

Large radius — Good

Best

**2**

Unequal sections — Wrong

Equal sections — Right

**3**

Sharp corners — Wrong

Generous fillets and radii — Right

**4**

Fillets especially needed here

Wrong

Right

**5**

Non-cutting holes — Wrong

Round off all holes where possible. e.g. die plate — Right

# heat treating

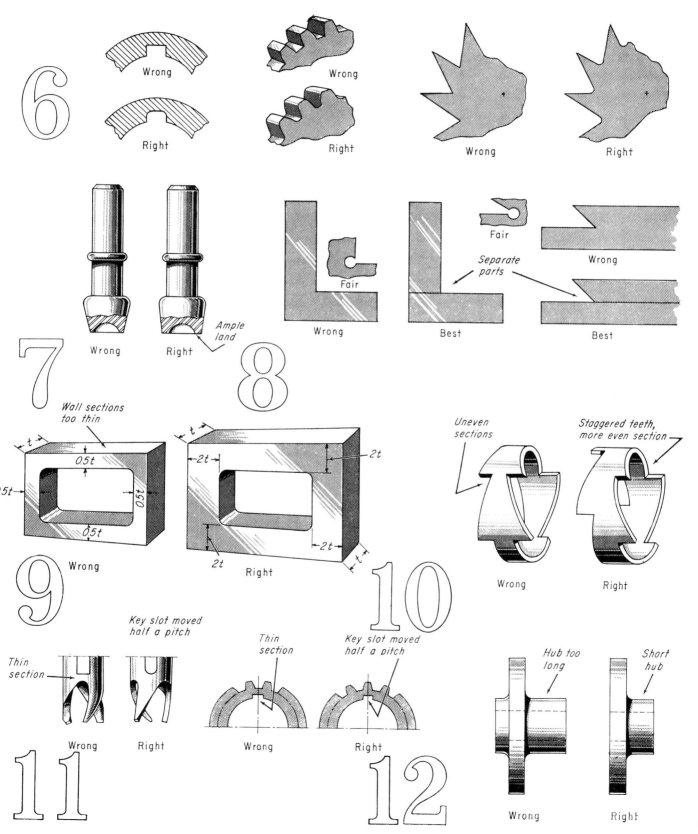

**6** Wrong / Right — Wrong / Right — Wrong / Right

**7** Wrong / Right — Ample land — Wrong / Fair / Best — Fair / Separate parts / Wrong / Best

**8** Wall sections too thin — 0.5t — 0.5t — 0.5t — 0.5t — Wrong — t — 2t — 2t — 2t — 2t — t — Right

**9** Uneven sections — Staggered teeth, more even section — Wrong / Right

**10** Key slot moved half a pitch — Thin section — Thin section — Key slot moved half a pitch — Hub too long — Short hub

**11** Wrong / Right — Wrong / Right

**12** Wrong / Right

# More design hints for

Watch out for faulty designs such as thin sections, blind holes, unbalanced slots, and other weaknesses that can cause cracking and warping in heat-treated parts. Follow these how-to tips.

*FEDERICO STRASSER, Mankowitz & Strasser, Santiago, Chile*

Nearly all serious failures of hardened steel parts are caused by internal stresses. Avoiding sudden changes of section is one good way to ensure balanced heating and cooling, the secret of success in all heat treating. Some other good design tips, which supplement those in our last issue, are illustrated.

**1**

*More uniform sections*

Wrong    Right

**2**

*Thin sections*    *Thicker sections*

Wrong    Right

**3**

Wrong    Right

**4**

< 1.5d    > 1.5d

**5**

*Deep, blind hole poor for quenching*

Wrong    Right

**6**

*Avoid junctions of holes in steel block*

**7**

*Grind punch after heat treating*

# heat treating

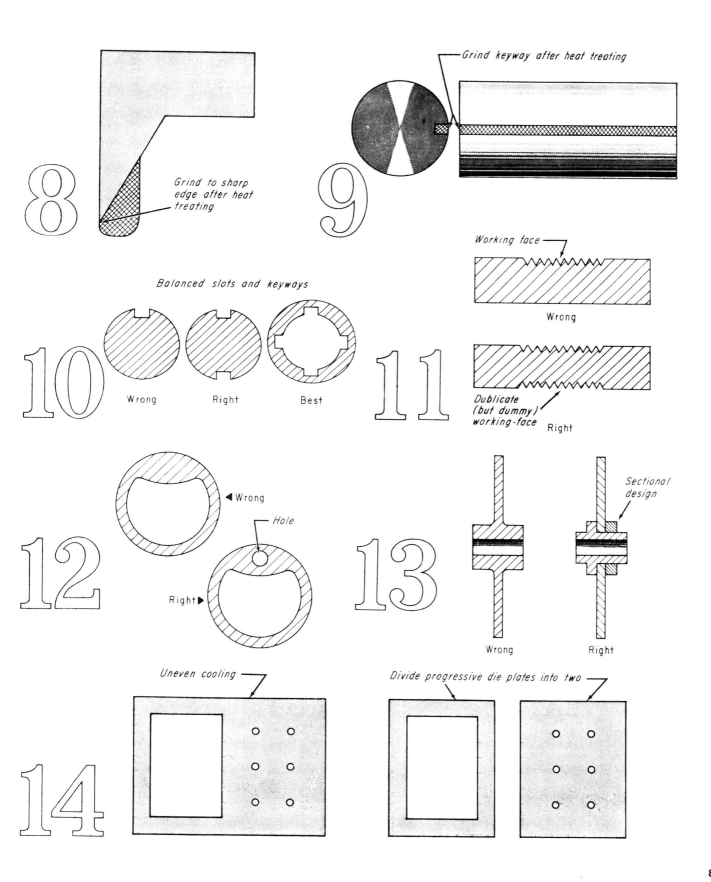

**8** — Grind to sharp edge after heat treating

**9** — Grind keyway after heat treating

Balanced slots and keyways

**10** — Wrong — Right — Best

**11** — Working face — Wrong — Dublicate (but dummy) working-face — Right

**12** — Wrong — Hole — Right

**13** — Sectional design — Wrong — Right

**14** — Uneven cooling — Divide progressive die plates into two

# PART I

# Designing for Production

Efficient, simple and economical production calls for the most advantageous use of labor, machines and methods. Often a simple design change will increase machine

FIG. 1—Casting or forging with a large tapered hole. If the conical section is to be held to close tolerances and is not a standard taper for which a plug gage is available, the size will be difficult to check during machining and inspection. Repeated caliper checks would have to be made during the boring operation, (A). An accurate measurement would be difficult to obtain, because the depth at which the diameter is measured is hard to define. (B) shows a simple change that eliminates these problems. The counterbore or recess need only be about ⅛ in. deep, but should be approximately 0.004 in. less than the critical maximum diameter of the finished hole.

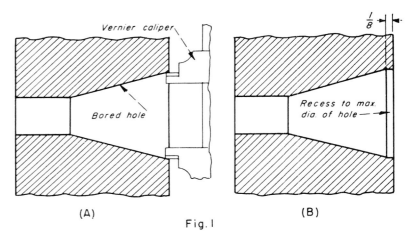

Fig. 1

FIG. 2—Lug formed on the external wall of an iron, brass or light-metal casting. To form a flat, clean seat for the bolt head, these lugs are cleaned with a pilot-type spotfacing tool, (A). If a large radius strengthening fillet adjoins the lug, an unsatisfactory finish can result. The spot-facing tool will cut partially into the fillet and leave triangular raised ledges. Moreover, an unequalized pressure—caused by cutting into the fillet—is imposed upon the tool. This can cause the pilot to be broken or bent, or else the teeth of the tool can be damaged. Cost is thus increased and production reduced. If a raised circular pad is cast, (B), there is no danger of tool catching or fillet damage. A clean, smooth surface is assured.

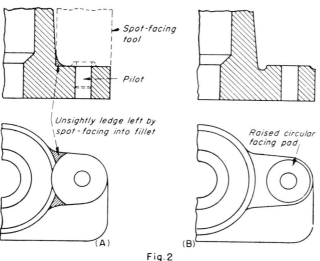

Fig. 2

FIG. 3—A slotted shackle milled from mild steel stock. (A) shows the part with the central parallel slot milled with a perfectly flat base. This requires the table carrying the part to travel a considerable distance to allow for tool curvature. By allowing the base of the central slot to be curved, (B) to the radius of the milling cutter, it is possible that only a vertical feed, to the necessary depth, will be required.

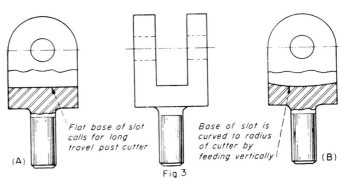

Fig. 3

# .... Machining

**W. M. HALLIDAY**
Engineer — Consultant
Southport Lancs., England

production and reduce labor cost. This, the first of a series, shows various design modifications that can be used to simplify machining operations to improve production.

FIG. 4—Drilling a casting where hidden hole exists. To drill and tap the hole, (*A*), a long extension drill would be needed to clear the long side wall. Frequent drill and tap breakage should be expected, as well as design difficulties in providing a jig or fixture to guide the tools. If a large diameter hole can be cored through the back wall, (*B*) a standard drill and tap can be used. A simple fixture can be used to mount the part.

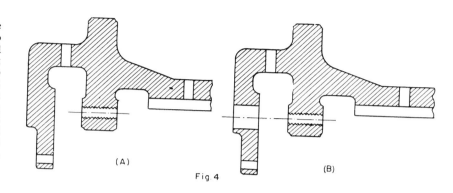

(A)     (B)

Fig. 4

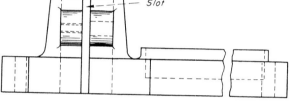

—Slot

Fig. 5

FIG. 5—Drilling and tapping a slotted lug on a bored cast boss. The left wall of the lug is tapped and the right wall clearance drilled. Drilling will be difficult both in setting the part and tooling, because of the closeness of the rectangular flat base of the casting. If the holes are transposed, drilling is simplified, and the drilled hole can be used as a guide to tap the core-drill diameter.

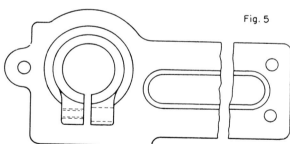

FIG. 6—Drilling holes in flanges for the fixing of a cover. A step-up or step-down design. (*A*) and (*B*) will require a new setting or a readjustment of the milling machine. Also, in (*A*) the underside of the flange is inclined, which can cause trouble when the drill breaks through. In (*B*) the drill breaks through partially into the side wall. (*C*) provides for a single milling operation, and the parallel underside assures that the drill breaks through cleanly.

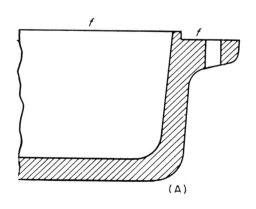

(A)

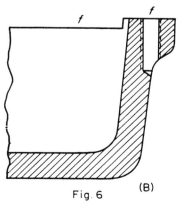

Fig. 6     (B)

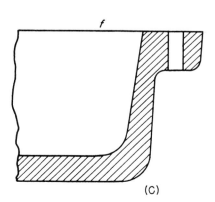

(C)

# PART II

# Designing for Production

Adapting designs to simplify work setting and retention can result in efficient, simple and economical production. These are some useful principles of design that permit

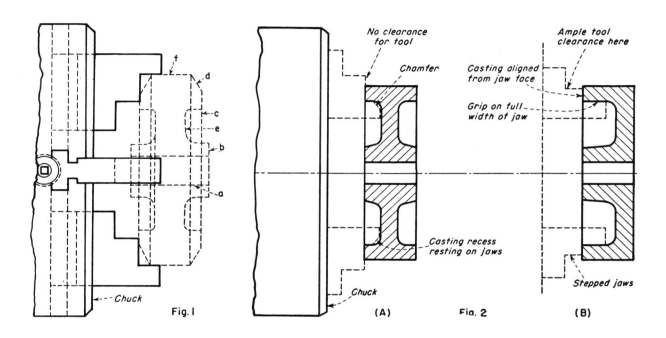

Fig. I

FIG. 2

FIG. 1—Phosphour - bronze worm wheel casting chucked for machining. This unit is cast to outline shape shown, by the heavy dotted lines with the angular side-faces. These are for clearance purposes and are finally machined to assure good balance. They prevent, however, an effective grip being obtained by jaws and permit machining only of portions *a* to *e*. A step would be left on the periphery *e* when the part is reversed and where the second cut joins the first. A simpler method would be to cast the wheel without the angular face. Machine *b* through *e* reverse and inside chuck part at *e* and finish machine second side. Inside and outside diameters *a* and *f* are machined at the same time to be sure of concentricity. Angular faces *d*, machined later from a mandrel setting. Since the angular faces are machined for balance only, it is easier to cast the part without these faces and then machine. Better balance and more accurate material removal is assured.

FIG. 2—Gear wheel blanks, in various metals, are usually designed and chucked as shown in *A*. This leaves a shallow grip for the chuck and a large radii must be used to clear the radius fillet in root and recess. It is also impossible to completely turn the O. D., since insufficient clearance exists between edge and squaring face of chuck. A blank designed as in *B* permits an effective grip to be obtained, as well as allowing all surfaces to be machined at one setting. This change does not alter the weight or change the mechanical properties of the part. Outside and inside diameters can be turned together to assure concentricity. The blank design, *B*, is also easier to cast and there is less chance of having blow holes or inclusions in the web. Inspection is also simplified.

FIG. 3—Large, circular, flanged castings or pressings having a long hollow conical boss. The casting shown, *A*,

is a shaft and roller bearing housing that must be accurately turned, bored and faced on the surfaces marked. As illustrated, only line contact is possible on the conical boss. To arrest any tilting when machining the periphery, jacks, supporting screws, or similar packing would be necessary. If an extension boss is cast with the housing, the setup and machining are greatly simplified, *B*. The square shoulder on the boss prevents the workpiece from being punched into the jaws when a heavy cut is taken.

FIG. 4—Large diameter end shield casting made from cast-iron or some light metal alloy. Parts of this type usually require machining on those surfaces denoted by heavy lines. In *A*, the shield is chucked over the outside rim. Because of the relatively thin base wall, gripping in this manner can easily induce distortion or rim cracking. Out-of-roundness often results. Also, face *a* should be machined at the same set-

# ... Retaining

W. M. HALLIDAY
Engineer · Consultant
Southport, Lancs., England

simplicity in setting up the work and ensure a powerful and safe retention of the part during machining. In most instances, final part shape is unchanged.

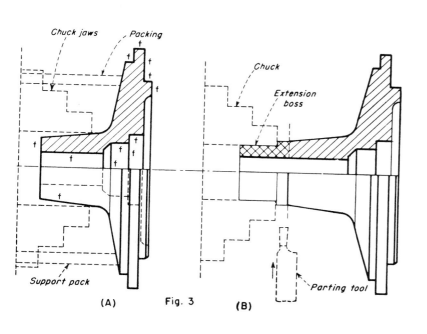

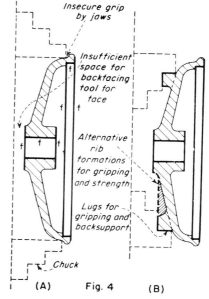

(A)  Fig. 3  (B)

(A)  Fig. 4  (B)

ting, to ensure concentricity with the remainder of the part. Here, insufficient space exists between part and chuck. Design modification, *B,* overcomes all these objections. Stiffness can be increased by using the alternative rib construction.

FIG. 5—Thin walled hollow dish-type casting that must be machined as noted. Normal chucking pressure on the thin wall section could cause distortion, fracture or out-of-roundness. In *A,* holes are drilled or cast, and shouldered studs locate and support the casting. This is the driving member. The other jaws are fitted with headed support studs that are equal in height to the shoulder of the driving stud. The jaws are drawn up snug, but not tight enough to deform the thin wall casting. Where cored holes are not possible, a well can be cast or drilled, *B.* A boss, lug or rib can also be used with the chuck jaw driving against the member.

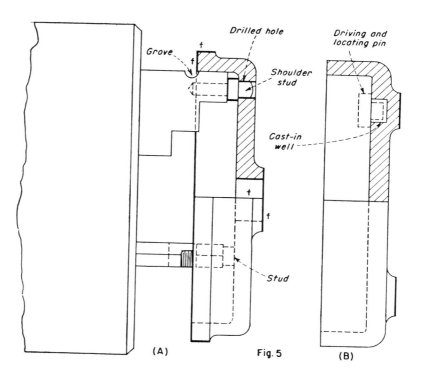

(A)  Fig. 5  (B)

# PART III

# Designing for Production

Advantages and economies can be derived if components are designed to reduce non-cutting motions of machine members or tools. Simple modifications of the

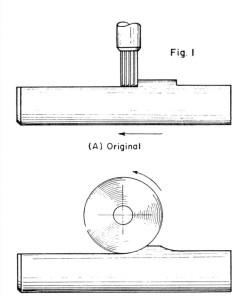

Fig. 1

(A) Original

(B) Redesign

Fig. 1—Milling flats and keyways on shafts. In (A) small diameter end-mill generates a square step requiring axial and transverse movement of the worktable. Cuts must be light. A large diameter circular cutter as in (B) has a curved runout—equal to radius of cutter—but requires only axial worktable travel. Cutter is slightly wider than required flat. Heavy cuts can be taken and flat milled in a single pass. Machine cutting time savings can range from 10 to 30 per cent.

Fig. 2—Bellcrank lever bossed to simplify holding. Casting has bossed surfaces a, b, c, and e that must be accurately faced. Workpiece must be located from a to machine other faces. Since a, b, c, are not in line, b, and c must be braced during cutting. As redesigned in (B), these problems are minimized. Cast-on lugs, h and j, equalize boss height. Lugs ensure a rigid three point support on machine table or against a chuck face and are removed when holes f and g are drilled.

Fig. 3—Split rings replace machined shoulder to reduce material and machining costs. Because diameter of stock in (A) must be greater than x, machining of shoulders results in material waste of about 45 per cent. Shoulders locate a roller bearing set, a gear with a locknut, a thrust bearing, and a ball bearing with an end nut. Design in (B) has a material loss of less than 15 per cent of original bar. Eliminating threads and locknuts mean additional savings.

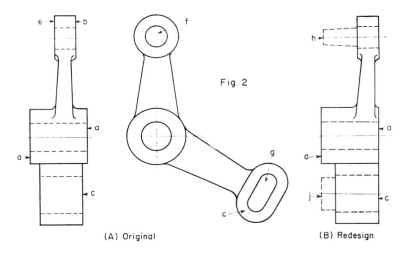

Fig. 2

(A) Original

(B) Redesign

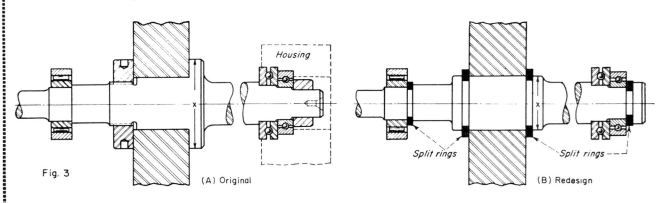

Fig. 3

Housing

(A) Original

Split rings

Split rings

(B) Redesign

# ....Reducing Waste

W. M. HALLIDAY
Engineer — Consultant
Southport Lancs., England

shape of a part can often increase production. Also, scrap loss can be reduced. This, the third of a series, shows various methods of saving machining time and material

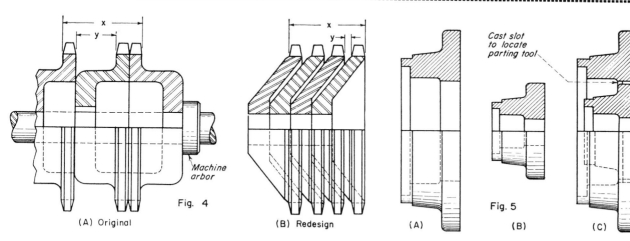

Fig. 4—Redesign of sprocket and gear blanks for faster machining. Teeth are reproduced either by a circular hobbing tool or a rack-shaped cutter which travels parallel to the axis of the shaft. In (A) only three blanks can be mounted within distance x which is the effective machine travel, leaving wide gap y. In (B) is a design modification that permits mounting four components within the same distance. Thus y is reduced and a 25 per cent saving on cutting time can be realized.

Fig. 5—Single casting for two components. Two castings of identical shapes but different size are shown in (A) and (B). Originally, two patterns and molds were needed as well as separate setup and machining operations. By combining the units as shown in (C), all surfaces are machinable at two lathe settings and only a single pattern is required. A final machining separates the castings.

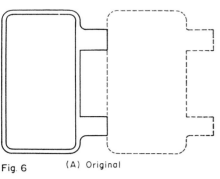

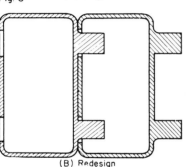

Fig. 6—Box casting has two lug extensions used for attaching hinge. Top surfaces are milled. In (A) lugs increase the table travel by about 15 per cent. A modification, (B), decreases machine time without increasing setup time. Two slots are cast or machined into the wall of the casting to engage lugs.

Fig. 7—Material saving on punching operation. Usually, sheet metal links are designed as shown in (A). Stock is about 25 per cent wider than link to ensure safe and accurate cutting. Altering the design as in (B) reduces waste. Cropping-tool is simpler, less costly and easier to operate than punch; also, length of cut is $2\frac{1}{2}$ times less than that of the blanking punch. Thus, less pressure is required, tool is more durable and closer accuracy is possible.

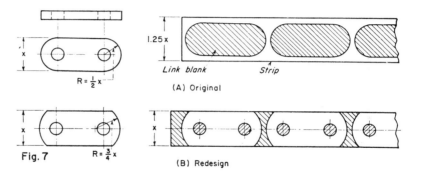

# DIMENSIONS for HAND GRIPS

*To get maximum advantage from knobs and handles, use the size suggested in these sketches.*

**FRANK WILLIAM WOOD JR**
*President, Advanced Designs Inc*
*Vienna, Va*

## KNOBS

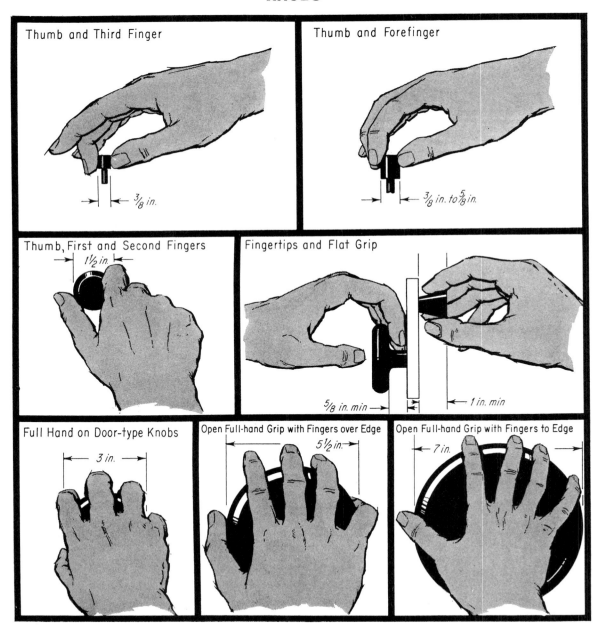

# HANDLES

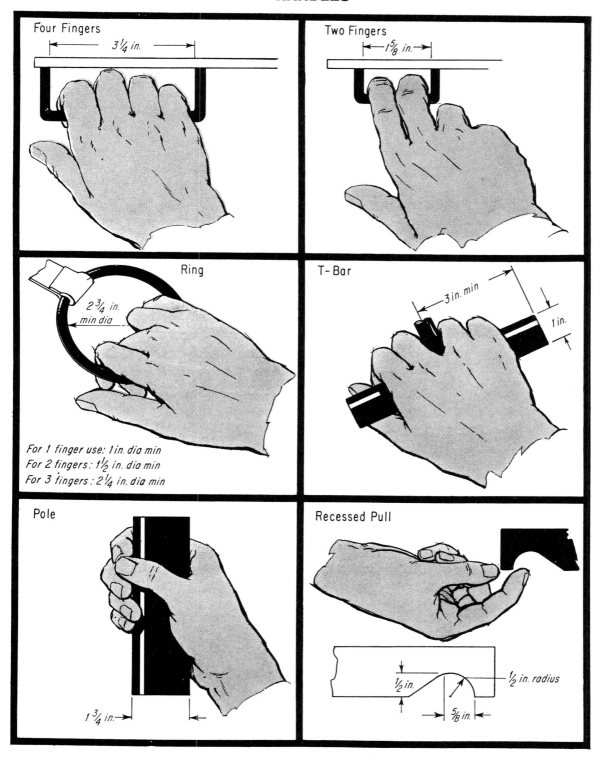

**Four Fingers** — 3 1/4 in.

**Two Fingers** — 1 5/8 in.

**Ring** — 2 3/4 in. min dia

For 1 finger use: 1 in. dia min
For 2 fingers : 1 1/2 in. dia min
For 3 fingers : 2 1/4 in. dia min

**T-Bar** — 3 in. min — 1 in.

**Pole** — 1 3/4 in.

**Recessed Pull** — 1/2 in. — 1/2 in. radius — 5/8 in.

# Dimensioning Parts for

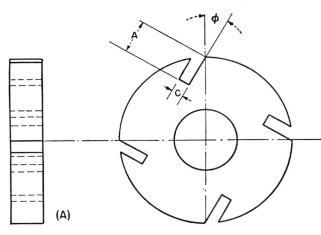

(A)

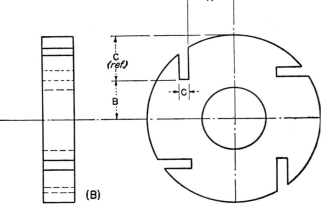

(B)

**1** (A) According to accepted practice, the position of each slot is completely defined by the two linear and one angular dimensions shown. But this form makes it difficult to lay out the part for production on standard equipment because the exact position for the milling cutter is not known. (B) By rotating the part and defining the distance *A* from the center line, the milling cutter can be immediately positioned. Reference dimension *C*, which varies with the tolerance of the blank diameter, is added to preclude shop miscalculations.

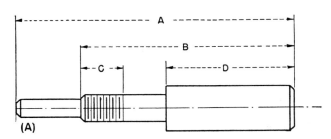

(A)

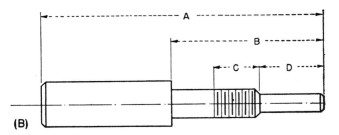

(B)

**3** (A) A shaft dimensioned in this manner can be turned directly using the data given. However, shop calculations must be made to locate the shoulders so that carriage stops can be properly positioned. Furthermore, it is impractical to scale the given dimensions while the lathe is running. (B) Lathe operations are simplified when the dimensions appear as above and carriage stops can be set immediately. It is convenient to hold a scale against a shoulder during a turn and then disengage the carriage when *C* and *D* cuts are completed.

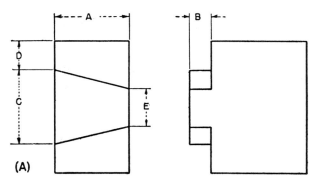

(A)

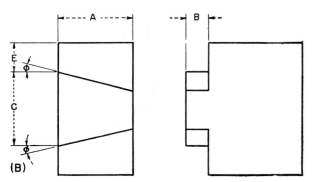

(B)

**5** (A) Layout of this block as dimensioned requires trial-and-error location of reference marks or shop-calculation of the angle shown in (B). Either method takes time and can lead to errors that result in costly scrap losses. (B) If the angle ϕ is on the drawing when it is received in the production department, the block can be clamped in a vise on a machine table and swung around to the correct position ready for machining. Shop errors are therefore less apt to occur, as well as appreciable time and material saved.

# Economical Production THOMAS L. LANE

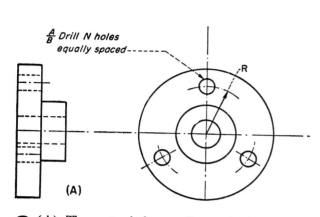

**(A)**

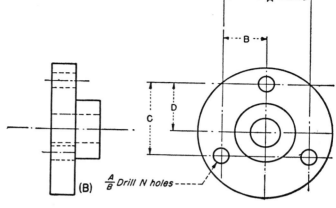

**(B)**

**2** (A) The center hole complicates the layout of flange holes, a dividing head or rotary table being required. By specifying the radius R for the small holes, the error caused by tolerances is doubled when there is an even number of flange holes. (B) This revision of dimensions permits the direct use of a height gage. If the small holes are drilled on a jig borer, the machine can be easily set up from the information as given because the dimensions are already in the required form, thereby reducing errors and saving costly setup time.

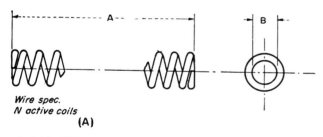

**(A)**

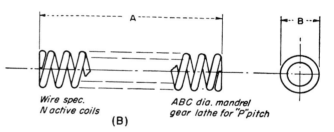

**(B)**

**4** (A) When a spring is dimensioned as above, the mandrel size, as well as winding lead, is determined by trial and error. This condition results because the spring becomes larger in diameter and coarser in pitch when the wire is relaxed after winding. (B) Handbooks contain tables that list mandrel sizes and winding pitches for a given wire size. Handbook data should be put on the drawing and the spring dimensioned to show the outside diameter. Setup time is thus reduced and checking of the diameter between parallels is simple.

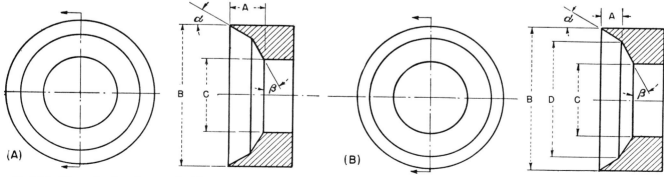

**(A)**

**(B)**

**6** (A) Though the shape of this part is geometrically determined, the intersection between the two tapers is not fully defined in terms of shop procedures. Without the use of algebraic computations, the length of cut is unknown. (B) The change in dimension A and the addition of dimension D fully define the end of the larger taper cut and the start of the smaller cut. No knowledge of algebra is required so that this source of costly shop errors disappears completely. Shop procedure is thus simplified and scrap reduced.

# HOW TO DIMENSION PERSPECTIVE

Perspective drawings are now in general use by aircraft companies and other firms are becoming increasingly interested in their use. This review of the principles of dimensioning perspective drawings is based on the practices of Fleetwings Division of Kaiser Cargo, Inc.

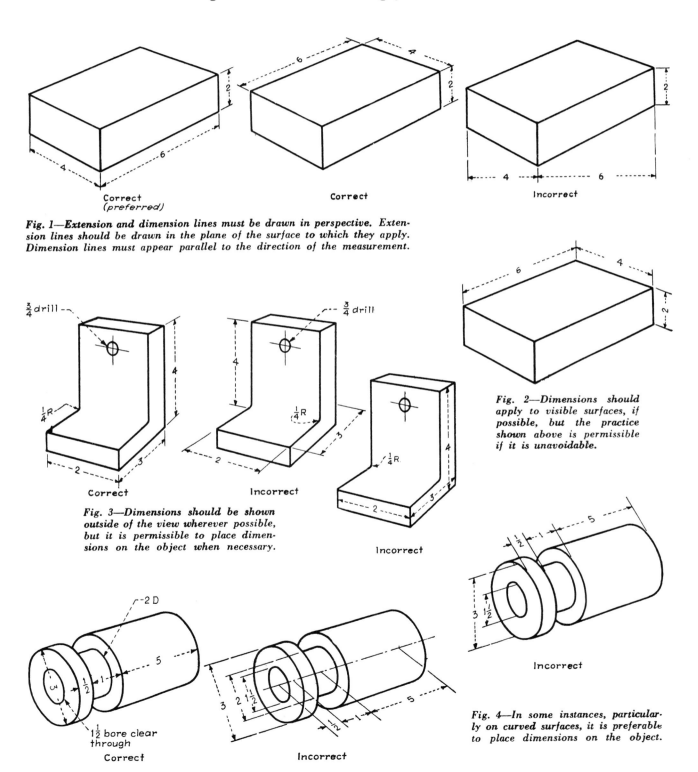

**Correct** (preferred)

**Correct**

**Incorrect**

*Fig. 1—Extension and dimension lines must be drawn in perspective. Extension lines should be drawn in the plane of the surface to which they apply. Dimension lines must appear parallel to the direction of the measurement.*

**Correct**

**Incorrect**

**Incorrect**

*Fig. 2—Dimensions should apply to visible surfaces, if possible, but the practice shown above is permissible if it is unavoidable.*

*Fig. 3—Dimensions should be shown outside of the view wherever possible, but it is permissible to place dimensions on the object when necessary.*

**Correct**

**Incorrect**

**Incorrect**

*Fig. 4—In some instances, particularly on curved surfaces, it is preferable to place dimensions on the object.*

# DRAWINGS

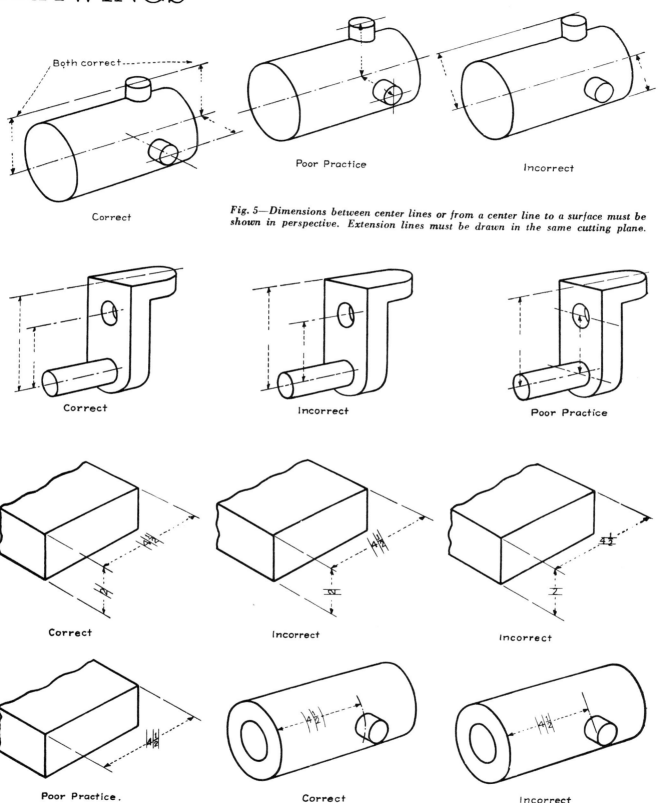

Fig. 5—Dimensions between center lines or from a center line to a surface must be shown in perspective. Extension lines must be drawn in the same cutting plane.

Fig. 6—Numerals and arrowheads should be drawn in perspective. Guide lines for numerals should appear parallel to the corresponding perspective plane. Numerals and arrowheads on curved surfaces should follow the contour of the surface. Arrowheads should appear parallel to the respective perspective plane. Notes need not be lettered in perspective but it is preferred that vertical rather than inclined lettering be used.

# CHECKLIST FOR PLANETARY-GEAR SETS

These five tests quickly tell whether the gears will
mesh, and whether there is room for them to fit together.

**HUGH P HUBBARD,** *mechanical engineer*
*Seattle, Wash*

## SYMBOLS

$CP$ = Circular pitch, in.
$L$ = Distance from center of sun gear to center of planet gear, in.
$M$ = Major or outside diameter of gear, in.
$DP$ = Diametral pitch, teeth/in.
$m$ = Minor, or working depth diameter of gear, in.
$N$ = Number of teeth per gear
$PD$ = Pitch diameter, in.
$x$ = The whole number in dividend when $N_s$ is divided by number of planets
$y$ = The whole number in dividend when $N_r$ is divided by number of planets
$z$ = Increment for locating planet gear
$\alpha$ = Angular location of planet gear

**Y**ou have decided to design a planetary-gear system
with a certain gear ratio, and have chosen the number
of teeth for each gear to get that ratio. Will it work?
Will the gears fit together to make a workable system?

If they can pass the following five tests, they will.

### 1—Do all gears have the same circular pitch?

If they do not, the gears will not mesh.

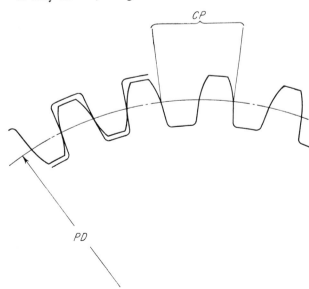

Circular pitch $CP = \pi/DP = PD/N$

Circular pitch and number of teeth determine pitch
diameter, which leads to the next test:

### 2—Will the gears mate at the pitch diameters?

This equation shows whether the planet gear will fill
the space between the sun gear and the ring gear:

$$N_p = \frac{N_r - N_s}{2}$$

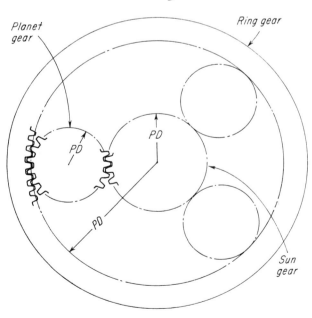

### 3—Will the teeth mesh?

Gears that pass the first two tests will not necessarily
pass this one. If the gears have the wrong number of

teeth, the planet gear will not mesh with the sun gear and the ring gear at the same time. Gears with numbers of teeth divisible by three will mesh. There are two other possible cases.

Case I—The number of teeth on the sun gear divides evenly into the number of teeth on the ring gear. This set will mesh, if allowance is made by spacing the planet gears unevenly around the sun gear.

EXAMPLE: In a set of planetary gears the ring gear has 70 teeth, the sun gear 14 teeth and each of the three planet gears 28 teeth. Even spacing would place the planet gears every 120°, but in this case they must be placed slightly to one side of the 120° point to mesh. Since $N_s$ divides evenly into $N_r$ there is a tooth on the ring gear opposite every tooth on the sun gear. Therefore, it is possible to fit a planet gear opposite any tooth on the sun gear. Tooth 6, five circular pitches from tooth 1, is the choice because it is closest to being one-third of the way around. It is opposite tooth 26 on the ring gear, because $Nr/Ns = 70/14 = 25/5$.

Case II—The number of teeth on the sun gear does not divide evenly into the number of teeth on the ring gear. This set may or may not mesh; the following example shows how to tell.

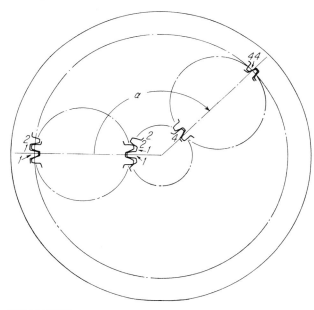

EXAMPLE: In a set of planetary gears with three planets, the ring gear has 134 teeth, the sun gear 14 and the planet gears 60 each. $N_s/3 = 14/3 = 4.67$, so the whole number $x = 4$. $N_r/3 = 134/3 = 44.67$, so the whole number $y = 44$.

Plug these numbers into the locating equation

$$(x+z)\, N_r/N_s = y+(1-z) = (4+z)\, 134/14 = 44 + (1-z)$$
$$10.57\, z = 6.72$$
$$z = 0.636$$

Location of the planet gear as a fractional part of the circular distance around the set is $(x + z)/N_s = 4.636/14 = 0.3311$, and $y + (1 - z)/N_r = 44.364/$

134 = 0.3311. The answers agree to four places, so the gears will mesh. If the answers don't agree to four places, there will be interference.

Angle $a = 0.3311 \times 360 = 119.2°$

### 4—Can three planets fit around the sun gear?

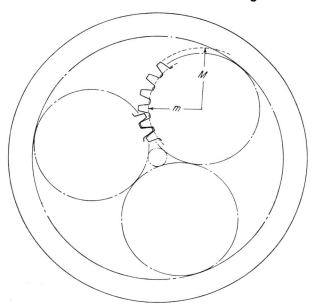

They will if the major diameters adhere to the limitation $M_p + m_s/2 < m_r$ by a safety clearance of $\tfrac{1}{32}$ in. more than maximum tolerances.

### 5—Will irregularly spaced planets hit each other?

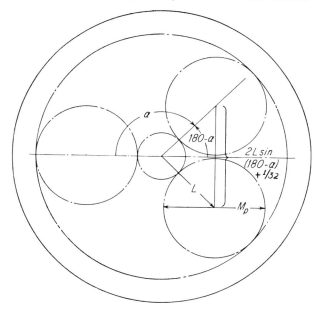

Two adjacent planets will not hit each other if $2L$ $\sin(180 - a) > M_p + \tfrac{1}{32}$ in. safety clearance. Sun-to-planet center-to-center distance $L = (PD_s + PD_p)/2$.  ∎

## worksheet streamlines

# BEVEL-GEAR CALCULATIONS

**B J MUMKEN,** *tool engineer, Sier-Bath Gear & Pump Co, North Bergen, NJ*

The following worksheet neatly gathers together the many mathematical problems that need solving when designing straight bevel-gears. And they are numbered in the correct sequence—no need to hunt "all over the place" as when using formulas in the usual bevel-gear tables. In fact, there are no formulas as such—and, therefore, no need for working with the many Greek symbols found in them.

Instead, the language here is in terms of the actual working operations. For example, space (9) tells you to obtain pitch diameter of the pinion—simply divide

the value in space (1) by the value in space (3). And to get root angle for the gear, you are told to subtract the value in space (24) from the value in space (14). Each bracketed number refers you to a value previously filled in.

Just fill in the known values for pinion and gear in the first eight spaces, then work through the sheet, which is based on the Gleason system for 90° straight bevel-gears. Final result (next page) is gear-blank dimensions.

Colored numbers show values obtained in a sample problem worked out by this method.

| | | | | | |
|---|---|---|---|---|---|
| I | No. of teeth, pinion | *40* | 5 | Working depth = $\frac{2.000}{(3)}$ | *0.200* |
| 2 | No. of teeth, gear | *80* | 6 | Whole depth = $\frac{2.188}{(3)}$ + 0.002 ("D + F") | *0.2208* |
| 3 | Diametral pitch | *10* | 7 | Pressure angle | *20°* |
| 4 | Face width | *0.750* | 8 | Total backlash | *0.003* |

| | P I N I O N | | G E A R | | |
|---|---|---|---|---|---|
| | | (Thick underlining indicates working dimensions) | | | |
| 9 | Pitch dia. $\frac{(1)}{(3)}$ | *4.000* | 10 | Pitch dia. $\frac{(2)}{(3)}$ | *8.000* |
| 11 | Tan $\frac{(1)}{(2)}$ | *0.5000* | 12 | Tan $\frac{(2)}{(1)}$ | *2.0000* |
| 13 | Pitch angle (11), in deg. | *26° 34'* | 14 | Pitch angle (12) | *63° 26'* |
| 15 | 2 X cos (13) | *1.7888* | 16 | Cone distance $\frac{(10)}{(15)}$ | *4.4722* |
| 18 | Addendum (5) – (17) | *0.135* | 17 | Addendum = $\frac{(see\ table)}{(3)}$ | *0.065* |

### Gear Addendum for 1 D. P.
### Ratio = (No. of gear teeth)/(No. of pinion teeth)

| Ratios | | Adden-dum, in. | Ratios | | Adden-dum, in. | Ratios | | Adden-dum, in. | Ratios | | Adden-dum, in. |
|---|---|---|---|---|---|---|---|---|---|---|---|
| From | To | | From | To | | From | To | | From | To | |
| 1.00 | 1.00 | 0.850 | 1.15 | 1.17 | 0.750 | 1.41 | 1.44 | 0.650 | 1.99 | 2.10 | 0.550 |
| 1.00 | 1.02 | 0.840 | 1.17 | 1.19 | 0.740 | 1.44 | 1.48 | 0.640 | 2.10 | 2.23 | 0.540 |
| 1.02 | 1.03 | 0.830 | 1.19 | 1.21 | 0.730 | 1.48 | 1.52 | 0.630 | 2.23 | 2.38 | 0.530 |
| 1.03 | 1.05 | 0.820 | 1.21 | 1.23 | 0.720 | 1.52 | 1.57 | 0.620 | 2.38 | 2.58 | 0.520 |
| 1.05 | 1.06 | 0.810 | 1.23 | 1.26 | 0.710 | 1.57 | 1.63 | 0.610 | 2.58 | 2.82 | 0.510 |
| 1.06 | 1.08 | 0.800 | 1.26 | 1.28 | 0.700 | 1.63 | 1.68 | 0.600 | 2.82 | 3.17 | 0.500 |
| 1.08 | 1.09 | 0.790 | 1.28 | 1.31 | 0.690 | 1.68 | 1.75 | 0.590 | 3.17 | 3.67 | 0.490 |
| 1.09 | 1.11 | 0.780 | 1.31 | 1.34 | 0.680 | 1.75 | 1.82 | 0.580 | 3.67 | 4.56 | 0.480 |
| 1.11 | 1.13 | 0.770 | 1.34 | 1.37 | 0.670 | 1.82 | 1.90 | 0.570 | 4.56 | 7.00 | 0.470 |
| 1.13 | 1.15 | 0.760 | 1.37 | 1.41 | 0.660 | 1.90 | 1.99 | 0.560 | 7.00 | ∝ | 0.460 |

| | | | | | |
|---|---|---|---|---|---|
| 19 | Dedendum = $\frac{2.188}{(3)}$ – (18) | *0.0838* | 20 | Dedendum = $\frac{2.188}{(3)}$ – (17) | *0.1538* |
| 21 | Tan $\frac{(19)}{(16)}$ | *0.0187* | 22 | Tan $\frac{(20)}{(16)}$ | *0.0343* |
| 23 | Ded angle (21) | *1° 4'* | 24 | Ded angle (22) | *1° 58'* |
| 25 | Face angle (13) + (24) | *28° 32'* | 26 | Face angle (14) + (23) | *64° 30'* |
| 27 | Root angle (13) – (23) | *25° 30'* | 28 | Root angle (14) – (24) | *61° 28'* |

| 29 | cos (13) | 0.8944 | 30 | cos (14) | 0.4472 |
|----|----------|--------|----|----------|--------|
| 31 | $[2 \times (18)] \times (29)$ | 0.2414 | 32 | $[2 \times (17)] \times (30)$ | 0.0581 |
| 33 | OD = (9) + (31) | 4.2415 | 34 | OD = (10) + (32) | 8.0581 |
| 35 | (18) x (30) | 0.0603 | 36 | (17) x (29) | 0.0581 |
| 37 | Pitch-apex to crown = $[0.5 \times (10)] - (35)$ | 3.9396 | 38 | Pitch-apex to crown = $[0.5 \times (9)] - (36)$ | 1.9419 |
| 39 | Circular pitch = $\frac{3.1416}{(3)}$ | 0.3141 | 41 | (18) - (17) | 0.0700 |
| 40 | 0.5 x (39) | 0.1570 | 42 | (41) x tan (7) | 0.0254 |
| 44 | Circular tooth thickness = (39) - (43) | 0.1825 | 43 | Circular tooth thickness = (40) - (42) | 0.1316 |
| 45 | $(44)^3$ | 0.0060 | 46 | $(44)^3$ | 0.0022 |
| 47 | $(9)^2$ | 16.0000 | 48 | $(10)^2$ | 64.0000 |
| 49 | 6 x (47) | 96.0000 | 50 | 6 x (48) | 384.000 |
| 51 | $\frac{(45)}{(49)}$ | 0.00006 | 52 | $\frac{(46)}{(50)}$ | 0.0000 |
| 53 | Chordal tooth thickness = $(44) - (51) - [0.5 \times (8)]$ | 0.181 | 54 | Chordal tooth thickness = $(43) - (52) - [0.5 \times (8)]$ | 0.1301 |
| 55 | $(44)^2 \times (29)$ | 0.0298 | 56 | $(43)^2 \times (30)$ | 0.0077 |
| 57 | 4 x (9) | 16.0000 | 58 | 4 x (10) | 32.0000 |
| 59 | $\frac{(55)}{(57)}$ | 0.0019 | 60 | $\frac{(56)}{(58)}$ | 0.0002 |
| 61 | Chordal addendum (18) + (59) | 0.1369 | 62 | Chordal addendum (17) + (60) | 0.0652 |
| 63 | sin (28) | 0.8785 | 64 | sin (27) | 0.4771 |
| 65 | cos (28) | 0.4776 | 66 | cos (27) | 0.8788 |

PINION                                                                                  GEAR

| 67 | (4) x (63) | 0.6589 | 68 | (4) x (64) | 0.3577 |
|----|-----------|--------|----|-----------|--------|
| 69 | (4) x (65) | 0.3583 | 70 | (4) x (66) | 0.6591 |
| 71 | $\frac{(16) - (4)}{(16)}$ | 0.8323 | | | |
| 72 | (18) x (71) | 0.1124 | 73 | (17) x (71) | 0.0541 |
| 74 | (19) x (71) | 0.0697 | 75 | (20) x (71) | 0.1280 |
| 76 | $[(72) + (74)] \times (30)$ | 0.0815 | 77 | $[(73) + (75)] \times (29)$ | 0.1629 |
| 78 | $(33) - [2 \times (69)]$ | 3.5249 | 79 | $(34) - [2 \times (70)]$ | 6.7399 |
| 80 | (76) + mfg. std. | 0.125 | 81 | (77) + mfg. std. | 0.250 |

# 8 printed circuit

Printed circuit boards must be easily inserted, accurately guided, and supported firmly in place during service.

*IRWIN SCHUSTER, Product Design Consultant, Secane, Pa*

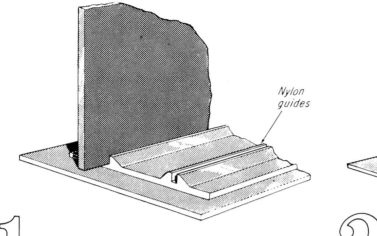

*Nylon guides*

**1** NYLON GUIDES grip the board along its entire length, lend support, and damp vibration during service.

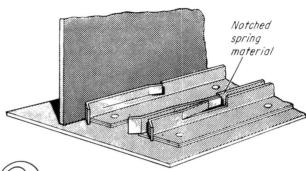

*Notched spring material*

**2** NOTCHED SPRING MATERIAL allows wide grooves for ease of alignment when mating with fixed connectors.

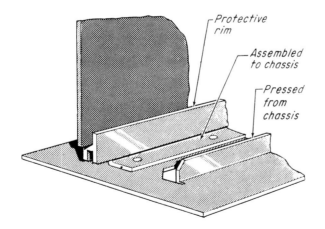

*Protective rim*

*Assembled to chassis*

*Pressed from chassis*

**5** PANEL STIFFENER and protective rim give excellent service. Guide can be pressed from chassis.

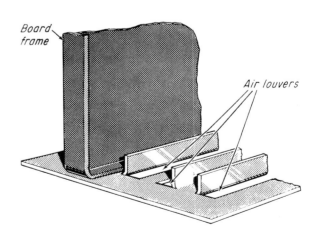

*Board frame*

*Air louvers*

**6** BOARD STIFFENER requires wide channel in chassis. When channel is pressed from chassis, air louvers are gained.

# guides

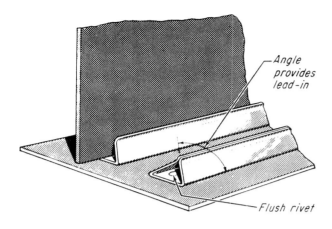

Angle provides lead-in

Flush rivet

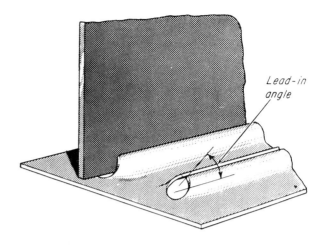

Lead-in angle

**FORMED SHEETMETAL GUIDE** is made of spring material, with the end cut off at an angle to guide the board.

**STAMPED-IN** board guide reduces weight of chassis while providing firm board mount. Note lead-in angle.

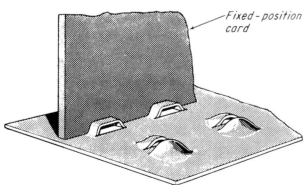

Fixed-position card

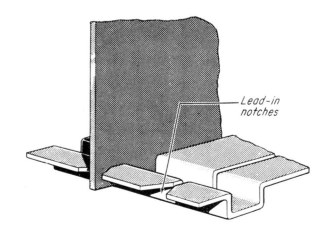

Lead-in notches

**SMALL SECTIONS** stamped in the chassis provide locating guides for cards mounted in fixed positions.

**INTEGRAL GUIDE** is ideal when stiff chassis is required and gives excellent lead-in characteristics.

# 8 more printed-circuit

They allow easy and quick insertion,
they guide accurately, and they support
the board firmly in place.

*IRWIN N. SCHUSTER, Product Design Consultant, Secane, Pa*

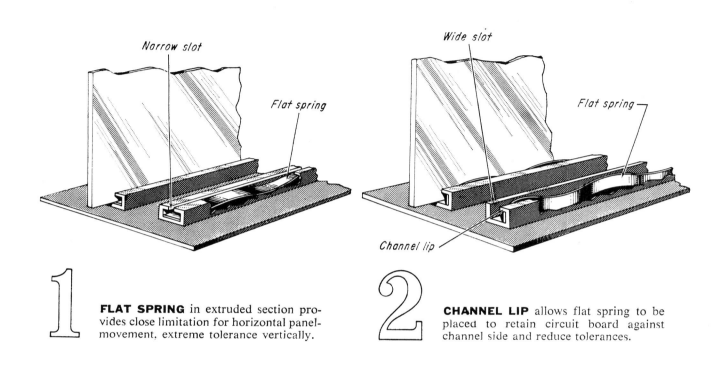

**1** **FLAT SPRING** in extruded section provides close limitation for horizontal panel-movement, extreme tolerance vertically.

**2** **CHANNEL LIP** allows flat spring to be placed to retain circuit board against channel side and reduce tolerances.

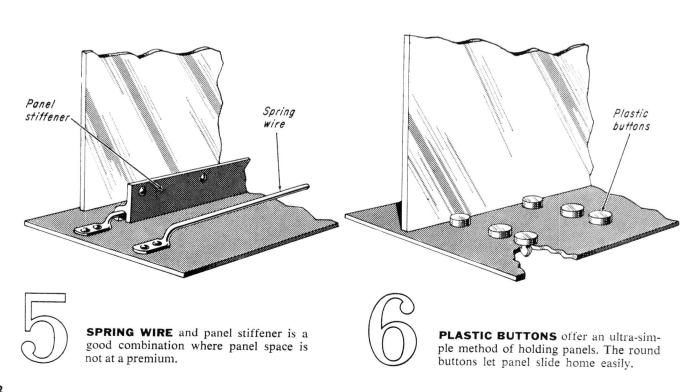

**5** **SPRING WIRE** and panel stiffener is a good combination where panel space is not at a premium.

**6** **PLASTIC BUTTONS** offer an ultra-simple method of holding panels. The round buttons let panel slide home easily.

# guides

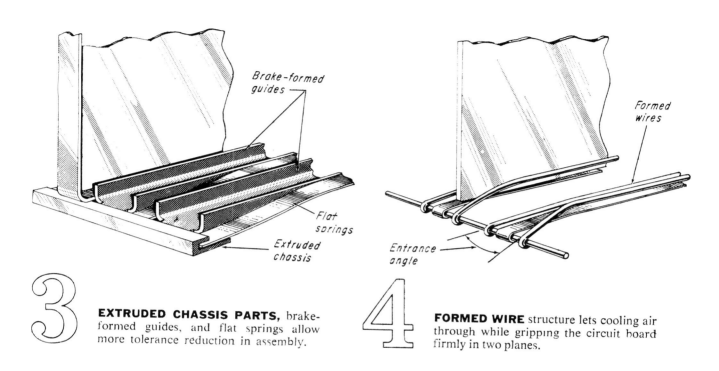

Brake-formed guides

Flat springs

Extruded chassis

**3** **EXTRUDED CHASSIS PARTS,** brake-formed guides, and flat springs allow more tolerance reduction in assembly.

Formed wires

Entrance angle

**4** **FORMED WIRE** structure lets cooling air through while gripping the circuit board firmly in two planes.

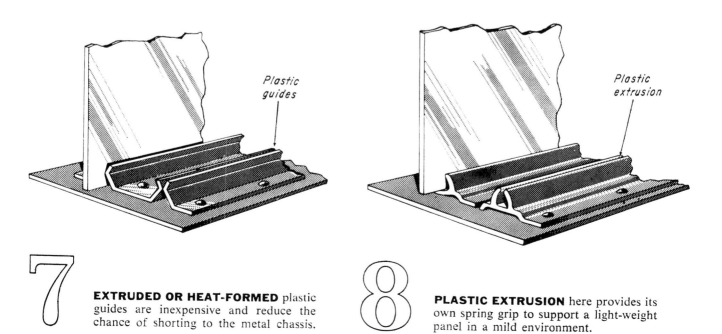

Plastic guides

**7** **EXTRUDED OR HEAT-FORMED** plastic guides are inexpensive and reduce the chance of shorting to the metal chassis.

Plastic extrusion

**8** **PLASTIC EXTRUSION** here provides its own spring grip to support a light-weight panel in a mild environment.

# These hinged lids

Keyslots, lid grooves, open hooks, sliding pins, and other features let hinged lids be completely removed.

*L. KASPER, Philadelphia*

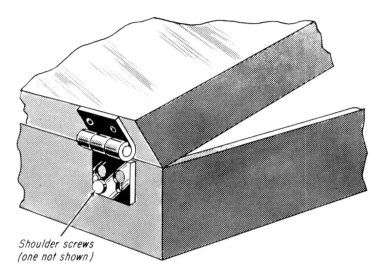

Shoulder screws
(one not shown)

**1** **KEYSLOTTING** one leaf of the hinge is a simple way to provide for separation of the lid from the box.

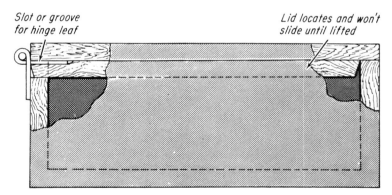

Slot or groove
for hinge leaf

Lid locates and won't
slide until lifted

**2** **LEAF CAVITY** in lid can be a simple groove. When lid locates against box sides, leaf cannot slip out.

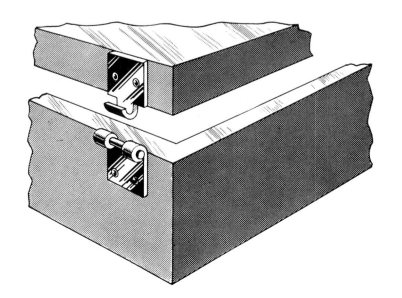

**3** **OPEN HOOK** is formed by partly uncurling one leaf. To disassemble the lid it must be opened through 180 deg.

# are separable

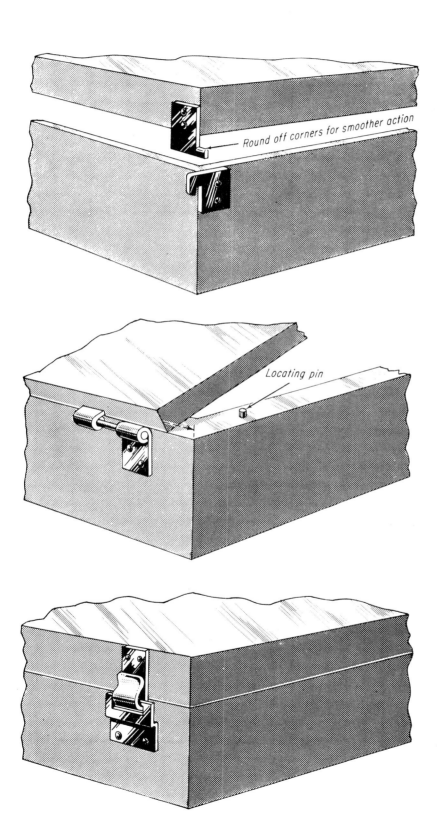

Round off corners for smoother action

Locating pin

**FLAT PLATES** are hook and pin that act as efficient but low-cost hinge for rigid lids. Round off pin corners.

**SLIDING PIN** is popular way of making lids separable. Locating pins must be provided if lid does not fit in box.

**SPRING-TYPE LEAF** must have enough clearance to accept retaining plate thickness unless spring is very light.

# CONTROL-LOCKS THWART VIBRATION AND SHOCK

Critical adjustments stay put—safe against accidental turning or deliberate fiddling with them.

**FRANK WILLIAM WOOD JR**
*President, Advanced Designs Inc*
*Vienna, Va*

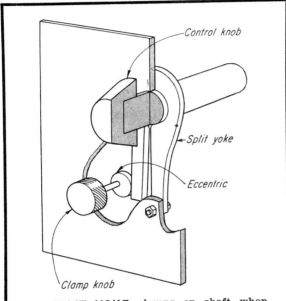

**1..SPLIT YOKE** clamps on shaft when eccentric squeezes ends of yoke together. Knurled knob is handy for constant use, and eliminates need for tool. Another advantage is high torque capacity. But this design needs considerable space on panel.

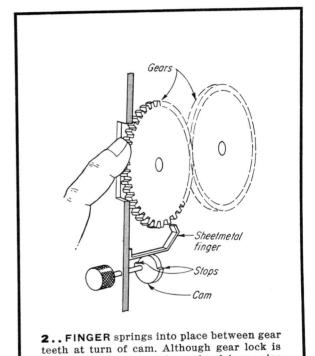

**2..FINGER** springs into place between gear teeth at turn of cam. Although gear lock is ideally suited for right-angle drives, size of teeth limits positioning accuracy.

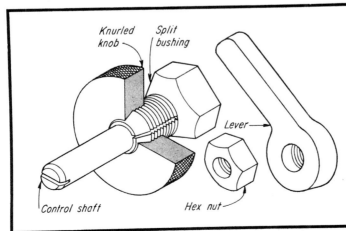

**3..SPLIT BUSHING** tightens on control shaft, because knurled knob has tapered thread. Bushing also mounts control to panel, so requires just one hole. Lever, like knob, does away with tools, but locks tighter and faster. For controls adjusted infrequently, hex nut turns a fault into an advantage. Although it takes a wrench to turn the nut, added difficulty guards against knob-twisters.

# CONTROL-LOCKS THWART
# VIBRATION AND SHOCK continued

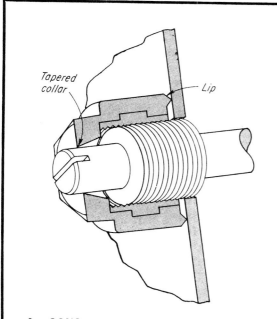

**4..CONSTANT DRAG** of tapered collar on shaft makes control stiff, so it doesn't need locking and unlocking. Compressed lip both seals out dust and keeps molded locking nut from rotating.

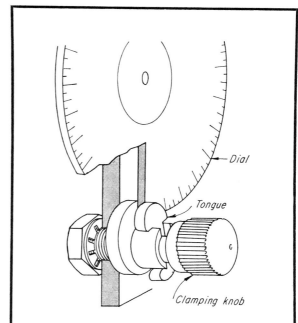

**5..TONGUE** slides in groove, clamps down on edge of dial. If clamp is not tight, it can scratch the face.

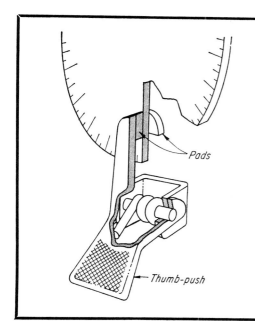

**6..SPOT-BRAKE** clamp is self-locking, which means it takes two hands to make an adjustment, one to hold the clamp open and one to turn the dial.

# BUILDING STRENGTH INTO BRACKETS

They must meet specific requirements—stability,
light weight, and the like. Here's your guide.

**S WARREN KAYE**

*Raytheon Co, Bedford, Mass*

**F**or stability, a good bracket must be able to carry load in three directions at right angles to each other—vertical, fore and aft, and sideways. Besides being able to withstand regular acceleration and operating loads, it must often be rugged enough to avoid damage from handling and accidental loads—for example, if it is stepped on, or used as a handhold, as in aircraft and missiles.

Space Age requirements also point up the frequent need to minimize weight of brackets. One way to do this is to place the equipment they support as near as possible to suitable attachment points on the basic structure. (Sometimes, in fact, by a minor rearrangement, such as shifting a stiffener or frame, the equipment can be attached directly to the structure, and the bracket eliminated.)

Other general rules for designing brackets: Avoid tension loads on riveted joints, do not combine rivets and bolts in the same local area; avoid using aluminum bolts in tension wherever possible; in a rivet pattern, avoid smaller rivets in the outer row; and don't overload first rivet or first row of rivets.

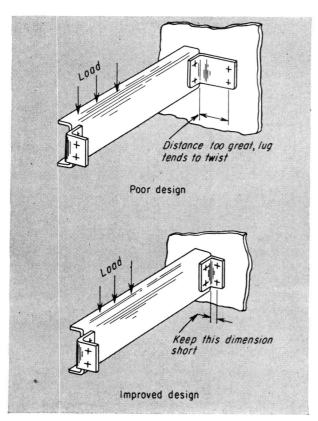

**1** MOUNTING LUGS should be either kept short or have rivet locations that reduce twisting.

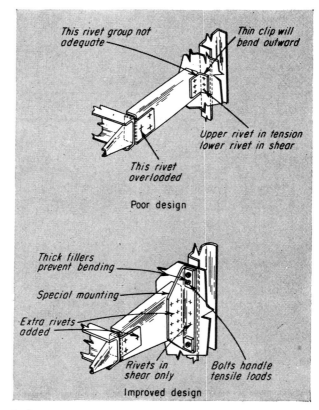

**2** SPECIAL MOUNTING is best for cantilever bracket where large moments cause high tensile stress at mounting. If possible, design a one-piece bracket.

**BRACKETS continued**

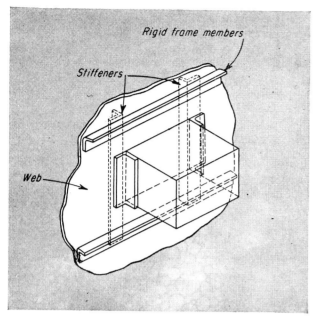

**3** STIFFENERS carry moment loads to rigid frame, prevent unsupported web from "oilcanning."

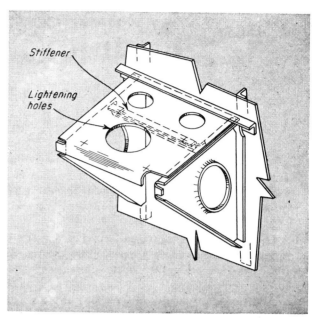

**4** SHELF SHEET can be thinner and lighter if stiffeners are provided. Lightening holes are flanged where possible.

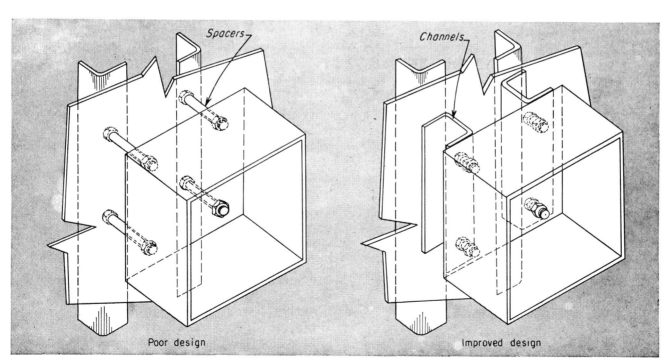

**5** CHANNELS are best for spacing mounted equipment from attachment wall. Channel thickness must be sufficient to withstand bending from side loads. If necessary, extra stiffening should be provided.

# Cleaner lines for control

How to improve the appearance of consoles and similar functional cabinets with divider strips, concealed catches, recesses, baffles, and trim.

*F. W. WOOD, Senior Engineer, Farrington Electronics, Alexandria, Va*

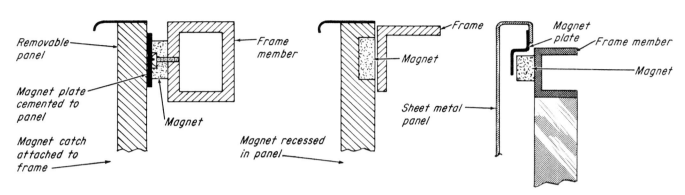

**1** **CONCEALED CATCHES** permit a clear, uncluttered exterior panel appearance. Catches not requiring close alignment are preferable.

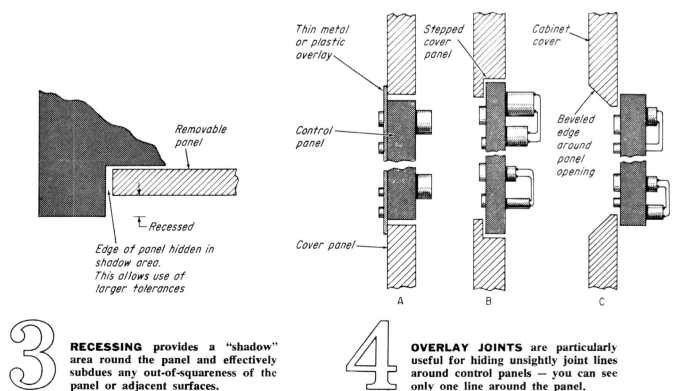

**3** **RECESSING** provides a "shadow" area round the panel and effectively subdues any out-of-squareness of the panel or adjacent surfaces.

**4** **OVERLAY JOINTS** are particularly useful for hiding unsightly joint lines around control panels — you can see only one line around the panel.

# cabinets

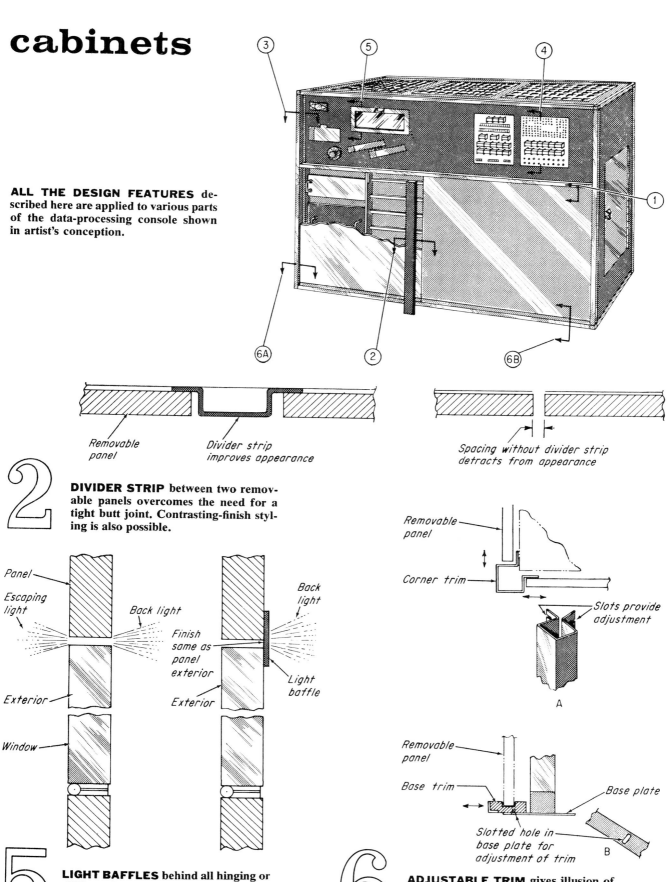

**ALL THE DESIGN FEATURES** described here are applied to various parts of the data-processing console shown in artist's conception.

Removable panel

Divider strip improves appearance

Spacing without divider strip detracts from appearance

## 2

**DIVIDER STRIP** between two removable panels overcomes the need for a tight butt joint. Contrasting-finish styling is also possible.

Panel

Escaping light

Back light

Exterior

Window

Back light

Finish same as panel exterior

Exterior

Light baffle

Removable panel

Corner trim

Slots provide adjustment

A

Removable panel

Base trim

Base plate

Slotted hole in base plate for adjustment of trim

B

## 5

**LIGHT BAFFLES** behind all hinging or sliding windows prevent back-lighting from emphasizing bad fits. Baffle and panel color should be the same.

## 6

**ADJUSTABLE TRIM** gives illusion of a good fit between non-squared panels and frames. Open-ended slots provide for easy assembly.

# Control Mountings

## When designing control panels follow this 8-point guide and check for...

*FRANK WILLIAM WOOD JR, president, Advanced Designs Inc, Vienna, Va*

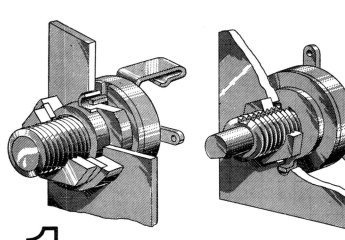

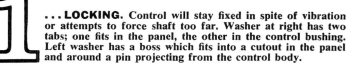

**1** ...**LOCKING.** Control will stay fixed in spite of vibration or attempts to force shaft too far. Washer at right has two tabs; one fits in the panel, the other in the control bushing. Left washer has a boss which fits into a cutout in the panel and around a pin projecting from the control body.

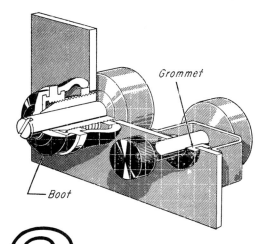

**2** ...**SEALING** against dust or water. Boot seals between shaft and bushing and between bushing and panel. With control behind panel rubber grommet seals only one place.

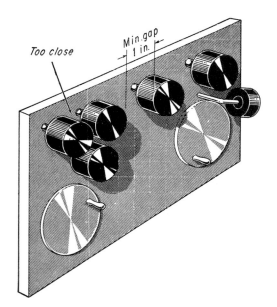

**5** ...**HAND-ROOM** at front of the panel. Space knobs at least one inch apart. Extending knob to save space puts it where the operator can bump into it and bend the shaft. Best rule is to keep shaft as short as possible.

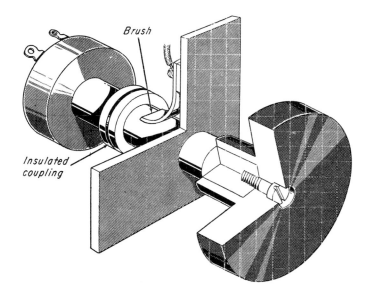

**6** ...**"HOT" CONTROL KNOBS.** One approach is to ground them by installing a brush against the shaft. Another solution is to isolate the control by an insulated coupling or a plastic knob having recessed holding screws.

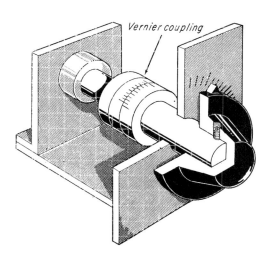

Vernier coupling

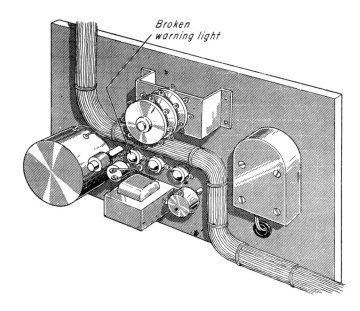

Broken
warning light

**3** **. . . RESETTING** to match controls to panel markings. For crude adjustments a set-screw is enough. Where matching is critical a three-piece vernier coupling permits more accurate calibration.

**4** **. . . ACCESSIBILITY** behind the panel. Easy access reduces down time and maintenance costs especially if one man can do most jobs alone. Here, technician can't replace a warning light without dismantling other parts.

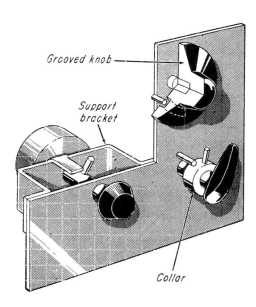

Grooved knob

Support
bracket

Collar

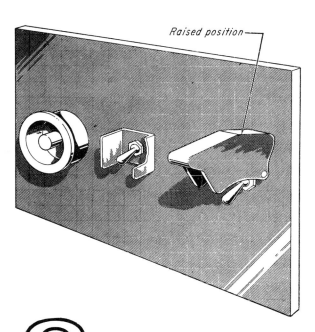

Raised position

**7** **. . . LIMIT STOPS** that are strong enough not to bend under heavy-handed use. Otherwise setting will change when stop moves. Collar and grooved knob permit adjustment; tab on bracket doesn't.

**8** **. . . GUARDS** to prevent accidental actuation of switches. Bell-shape guard for push-buttons is just finger-size. U-shape guard separates closely spaced toggle switches, and a swinging guard holds down special ones.

# EFFECT of CUTOUTS on MACHINE-TOOL PEDESTALS

These test results—38 variations on a design theme—are digested from an article by K Loewenfeld in *Der Maschinemarkt* (Wurzburg, W. Germany), No. 79, Oct '59.

**W**hat happens when you shoot a design full of holes? Investigators at Munich University found out. In the original machine-tool pedestal at right they cut round holes, square holes and slots at almost every possible location. This changed stiffness and natural frequency. The drawings and a summary (next page) of some of the results show the relative importance of cutout size, shape and location in bringing about the changes.

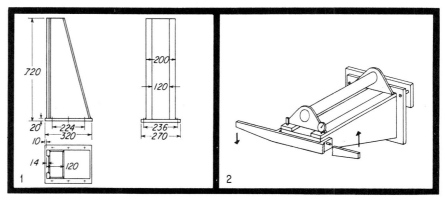

**STANDARD PEDESTAL** is comparison for all other configurations.

**TEST LOADS** act through lugs in side of horizontal pedestal.

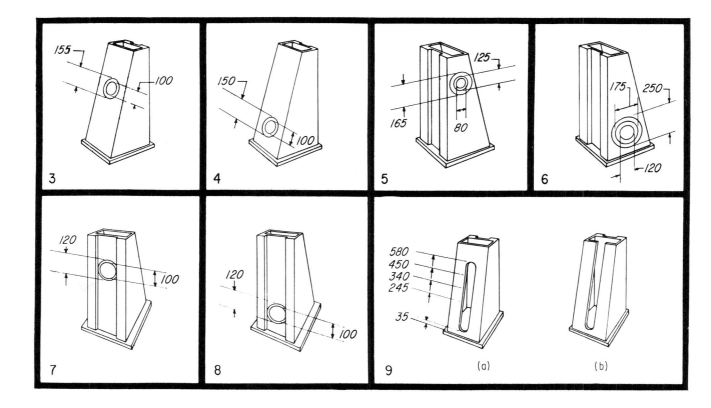

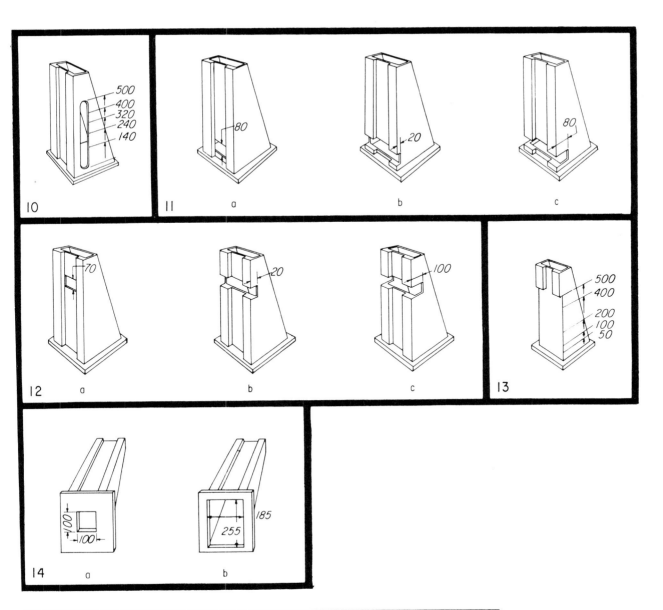

| Pedestal Number | 2 | 3 | | 4 | | 5 | | | 6 | | | 7 | | 8 | |
|---|---|---|---|---|---|---|---|---|---|---|---|---|---|---|---|
| Hole dia, mm.................... | — | 100 | 155 | 100 | 150 | 80 | 125 | 165 | 120 | 175 | 250 | 100 | 120 | 100 | 120 |
| Bending stiffness, %............. | 100 | 99 | 83 | 89 | 79 | 81 | 78 | 47 | 94 | 86 | 57 | 90 | 90 | 97 | 97 |
| Torsional stiffness, %........... | 100 | 97 | 96 | 97 | 94 | 80 | 72 | 62 | 98 | 94 | 93 | 86 | 86 | 97 | 95 |
| Bending natural frequency, cps...... | 455 | 454 | 451 | 390 | 390 | 433 | 428 | 426 | 411 | 420 | 402 | 450 | 448 | 411 | 403 |
| Torsional natural frequency, cps..... | 336 | 334 | 332 | 273 | 276 | 304 | 299 | 300 | 285 | 285 | 283 | 328 | 324 | 228 | 287 |

| Pedestal number | 9a | | | | 9b | 10 | | | | | 11a | 11b | 11c | 12a | 12b | 12c | 13 | | | | | 14a | 14b |
|---|---|---|---|---|---|---|---|---|---|---|---|---|---|---|---|---|---|---|---|---|---|---|---|
| Key dimension, mm................. | 245 | 340 | 450 | 580 | — | 140 | 240 | 320 | 400 | 500 | — | | | | | | 50 | 100 | 200 | 400 | 500 | — | |
| Bending stiffness, %.............. | 97 | 97 | 93 | 91 | 83 | 95 | 89 | 84 | 70 | 49 | 98 | 62 | 4.7 | 100 | 78 | 25 | 97 | 94 | 89 | 84 | 83 | 100 | 87 |
| Torsional stiffness, %............ | 99 | 94 | 93 | 83 | 45 | 96 | 94 | 94 | 93 | 86 | 100 | 59 | 27 | 100 | 62 | 28 | 98 | 96 | 96 | 92 | 90 | 100 | 69 |
| Bending natural frequency, cps...... | 418 | 410 | 402 | 394 | 182 | 445 | 408 | 369 | — | 310 | 392 | 360 | 352 | 438 | 435 | 430 | 392 | 384 | 382 | 378 | 378 | 412 | 406 |
| Torsional natural frequency, cps..... | 306 | 305 | 303 | 272 | 204 | 314 | 312 | 308 | 282 | 260 | 264 | 270 | 265 | 325 | 270 | 144 | 276 | 276 | 276 | 278 | 278 | 275 | 270 |

# HOW CUTOUTS and BRACES AFFECT MACHINE-TOOL TABLES

These comparative stiffness values for 30 designs are digested from an article by K Loewenfeld in *Der Maschinenmarkt* (Wurzburg, W. Germany), No. 79, Oct '59.

**A**dd braces to a machine-tool table and you increase stiffness; cut out slots or holes and you decrease it. To find the relative effect of various stiffeners and cutouts, researchers at the University of Munich found the relative torsional stiffness (based on an arbitrary standard shown below) of several representative designs. Tabulation on this page gives the results, including comparative stiffness-to-weight ratio for each design. Figures 1 to 8 show the reinforced designs; 9 to 18 show the cutout versions.

Dimension in millimeters.
7.5 mm plate except for back

**STANDARD DESIGN** received arbitrary rating of 1.0 for both torsional stiffness and stiffness-to-weight ratio.

**TEST RIG** determined the effect of stiffeners and cutouts by comparing each design against the standard.

| Table Number | 1 | 2 | 3 | 4 | 5 | 6 | 7 | 8 | STD | 9 | | 10 | | | 11 | | |
|---|---|---|---|---|---|---|---|---|---|---|---|---|---|---|---|---|---|
| Key dimension, mm | | | | | | | | | | 100 | 140 | 100 | 140 | 200 | 100 | 140 | 200 |
| Comparative torsional stiffness | 436 | 223 | 97 | 53 | 44 | 16 | 4.1 | 1.2 | 1.0 | 159 | 109 | 174 | 168 | 112 | 223 | 174 | 121 |
| Comparative torsional stiffness/weight | 279 | 175 | 69 | 39 | 35 | 14 | 3.4 | 1.0 | 1.0 | 123 | 86 | 136 | 133 | 91 | 176 | 140 | 101 |

| Table Number | 12 | | | 13 | | | 14 | | 15 | | 16 | 17 | 18 |
|---|---|---|---|---|---|---|---|---|---|---|---|---|---|
| Key dimension, mm | 100 | 140 | 205 | 100 | 140 | 200 | 230 | 300 | 230 | 300 | | 120 | 100 | 120 |
| Comparative torsional stiffness | 182 | 174 | 146 | 175 | 134 | 62 | 145 | 30 | 145 | 18.2 | 146 | 144 | 194 |
| Comparative torsional stiffness/weight | 145 | 142 | 123 | 139 | 109 | 53 | 115 | 24 | 107 | 13.4 | 116 | 112 | 142 |

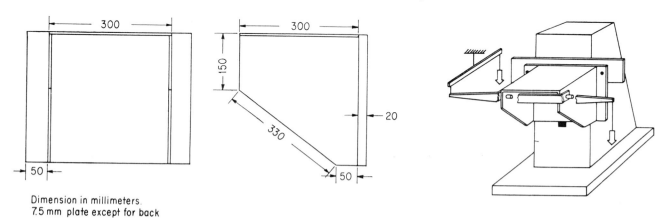

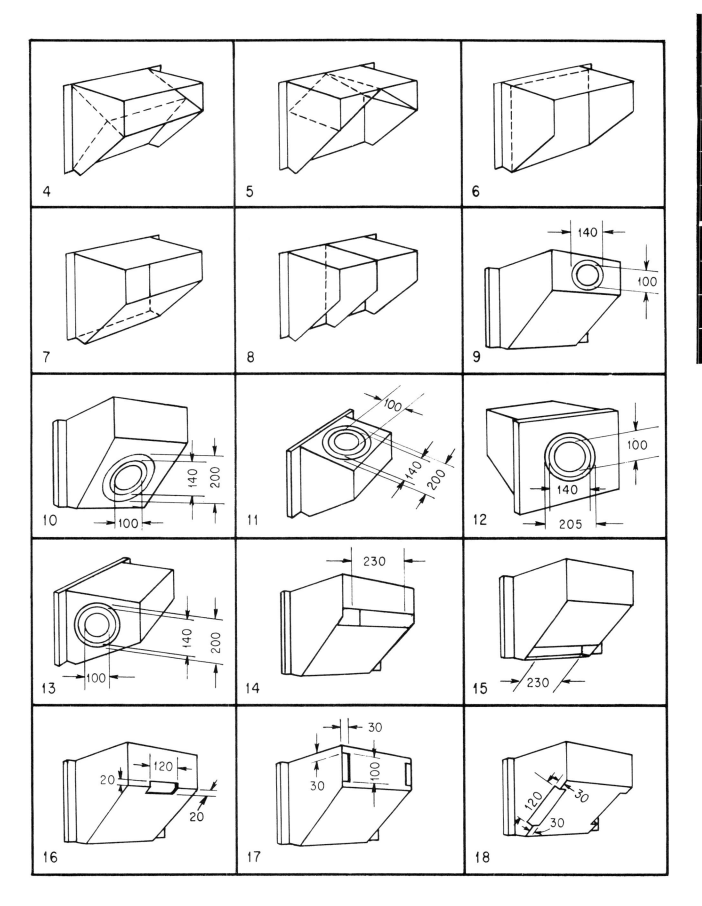

# HANDLES
# for PRINTED CIRCUITS

Seven simple designs for making maintenance easier.
More in a later issue.

**I N SCHUSTER,** *product design engineer, Raytheon Co*

**1**
**PUNCHED OR DRILLED HOLES**
are adequate if space between
boards is sufficient for finger insertion. Grommets may be required
in some materials.

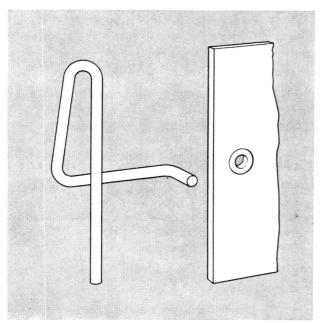

**2**
**SMALL EYELET** and removable extractor
works well when space and weight are at a
premium.

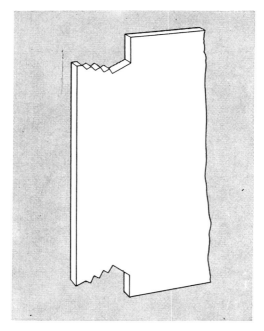

**3**
**SERRATED FINGER GRIPS** are often best when
spacing of boards is extremely close.

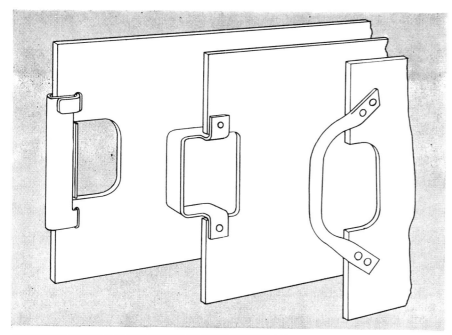

**4**
**INDIVIDUAL HANDLES,** tabbed or riveted in place, may be called for on large boards.

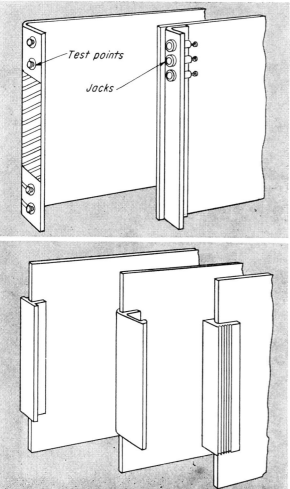

**5**
**FORMED BOARDS** do double duty when test points and jacks are incorporated into handles.

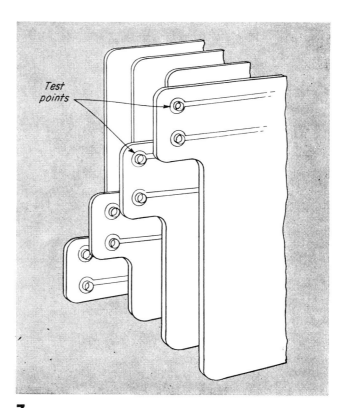

**6**
**EXTRUSIONS** staked, crimped or pinned in place form attractive withdrawal aids.

**7**
**STAGGERED POSITIONS** of removal tabs give easy access to test points on closely spaced panels.

# 7 more HANDLES
# for PRINTED CIRCUITS

A handy guide to easy withdrawal and handling of these
circuit boards. An earlier selection was presented in
the Oct 10 issue.

**I N SCHUSTER,** *product design engineer*
**Raytheon Co**
**Wayland, Mass**

**1** CABLE CLAMPS AND STRAPS are readily available in
many styles. By using solderable materials, handles can be
assembled during component-soldering operation.

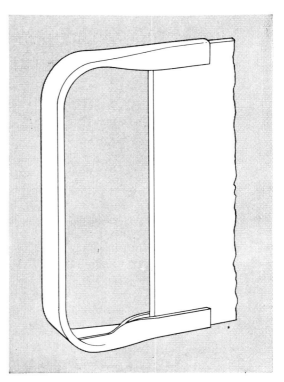

**2** MORE COMPLEX SHAPE of sheetmetal handle
is often preferred when appearance is an important feature of the design.

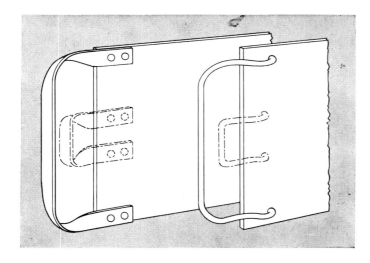

**3** WIRE OR SHEETMETAL parts may be easily
formed either as full handles or fingergrips.

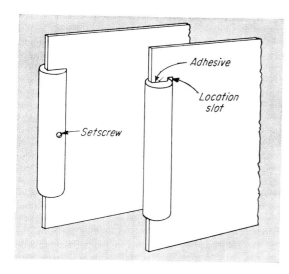

**4** SLOTTED ROD, held by either a screw or adhesive, is most suitable when more robust fastening is required.

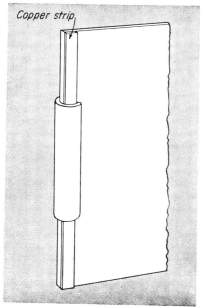

**5** SPLIT TUBING can be slipped onto panels and retained by spring effect, or a copper strip can be left to provide a shoulder.

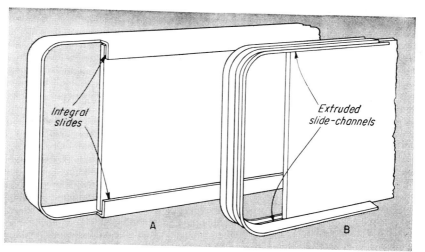

**6** BOARD-STIFFENING FRAMES have integral slide surfaces and handles. Method suitable for either press-forming (A) or extrusion (B).

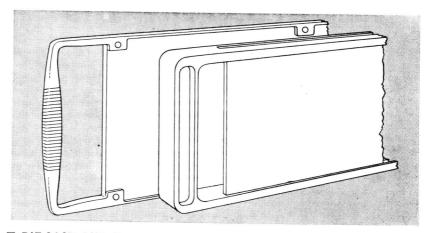

**7** DIE-CAST AND MOLDED. handles can be provided if needed in quantity large enough to justify added cost of tooling.

# 8 Retainers for

These retainers ensure that the board is properly seated and locked against shock and vibration.

*IRWIN N. SCHUSTER, Raytheon Co., Wayland, Mass.*

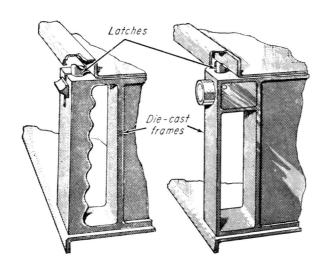

Latches

Die-cast frames

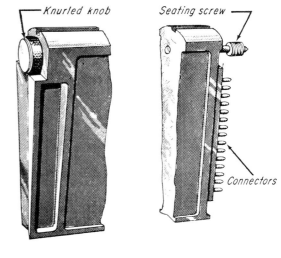

Knurled knob

Seating screw

Connectors

**1** **SPRING-LOADED LATCHES** for large die-cast frames are positive and clean looking. The cost is somewhat high.

**2** **TIGHT SEATING** is necessary for connectors of the plug and socket type. A screw and a knurled knob aid seating.

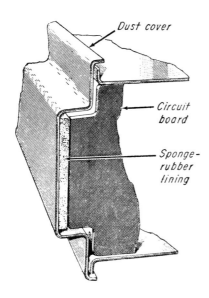

Dust cover

Circuit board

Sponge-rubber lining

Wing nut

Adjustable retainer

Adjusting slot

**5** **DUST COVER,** lined with sponge rubber, does double duty — it holds the board in place and helps protect it from shock.

**6** **ADJUSTABLE PLATES,** either flat or formed, are very easy to assemble and hold sliding parts firmly in place.

# circuit boards

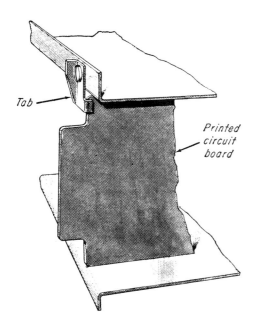

Tab

Printed circuit board

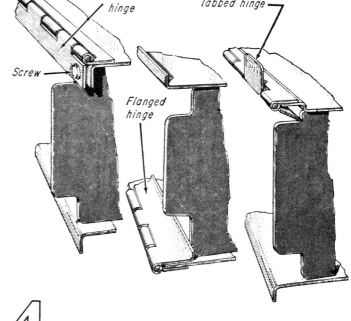

Screw-held hinge

Tabbed hinge

Screw

Flanged hinge

**SHEETMETAL TABS,** pivoting on either a shoulder screw or rivet, are always an efficient, low-cost way to retain parts.

**HINGES,** spring loaded or otherwise modified, provide a variety of suitable means for retaining circuit boards in place.

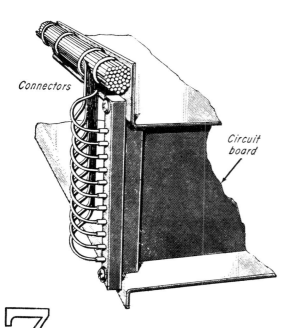

Connectors

Circuit board

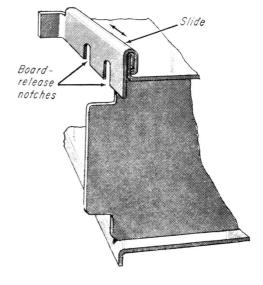

Slide

Board-release notches

**FRONT-MOUNTED CONNECTORS** do double duty here, providing test points for circuit leads and securing the board.

**NOTCHES** in the slide provide entrance and exit gates for circuit boards. Lubrication of the slide may be advisable.

# 8 More retainers

These methods for retaining circuit boards can give you some valuable ideas you can apply to other devices.

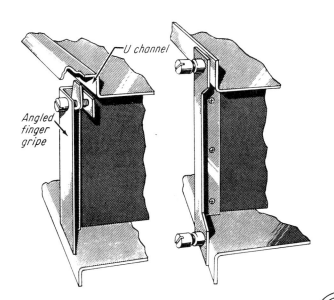

**1** ANGLED HANDLES fitted with standard hardware parts result in low-cost, yet efficient, slide retainers.

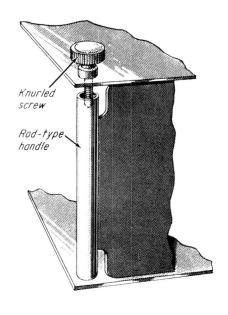

**2** ROD-TYPE HANDLE can be either solid, with tapped hole for screw, or hollow, with mating dowel-type spring latch.

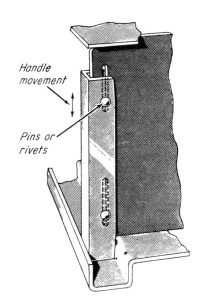

**5** SLIDING HANDLES can be arranged to fall into locking position when vertical; otherwise they need springs.

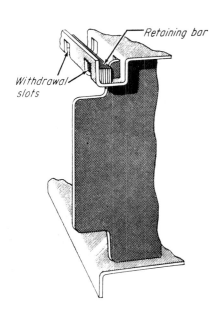

**6** SLOTTED U-CHANNEL not only locates the circuit boards at correct spacings but also accommodates a retaining bar.

# for circuit boards

*IRWIN N. SCHUSTER, Raytheon Co., Wayland, Mass.*

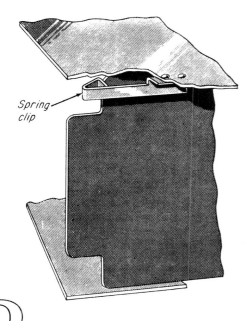

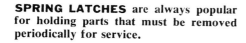

**3** **SPRING LATCHES** are always popular for holding parts that must be removed periodically for service.

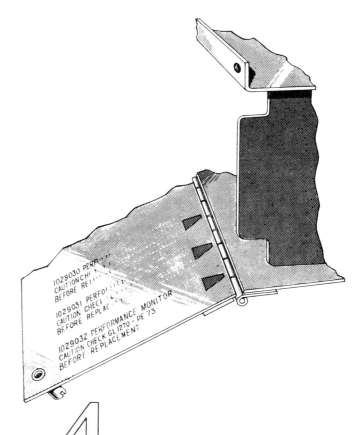

**4** **DOUBLE-DUTY COVERS** not only hold units in place but are also ideal locations for operating instructions.

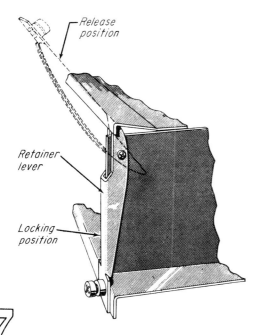

**7** **RETAINER LEVERS** jack the boards into and out of the receptacle. Such levers are usually locked in place.

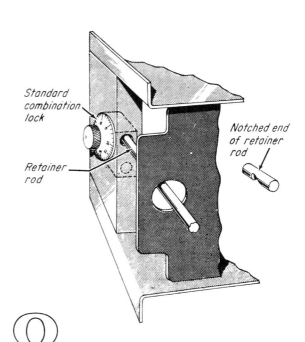

**8** **COMBINATION LOCK** and straight, notched bar provide a retaining assembly that is virtually tamperproof.

# When Instruments Need Feet

**These sketches illustrate many different solutions to the problem of how to mount instruments properly.**

**FRANK WILLIAM WOOD JR,**
*design engineer*
*Vitro Laboratories, Silver Spring, Md*

Always consider these factors carefully when choosing feet for instruments: instrument size and weight; cost of parts and installation; how and where instrument will be used; styling; height and angular adjustments that will be necessary.

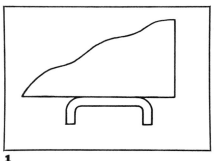

**1** FORMED SHEETMETAL foot can also strengthen the instrument case. Can be either four short sections at corners of instrument case or two

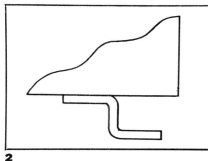

**2** members almost full length or width of case. This foot could also be inverted to secure case to mounting. Z-foot (2) provides easy access.

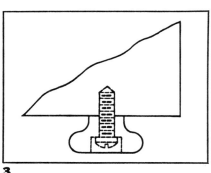

**3** "BUMPER" TYPE FEET are available in a large variety of sizes and rubberlike materials. These can

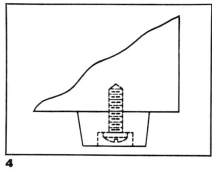

**4** be attached to the case with machine screws, self-tapping sheetmetal screws (3, 4), or push-in self-retaining types

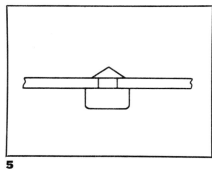

**5** (5). For sensitive equipment, rubber bumpers provide some isolation from vibration.

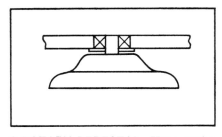

**6** ROTARY PEDESTAL. Here, entire case is supported at its center on a bearing.

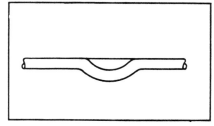

**7** "DIMPLE" FOOT can be pressed into a sheetmetal case during fabrication, is ideal for heavy instruments that must be moved by sliding.

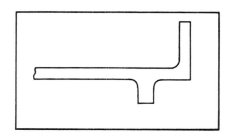

**8** "CAST" FOOT is another cost-cutting design—handling and assembly of separate feet is avoided.

**Instrument Feet** continued

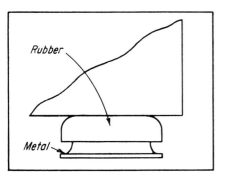

**9** SHOCK AND VIBRATION are isolated by this mount, available in sizes and materials to meet requirements.

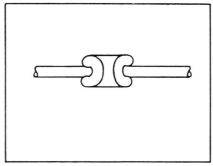

**10** RUBBER GROMMET is a satisfactory foot for a lightweight instrument or for a temporary mount.

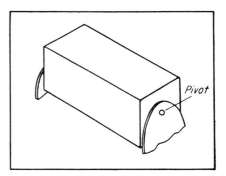

**11** ANGULAR ADJUSTMENT in the vertical plane is provided by this type of support. Suitable locking devices should be provided.

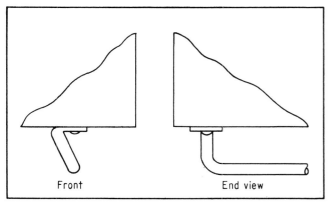

**12** METAL TUBING OR ROD makes efficient, good-looking foot. Can be used in pairs or at front only, if viewing face of instrument requires tilting.

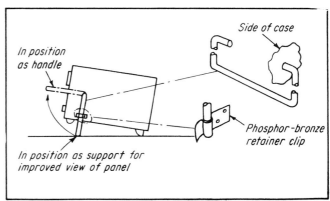

**14** DUAL-FUNCTION support doubles as handle. This is ideal for miniaturized oscilloscopes and other test equipment where space is at a premium.

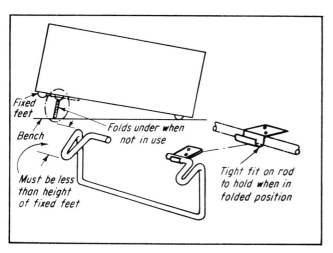

**13** HINGED ROD can combine with fixed feet to allow better viewing angle for instruments such as oscilloscopes.

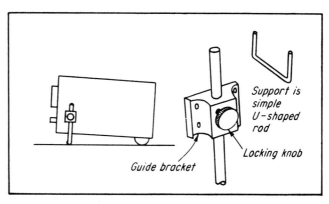

**15** HEIGHT ADJUSTMENT shown here is only one of many ways of providing small or large compensation in, for example, optical projectors.

# MANUFACTURING PROCESSES AND FINISHES FOR NAMEPLATES

| MANUFACTURING PROCESS | MATERIALS USUALLY USED | FINISHES | MANUFACTURING AND FINISHING PROCEDURE |
|---|---|---|---|
| Sand and Plaster Mold Casting | Nonferrous alloys; Brass, bronze, aluminum and magnesium on occasion. Also cast iron for sand castings. | Primarily organic finishes. Frequently raised characters are buffed to obtain a metallic finish against a dark painted background. See also, "Non-Metallic Finishes for Gray-Iron," Product Engineering, October, 1950 | Castings made in plaster or sand molds using only casting pressure. Types of finishes and manufacturing procedure not as flexible as for sheet metal forms. |
| Die Casting | Usually zinc, aluminum, or magnesium, although latter is seldom used for nameplates. | Plating is common, with chromium being widely applied; some gold plating done on high quality nameplates and emblems. Organic finishes also very common. | Conventional pressure die casting process. Finishing usually done on an automatic high production scale. Very high quality finishes can be obtained. |
| Die Striking | Any metal surface | Since die striking is selected primarily for unobtrusive markings, such markings are almost always done on unfinished or plated metals. However, depressed characters formed by the punch may be filled with paint to secure a better contrast. | Produced by a sharp blow with a punch. No female die required as for embossed plates. Punches can be combined with automatic numbering heads to number the product. |
| Cold Forging | Steel, magnesium, aluminum and copper. Brass is very popular for nameplates. | Electroplates, paints, lacquers, mechanical finishes, and porcelain enamel in a wide variety of combinations. | Die forging, followed by suitable trimming and finishing operations after proper surface pre-treatment. |
| Stamping | Sheet metal of any type, including steel, stainless steel, aluminum, brass, copper and Monel. | Same as forgings for blanked or embossed plates. Also, lithographed or etched plates, the etched plates being painted and the lithographed plates being printed. | BLANKED OR EMBOSSED—May be flat, skeleton, or embossed sheet metal type. Embossed types may have figures, characters or designs either in relief or intaglio.<br><br>ETCHED SHEET—Design exposed to zinc plate with light sensitive surface, which then is used to print on sheet metal form. Etching of sheet metal follows, and plate is painted.<br><br>LITHOGRAPHED SHEET—Preparation of drawings, reproduction on master printing plate, and printing on sheet essentially same as for etched plates except that no provision is made on the drawings for color separation. Colors are printed, not painted. |
| Fabricated plastic forms | Transparent or opaque thermosetting or thermoplastic materials. (Laminated engraving sheet and graphic sheet widely used.) | Most surfaces are printed, painted, or left in their natural state. | Engraving, etching, printing, stenciling, laminating, branding, or embossing. Electroplates can be applied to plastics, although they seldom are. |
| Molded plastic forms | Both thermosetting and thermoplastic materials. | Painted or natural finish of the plastic, which can be transparent or colored opaque. | Standard molding processes, plus painting; or double or triple injection molded forms in several colors; or acrylic plastic with painted backs to give three dimensional effects. |
| Decalcomanias | Standard decals are paper with an adhesive backing. Vitreous decals also are available, as are aluminum foil "Metal-Cals." | Printed in any color and with color overlays. | Decal is slid off paper backing and is attached to surface by adhesive backing. Decal is lacquered so it is unnecessary to give it another coat on application to the product. |

| ADVANTAGES AND LIMITATIONS | APPLICATIONS | REMARKS |
| --- | --- | --- |
| Low production processes. Detail not as good as die casting, although plaster cast plates are sharper than those produced by sand casting. Sand casting ideal when identification is cast integral with machine. | Nameplates for large equipment where only limited production is anticipated. Seldom used for consumer goods. | Either raised or depressed lettering can be used. Individual plates are generally cast with raised nomenclature and border. Produces a very substantial appearance. |
| High production process. Script or block nameplates, with characters connected by bar or border running through characters is excellent. Can be made integral with product or as separate plate. Excellent detail. Dies can be made to produce several plates in one casting cycle. | Automobiles, household appliances, radio and television receivers, office equipment, industrial equipment, when high quality and large production justifies tooling required. | Provides excellent detail. Raised letters on depressed background less costly than depressed letters. Characters should not be undercut to facilitate easier removal from the die. Plates can be cast in one plane or in curved or V-form, although dies for the latter are more costly. |
| Probably the most economical method of identifying a product. Not particularly attractive and not an attention focusing form. Since characters are formed in the product, however, they will last as long as the product. | Hand tools, cooking utensils, fuse links, thermostatic bimetals, and other parts on which an unobtrusive marking is required; or parts too small to be marked in any other way. | Detail is good. Trademarks or company initials often marked in this way. Method also can be used on sand, plaster mold, or die cast parts when there is no danger of the impact from the punch fracturing the base metal. |
| Nameplates made in this manner are solid, high quality items. Cost is higher than some of the stamped forms. | High quality nameplates and emblems for industrial equipment, automotive trim, and other devices when moderately high production and solid appearance is essential. | Detail is sharp. Forged identification can be made a part of the product, although separate plates are more common. |
| Low cost, high production. Almost unlimited design freedom. Any type of finish practical that is adaptable to the base metal. Size limited only by press capacities. | Process is used mostly for name and identification plates. Embossed sheet metal plates combine relief with light weight. All types of industrial and consumer equipment. | Embossing often applied to structural or decorative members, with name identification made a part of the design. Freezer doors and storage bins for household refrigerators are examples. |
| No tooling cost except for final blanking of the sheet into individual plates. Excellent reproduction of drawing. Low cost. Wide variety of colors and designs. However, different colors must be separated by a raised metal barrier. | Etched plates are ideal for control accessories that are subject to extensive handling because paints lie protected in depressed etched areas. Also widely used for instruction and nameplates. | Metal or plated-metal border prevents paint from chipping on blanking operation. If border is impossible, plate should be blanked with the bottom side up. Lettering may be produced in either depressed or relief forms. |
| Economical. Can be reproduced as faithfully as any printed matter. Different colors can be printed adjacent to, or superimposed over, one another. Adaptable to both medium and large production quantities. | For name, instruction or scale plates on indoor equipment. Does not resist abrasion as well as other forms. Semi-permanent. | Plates with open designs usually given a brushed satin mechanical finish prior to printing to conceal surface imperfections. Brushed treatment also decreases light reflections, increases plate legibility. Aluminum is widely used for litho plates, but almost any sheet metal is adaptable. |
| Slightly more costly than sheet metal forms. Good contrast. Wide variety of finishing processes can be used. Various colors can be obtained in the sheet. Have permanence, and will withstand wear and abuse. | Wiring diagrams, instrument panels, plotting boards, fluorescent scales, dials, and nameplates. Engraved graphic sheets usually used when quantities are small or similar types of plates are to have slightly different markings. | Translucent engraving stock can be used with rear illumination to obtain high contrast letters and markings. Sheet can also be obtained in various designs, as for example, wood graining. |
| Can be molded in several colors by multiple shot process. Acrylic plastics, painted on back in single or multiple colors, gives a beautiful three-dimensional effect. Adaptable to high production. Fairly high in cost. | Automobile insignia, radio and television control panels, and other consumer products. As yet, seldom applied to industrial equipment. | Metallic roll leaf, fused to the back of clear plastic, is particularly effective when gold or silver are reproduced. Additional cost of three-dimensional molded forms usually justified because of their eye-arresting appeal. |
| Complete freedom of design and coloring possible with lithographed printing process. Can be applied to almost any type of surface including wrinkle, or crackle organic finishes; ceramics, porcelain, rubber, glass, plastic or metal. No fastening devices required. | Unlimited use in consumer and industrial fields when cost is a factor and maximum in appearance not required. Wiring diagrams, name or trademark identification, operating instructions. etc. | Equipment ratings can be inserted as a separate transfer in combination with the regular marking. Providing a shallow nest or depression for the decal will protect it in service and provide a convenient painting guide for future reconditioning of the equipment. |

# SNAP-IN ACCESS PANELS
# PRESERVE CLEAN LOOK

**FRANK WILLIAM WOOD JR**
*President, Advanced Designs Inc*
*Vienna, Va*

These doors show no hinges or handles, need only finger holes or prying lips for positioning.

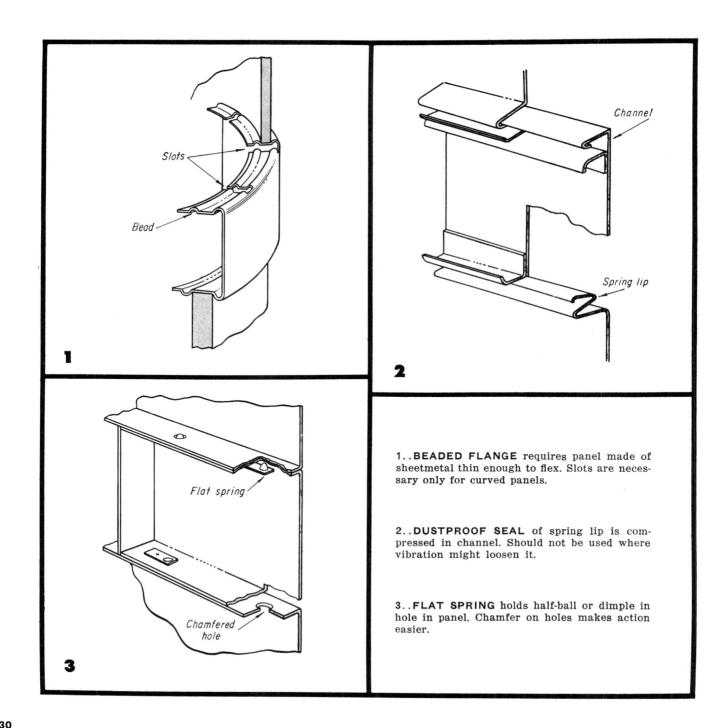

1..**BEADED FLANGE** requires panel made of sheetmetal thin enough to flex. Slots are necessary only for curved panels.

2..**DUSTPROOF SEAL** of spring lip is compressed in channel. Should not be used where vibration might loosen it.

3..**FLAT SPRING** holds half-ball or dimple in hole in panel. Chamfer on holes makes action easier.

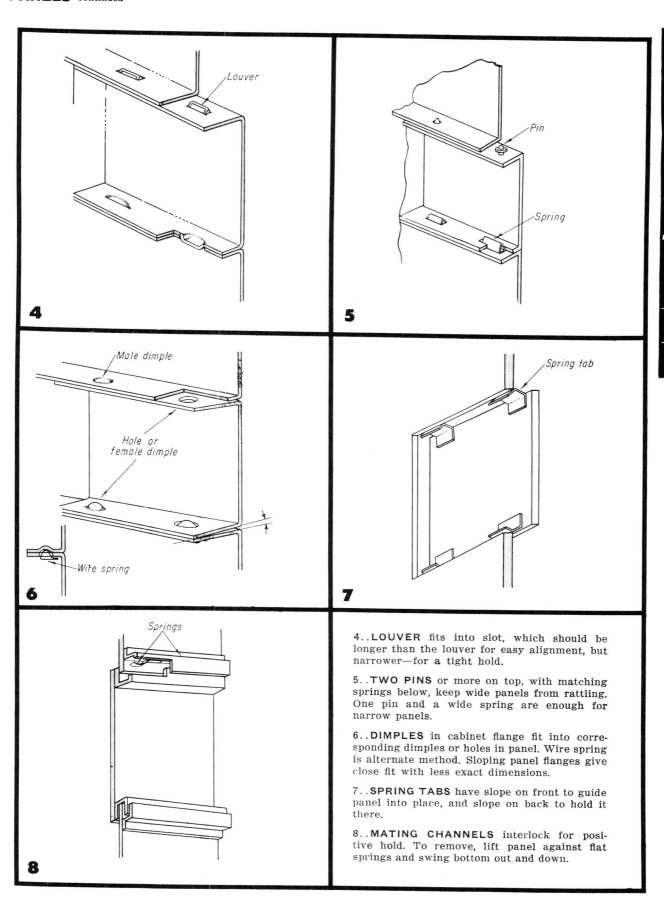

**4..LOUVER** fits into slot, which should be longer than the louver for easy alignment, but narrower—for a tight hold.

**5..TWO PINS** or more on top, with matching springs below, keep wide panels from rattling. One pin and a wide spring are enough for narrow panels.

**6..DIMPLES** in cabinet flange fit into corresponding dimples or holes in panel. Wire spring is alternate method. Sloping panel flanges give close fit with less exact dimensions.

**7..SPRING TABS** have slope on front to guide panel into place, and slope on back to hold it there.

**8..MATING CHANNELS** interlock for positive hold. To remove, lift panel against flat springs and swing bottom out and down.

# 8 STOPS FOR PANEL DOORS

They protect hinges from overtravel and hold doors in working position.

**FRANK WILLIAM WOOD JR**
*President, Advanced Designs Inc*
*Vienna, Va*

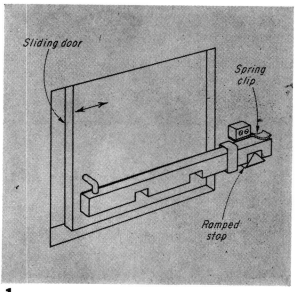

**1.**
**SPRING CLIP** presses notched bar down on stop for sliding door.

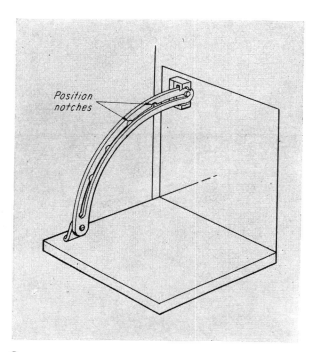

**2.**
**SLOTTED BAR** stops when pin jams against end; notches hold drop panel in intermediate positions.

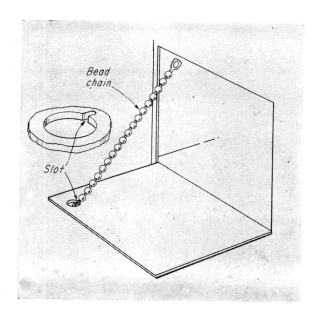

**3.**
**BEADED CHAIN** provides as many positions as there are beads. Keyhole slot allows repositioning.

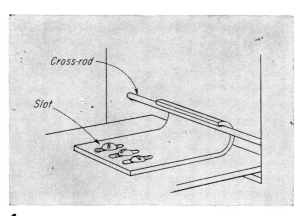

**4.**
**WRAPAROUND** back of bar comes to a stop against the cross-rod. Slots permit adjusting bar for different door opening.

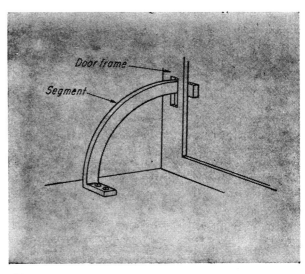

**5.**
**DOG-LEG** on end of segment butts against door frame.

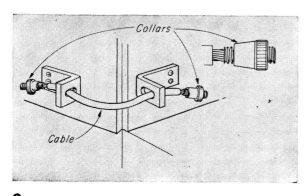

**6.**
**CABLE** pulls taut on end collars, which screw back and forth for slight adjustment.

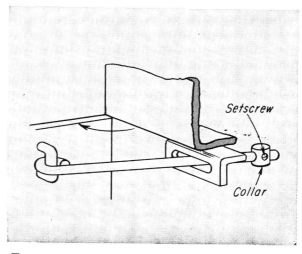

**7.**
**COLLAR** slides along rod to adjust stopping point.

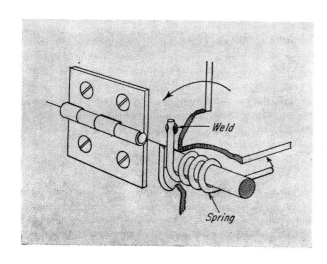

**8.**
**COIL SPRING** swings into underside of shelf and cushions door to a soft stop.

# How to seal air ducts

These slip joints reseal and realign ducting that is often taken apart. They also take care of expansion, vibration, and joint locations difficult to reach.

*JAMES H. LaPOINTE, Product Designer, Fairbanks, Morse & Co, Beloit, Wis*

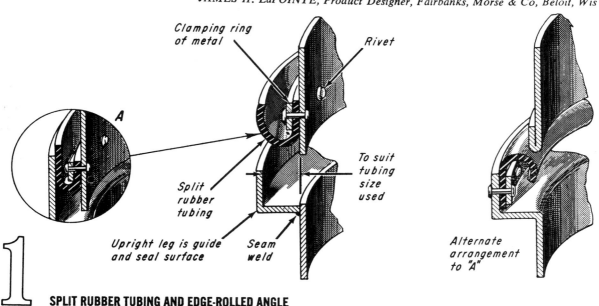

Clamping ring of metal

Rivet

A

Split rubber tubing

To suit tubing size used

Upright leg is guide and seal surface

Seam weld

Alternate arrangement to "A"

**1** SPLIT RUBBER TUBING AND EDGE-ROLLED ANGLE

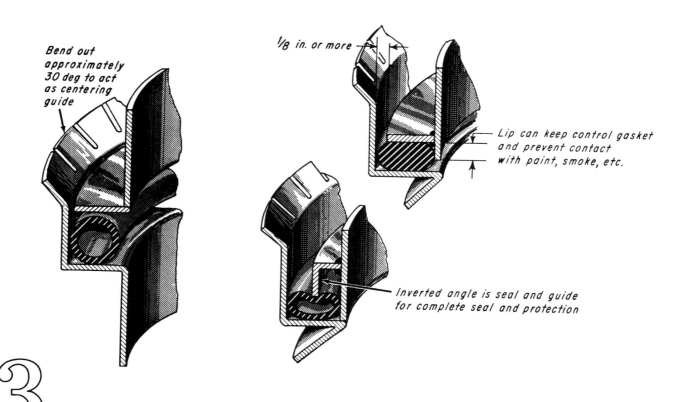

Bend out approximately 30 deg to act as centering guide

1/8 in. or more

Lip can keep control gasket and prevent contact with paint, smoke, etc.

Inverted angle is seal and guide for complete seal and protection

**3** PLAIN RUBBER TUBING OR SOLID RING IN COMPRESSION

# that separate

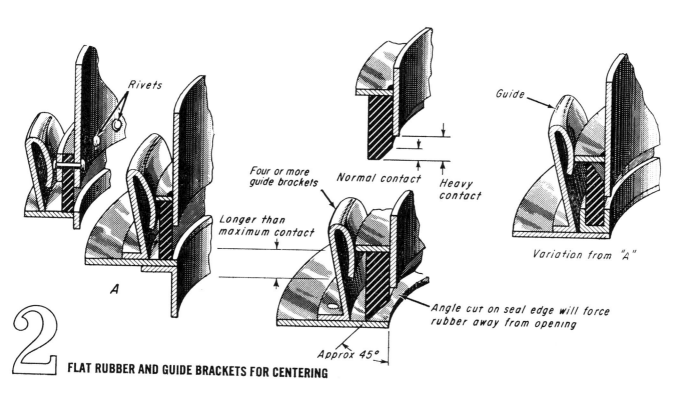

Rivets

Four or more guide brackets

Normal contact

Heavy contact

Longer than maximum contact

Guide

Variation from "A"

A

Angle cut on seal edge will force rubber away from opening

Approx 45°

## 2 FLAT RUBBER AND GUIDE BRACKETS FOR CENTERING

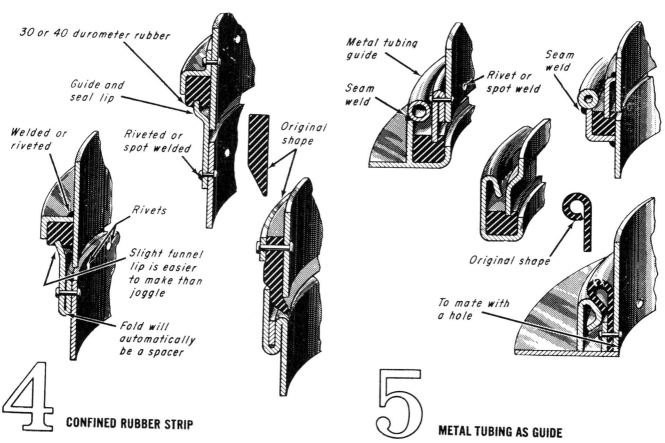

30 or 40 durometer rubber

Guide and seal lip

Welded or riveted

Riveted or spot welded

Original shape

Rivets

Slight funnel lip is easier to make than joggle

Fold will automatically be a spacer

## 4 CONFINED RUBBER STRIP

Metal tubing guide

Seam weld

Rivet or spot weld

Seam weld

Original shape

To mate with a hole

## 5 METAL TUBING AS GUIDE

# More seals for ducting

Six more seals for round ducts and others.
Make sure the gasket material can withstand
the ducted media.

*JAMES H. LaPOINTE, Product Designer, Fairbanks, Morse & Co, Beloit, Wis*

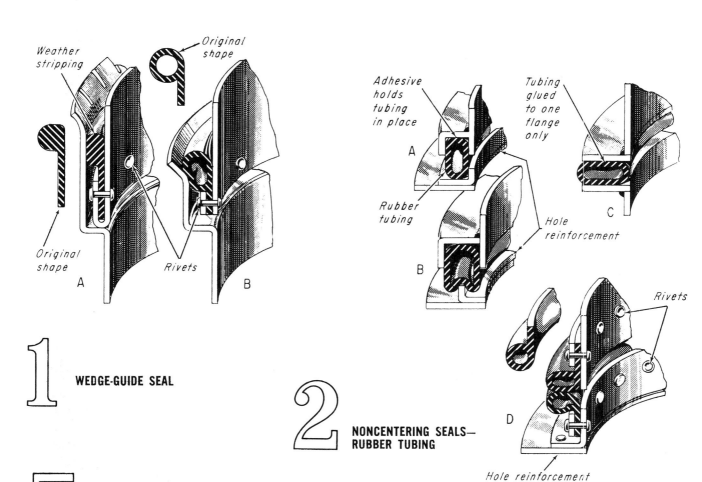

**1  WEDGE-GUIDE SEAL**

**2  NONCENTERING SEALS—
RUBBER TUBING**

**5  ROUND-BAR GUIDE SEALS AND VARIATIONS**

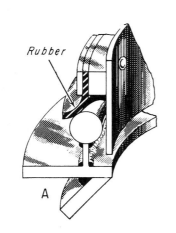

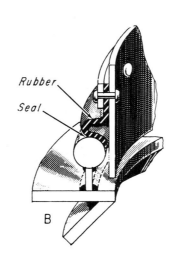

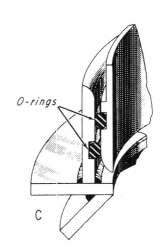

# that separates

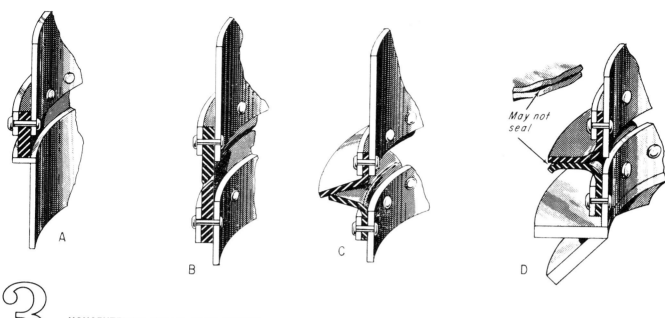

A

B

C

D

May not seal

**3** NONCENTERING SEALS—FLAT RUBBER

**4** SLIP SLEEVES THAT SEAL WITHOUT GASKETS

**6** METAL TUBING GUIDE AND VARIATIONS

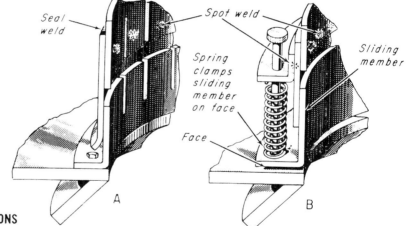

Seal weld

Spot weld

Spring clamps sliding member on face

Sliding member

Face

A

B

Seal and guide

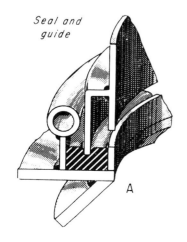

A

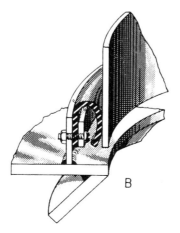

B

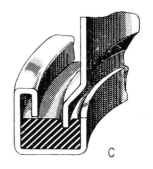

C

# FOR BETTER GRIP . . .
# LONGER HOLES IN SHEETMETAL

In steel or brass, depth of a threaded hole should be at least half its width, and in zinc or aluminum the right ratio is 2/3. If the metal is too thin, here's what to do.

**FEDERICO STRASSER,** Mankowitz & Strasser, Santiago, Chile

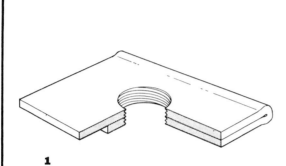

**1**

**BENT-OVER SHEET** doubles depth of holes near edge. Sometimes one more bend, for triple depth, is possible.

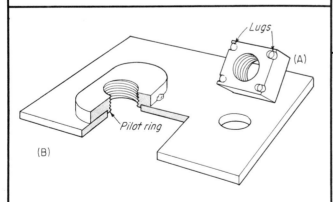

**2**

**PROJECTION-WELDING** fuses lugs on nut (A) to sheet. Flanged nut (B) for spotwelding has pilot rim to locate it on hole.

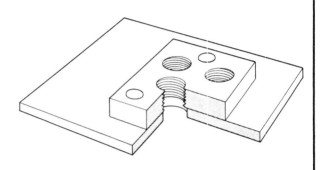

**3**

**PATCH OF SHEET** or plate, for a longer thread, serves holes away from edge; needs at least two rivets or welds to keep it from turning. Larger pieces cover group of holes.

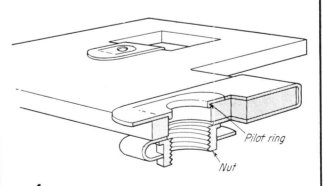

**4**

**CLIP** slips over edge of sheet, and positions on hole when pilot rim springs into place. Extra cutout next to hole allows installation away from edge.

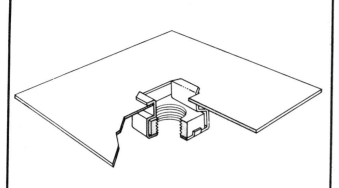

**5**

**FLOATING NUT** snaps into square hole and allows misalignment of bolt. If the thread strips, replacement is easy.

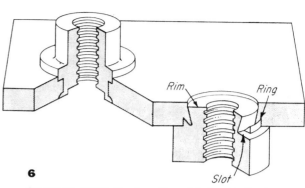

**6**

**STAKED NUT** fits in relieved hole. Relieving nut makes it easier to stake. Squeeze on clinch nut forces sheet to flow under tapered rim. Slots in ring keep nut from turning.

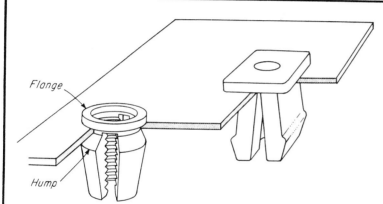

**7**

**TAPPED HOLE** snaps into sheet and grips it between flange and hump. Screw forces prongs apart so hump presses even harder on sheet. Slot digs into side of hole to prevent turning. Another version sits flush.

Square-shape plastic grommet, which doubles as insulator, cannot turn in square hole. Screw must make its own threads in smooth grooves, as it wedges grommet tightly in place.

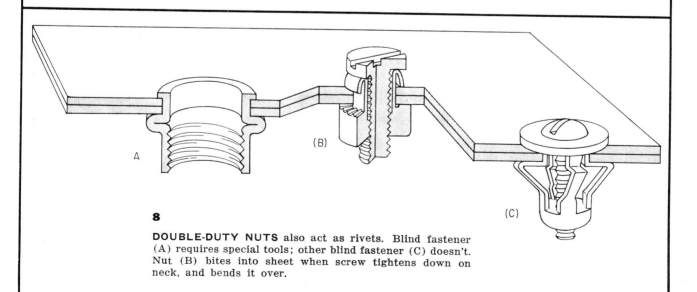

**8**

**DOUBLE-DUTY NUTS** also act as rivets. Blind fastener (A) requires special tools; other blind fastener (C) doesn't. Nut (B) bites into sheet when screw tightens down on neck, and bends it over.

# Metal Stamping Design

Stampings are made by pressworking sheet material to change its shape and can be divided into two general classifications: (1) Material formed without being cut—bending, forming, drawing and coining; and (2) mate-

## BEADS

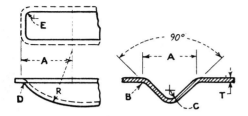

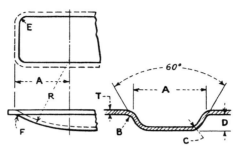

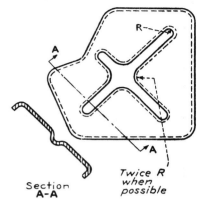

| A | B<br>Radius | C<br>Radius | D<br>Radius | E<br>Radius |
|---|---|---|---|---|
| 0.25 | T | 3 T | 3 T | 2 T |
| 0.38 | T | 3 T | 3 T | 2 T |
| 0.50 | T | 3 T | 3 T | 3 T |
| 0.62 | 3 T | 5 T | 3 T | 3 T |
| 0.75 | 4 T | 6 T | 3 T | 4 T |
| 1.00 | 4 T | 6 T | 3 T | 4 T |

Maximum radius as determined by "T," and multiples of "T," is not to exceed 0.25 of an inch

| A | B<br>Radius | C<br>Radius | D | E<br>Radius | F<br>Radius |
|---|---|---|---|---|---|
| 1.00 | 2 T | 3 T | 0.25 | 5 T | 3 T |
| 1.50 | 2 T | 3 T | 0.25 | 5 T | 3 T |

Maximum radius as determined by "T," and multiples of "T," is not to exceed 0.19 of an inch

Section A-A

BEADS OF THIS TYPE SHOULD BE FORMED IN SAME DIRECTION AS OUTER FLANGES TO FACILITATE DIE CONSTRUCTION

STRENGTHENING BEADS FOR FLAT SURFACES AND ANGULAR OR CURVED SURFACES

## FLANGES

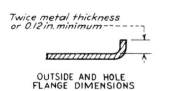

Twice metal thickness or 0.12 in. minimum

OUTSIDE AND HOLE FLANGE DIMENSIONS

To facilitate trimming, maximum flange should be twice metal thickness
PREFERRED

Flange shape when a sharp edge is not objectionable
PERMISSIBLE

Absence of flange causes expensive trim if X is maintained
NOT RECOMMENDED

Twice metal thickness or minimum of 0.12 in

FLANGE SHOULD NOT TAPER TO METAL FACE

Notch used for relief of smaller flanges

Circular hole relief used when maximum flange height is necessary

PARTIAL FLANGES IN HIGHLY STRESSED PARTS SHOULD BE RELIEVED BY NOTCH OR HOLE

A HEMMED EDGE SHOULD BE NOTCHED AT CORNERS

## RADII

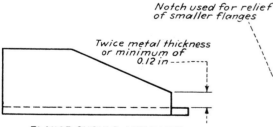

Large as practical; metal thickness is minimum
BEND FOR STAMPINGS

Bad

Good

Fracture

Radius four times metal thickness at bottom of drawn stamping saves drawing operations and prevents fractures
STAMPING DIES

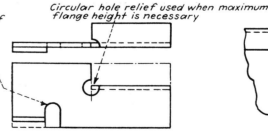

Radius as large as possible
RECTANGULAR HOLES

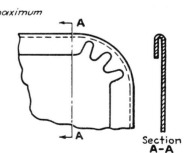

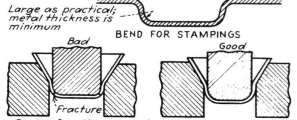

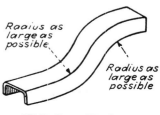

Radius as large as possible

Radius as large as possible

BENT FLANGED PIECE

# For Economy in Production

rial cut to shape—blanking, punching and trimming. The majority of stampings are made from flat sheet steel specified SAE 1008 for deep draws and SAE 1010 for simple forming operations.

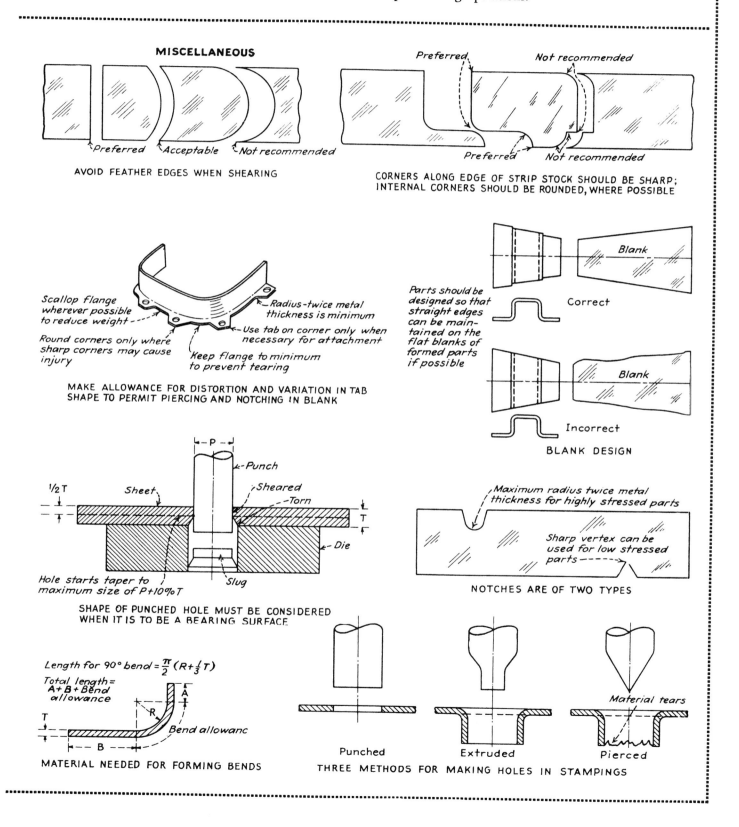

**MISCELLANEOUS**

Preferred   Acceptable   Not recommended

AVOID FEATHER EDGES WHEN SHEARING

Preferred   Not recommended
Preferred   Not recommended

CORNERS ALONG EDGE OF STRIP STOCK SHOULD BE SHARP; INTERNAL CORNERS SHOULD BE ROUNDED, WHERE POSSIBLE

Scallop flange wherever possible to reduce weight

Round corners only where sharp corners may cause injury

Radius-twice metal thickness is minimum

Use tab on corner only when necessary for attachment

Keep flange to minimum to prevent tearing

MAKE ALLOWANCE FOR DISTORTION AND VARIATION IN TAB SHAPE TO PERMIT PIERCING AND NOTCHING IN BLANK

Parts should be designed so that straight edges can be maintained on the flat blanks of formed parts if possible

Blank
Correct

Blank
Incorrect

BLANK DESIGN

1/2 T
Sheet
Punch
Sheared
Torn
Die
Slug

Hole starts taper to maximum size of P+10%T

SHAPE OF PUNCHED HOLE MUST BE CONSIDERED WHEN IT IS TO BE A BEARING SURFACE

Maximum radius twice metal thickness for highly stressed parts

Sharp vertex can be used for low stressed parts

NOTCHES ARE OF TWO TYPES

Length for 90° bend = $\frac{\pi}{2}(R+\frac{1}{3}T)$

Total length = A+B+Bend allowance

Bend allowanc

MATERIAL NEEDED FOR FORMING BENDS

Punched   Extruded   Pierced
Material tears

THREE METHODS FOR MAKING HOLES IN STAMPINGS

# Chapter 4

# CONTROL AND MATERIALS HANDLING

# Graphic symbols for

Direction of movement, types of drive, screw threads, hydraulic components, and other machine features are symbolized in this proposed standard for graphic instructions.

THESE symbols are taken from the draft of a standard published by DNA — the German Committee for Standardization. Since no similar U.S. standard exists, maybe this one proposed by DNA will be useful for American design engineers as a guide to graphic machine-control symbols. When machines are to be exported to foreign-language markets, it is all the more desirable to indicate symbolically how a control functions.

| No. | Symbol | Description | No. | Symbol | Description | No. | Symbol | Description |
|---|---|---|---|---|---|---|---|---|
| 1 | | Straight-line movement in one direction | 10 | | Limited rotary movement | 19 | | Continuous adjustment (stepless control) |
| 2 | | Straight-line movement in both directions | 11 | | Limited rotary movement back and forth | 20 | | Adjustable (used only in conjunction with another symbol) |
| 3 | | Intermittent movement in one direction | 12 | | Limited, equal back-and-forth movement | 21 | | Tool advance (four 30-deg angles) |
| 4 | | Limited straight-line movement | 13 | | One or more turns | 22 | | Rapid feed (two 60-deg angles) |
| 5 | | Reciprocating movement | 14 | | Direction of rotation | 23 | | Rough finish |
| 6 | | Limited reciprocating movement | 15 | | Slope down | 24 | | Fine finish |
| 7 | | Rotation in one direction | 16 | | Slope up | 25 | | Tighten |
| 8 | | Rotation in both directions | 17 | | Increase | 26 | | Loosen |
| 9 | | Intermittent rotation in one direction | 18 | | Decrease | 27 | | Apply brake |

# machine control

| | | | | | | | | |
|---|---|---|---|---|---|---|---|---|
| 28 | | Release brake | 41 | | Relief outline | 54 | | Drain |
| 29 | | Gear drive | 42 | | Copying | 55 | | Lubrication |
| 30 | | Belt drive | 43 | | Hydraulic | 56 | | Grease gun |
| 31 | | Chain drive | 44 | | Conventional pump | 57 | | "Grease here" |
| 32 | | Control lever | 45 | | Gear pump | 58 | | Square table |
| 33 | | Two positions from neutral | 46 | | Vane pump | 59 | | Round table |
| 34 | | Right-hand thread | 47 | | Piston pump | 60 | | Overload protection |
| 35 | | Left-hand thread | 48 | | Coolant supply | 61 | | Electric motor |
| 36 | | Pitch, L-H thread | 49 | | Blow | 62 | | Main switch |
| 37 | | Pitch, R-H thread | 50 | | Suck | 63 | | Light |
| 38 | | Conventional outline | 51 | | Filler opening | 64 | | Caution! |
| 39 | | Plate cam | 52 | | Overflow | 65 | | Temporary limit of movement |
| 40 | | Drum cam | 53 | | Filler overflow | 66 | | Attention |

# Typical Trolley Conveyor System

**TAKE-UPS.** Take-ups are not necessary when there is a definite down run following a drive unit, but should be used in level conveyor systems. It is often necessary to put an extra loop in the system so that the take-up can use a 180 degree turn. Conveyors operating through ovens should have automatic take-ups. Short systems use spring type, and long conveyors are built with counterweighted take-ups for larger differential movement.

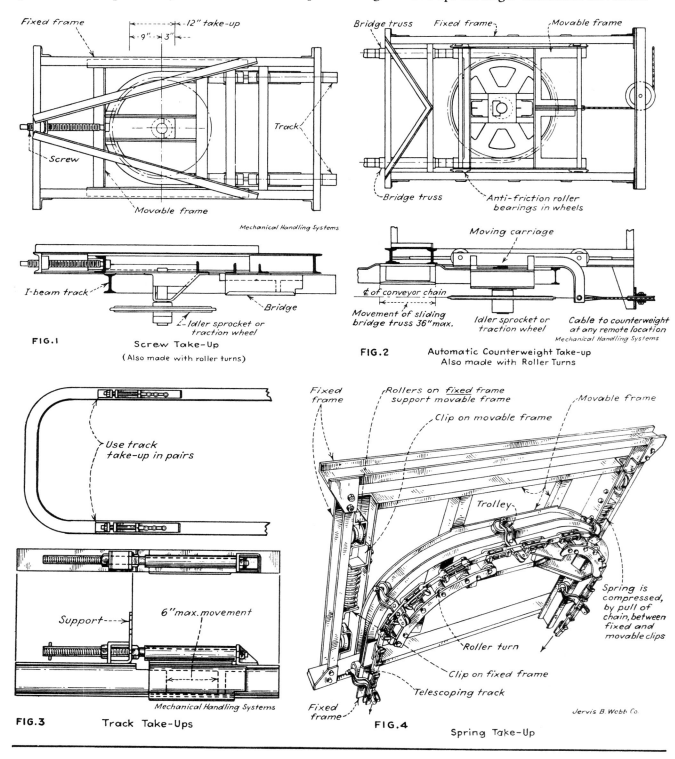

FIG.1    Screw Take-Up
(Also made with roller turns)

FIG.2    Automatic Counterweight Take-up
Also made with Roller Turns

FIG.3    Track Take-Ups

FIG.4    Spring Take-Up

# Components

**SIDNEY REIBEL**
Materials Handling Consultant,
Albert Kahn Associated Architects and Engineers

**CHAIN ATTACHMENTS.** The drop forged, rivetless Keystone chain is very flexible in use; not only because of its design, but also because of its application possibilities. Light objects can be carried by pin attachments and heavy objects can be transported on trolley attachments. Typical pin and trolley attachments are shown below. Attachments for special applications can be designed for each installation.

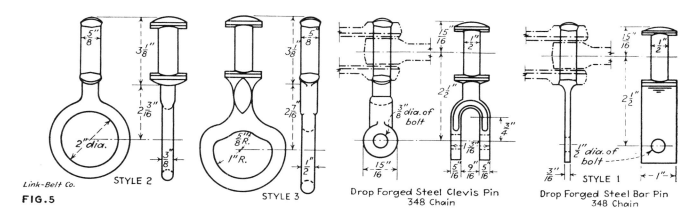

Link-Belt Co.
FIG.5

STYLE 2

STYLE 3

Drop Forged Steel Clevis Pin
348 Chain

Drop Forged Steel Bar Pin
348 Chain

STYLE 1

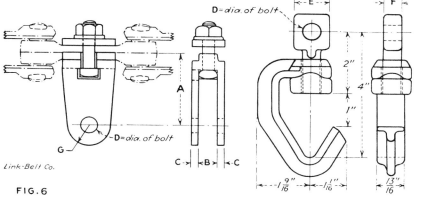

Link-Belt Co.

FIG.6

Malleable Iron
Intermediate Clevis Attachment

Malleable Iron
Swivel Hook

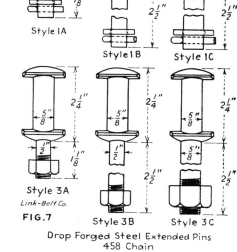

Style IA

Style1B

Style 1C

Style 3A

Link-Belt Co.

FIG.7

Style 3B

Style 3C

Drop Forged Steel Extended Pins
458 Chain

| CHAIN NUMBER | DIMENSIONS, IN. | | | | | | |
|---|---|---|---|---|---|---|---|
| | A | B | C | D | E | F | G |
| 348 | $2\frac{1}{2}$ | $\frac{9}{16}$ | $\frac{13}{16}$ | $\frac{1}{2}$ | 1 | $\frac{17}{32}$ | $\frac{5}{8}$ |
| 458 | $2\frac{7}{8}$ | $\frac{11}{16}$ | $\frac{1}{4}$ | $\frac{1}{2}$ | 1 | $\frac{17}{32}$ | $\frac{5}{8}$ |
| 678 | $3\frac{5}{8}$ | $\frac{13}{16}$ | $\frac{5}{16}$ | $\frac{3}{4}$ | $1\frac{1}{2}$ | $\frac{5}{8}$ | $\frac{7}{8}$ |

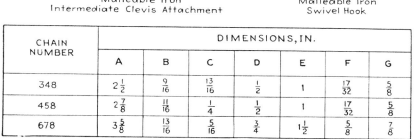
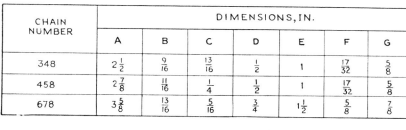
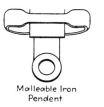
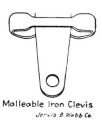

Rod
or "B"
Type
FIG.8

Special
Ring

Bar or
"P" Type

Steel Pendent or
"C" Type

Malleable Iron
Pendent

Malleable Iron Clevis

Trolley Attachments

Jervis B. Webb Co.

147

# Types of Trolley Conveyor Chain

JOINTS used in conveyor chain systems are designed for specific applications. The type of joint specified for a certain installation depends entirely on the lay-out of the supporting track. Joints can be designed for use with bends in the vertical or horizontal planes, and for combination service.

## VARIOUS TYPES OF JOINTS

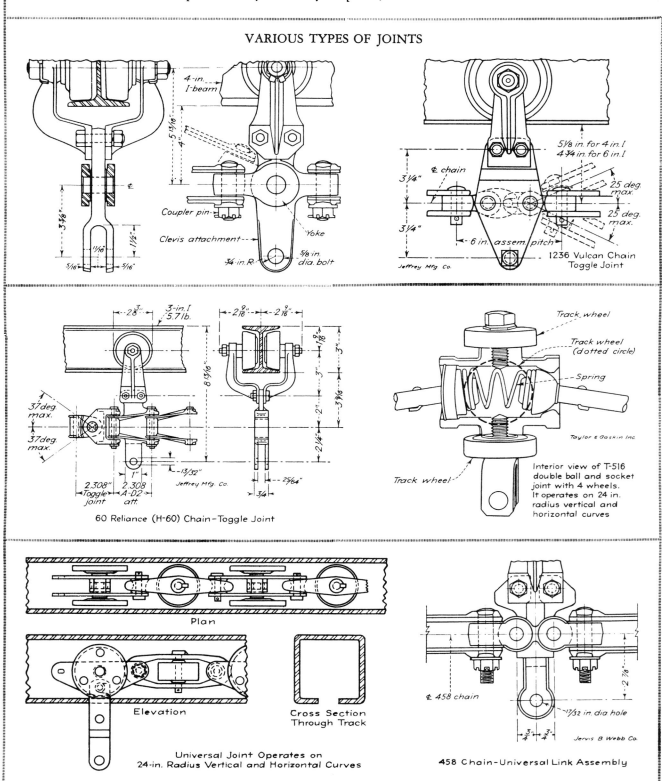

60 Reliance (H-60) Chain-Toggle Joint

1236 Vulcan Chain Toggle Joint

Interior view of T-516 double ball and socket joint with 4 wheels. It operates on 24 in. radius vertical and horizontal curves

Universal Joint Operates on 24-in. Radius Vertical and Horizontal Curves

458 Chain-Universal Link Assembly

# Links and Joints

**SIDNEY REIBEL**
Materials Handling Consultant
Albert Kahn Associated Architects and Engineers Inc.

THE SUCCESS of the overhead trolley conveyor is largely the result of the development and use of drop-forged, rivetless, Keystone chain. The dimensions of several sizes of Keystone chain links are shown below with two examples of pin-jointed chain. Standard Keystone chain parts are shown in three views.

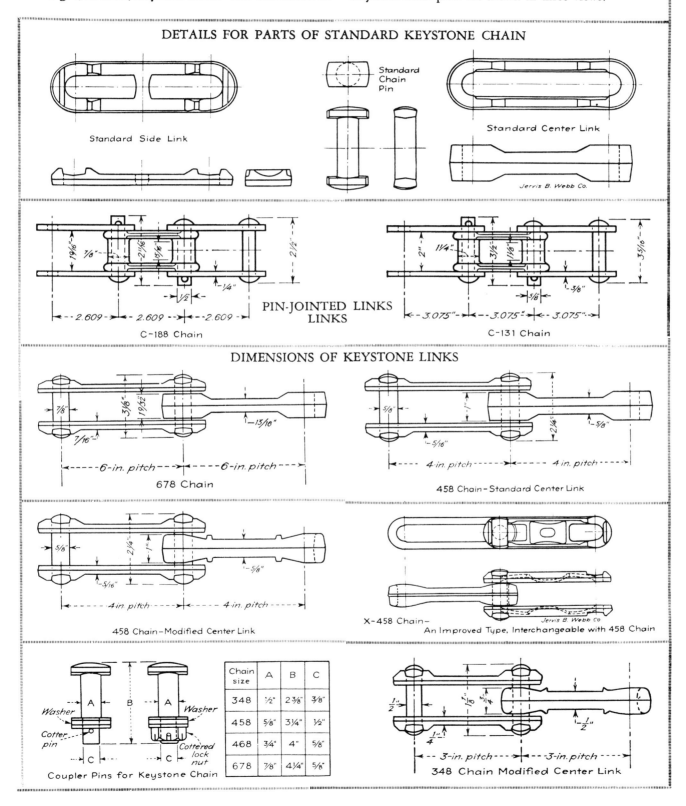

## DETAILS FOR PARTS OF STANDARD KEYSTONE CHAIN

Standard Side Link

Standard Chain Pin

Standard Center Link

Jervis B. Webb Co.

### PIN-JOINTED LINKS LINKS

C-188 Chain

C-131 Chain

## DIMENSIONS OF KEYSTONE LINKS

678 Chain

458 Chain – Standard Center Link

458 Chain – Modified Center Link

X-458 Chain –
An Improved Type, Interchangeable with 458 Chain

Jervis B. Webb Co

Coupler Pins for Keystone Chain

| Chain size | A | B | C |
|---|---|---|---|
| 348 | ½" | 2⅜" | ⅜" |
| 458 | ⅝" | 3¼" | ½" |
| 468 | ¾" | 4" | ⅝" |
| 678 | ⅞" | 4¼" | ⅝" |

348 Chain Modified Center Link

# AUTOMATIC FEED MECHANISMS

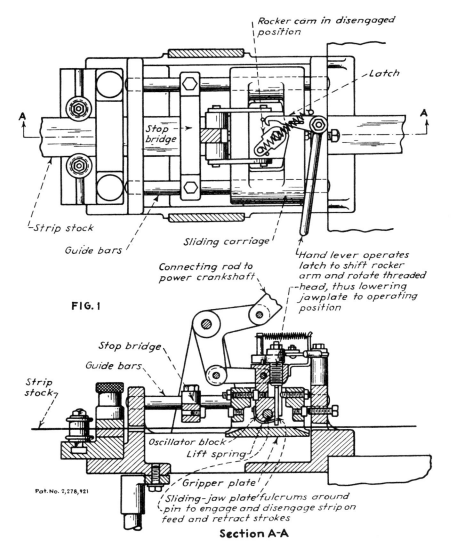

Rocker cam in disengaged position

Latch

A ——————— A

Stop bridge

Strip stock

Guide bars

Sliding carriage

Hand lever operates latch to shift rocker arm and rotate threaded head, thus lowering jawplate to operating position

Connecting rod to power crankshaft

FIG. 1

Stop bridge

Guide bars

Strip stock

Oscillator block

Lift spring

Gripper plate

Sliding-jaw plate fulcrums around pin to engage and disengage strip on feed and retract strokes

Pat. No. 2,278,921

**Section A-A**

Design of feed mechanisms for automatic or semi-automatic machines depends largely upon such factors as size, shape, and character of materials or parts being fed into a machine, and upon the type of operations to be performed. Feed mechanisms may be merely conveyors, may give positive guidance in many instances, or may include tight holding devices if the parts are subjected to processing operations while being fed through a machine. One of the functions of feed mechanism is to extract single pieces from a stack or unassorted supply of stock or, if the stock is a continuous strip of steel, roll of paper, long bar, and the like, to maintain intermittent motion between processing operations. All of these conditions are illustrated in the accompanying feed mechanisms.

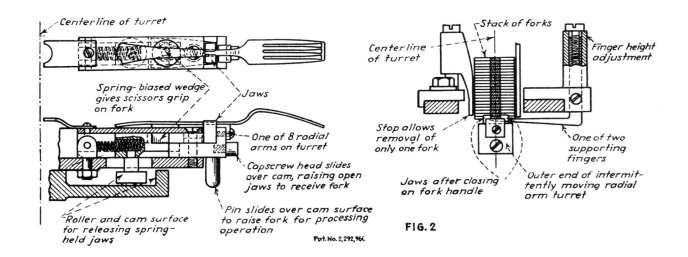

Centerline of turret

Spring-biased wedge gives scissors grip on fork

Jaws

One of 8 radial arms on turret

Capscrew head slides over cam, raising open jaws to receive fork

Roller and cam surface for releasing spring-held jaws

Pin slides over cam surface to raise fork for processing operation

Pat. No. 2,292,964

Stack of forks

Centerline of turret

Finger height adjustment

Stop allows removal of only one fork

One of two supporting fingers

Jaws after closing on fork handle

Outer end of intermittently moving radial arm turret

**FIG. 2**

# FOR VARIOUS MATERIALS

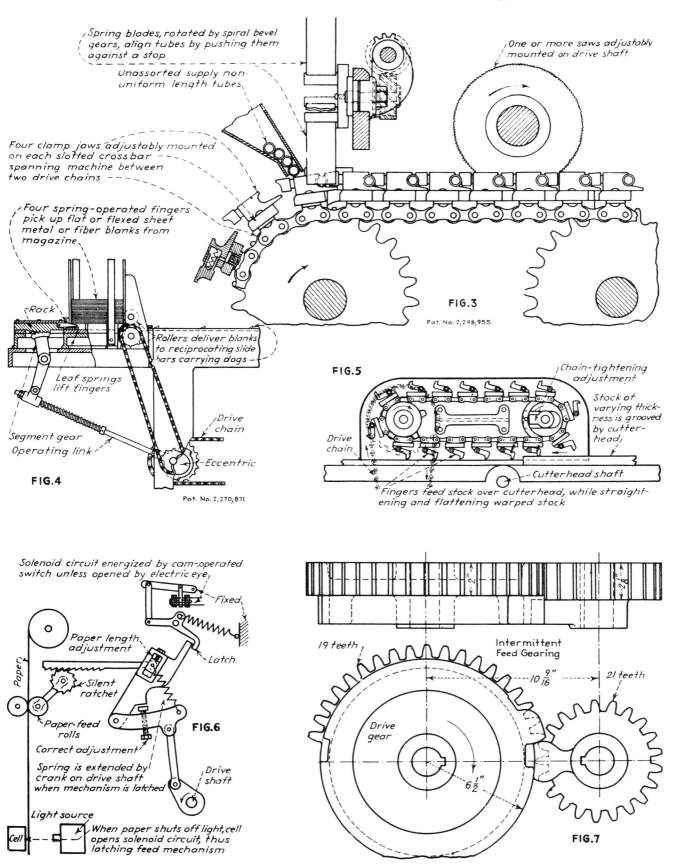

Spring blades, rotated by spiral bevel gears, align tubes by pushing them against a stop

Unassorted supply non-uniform length tubes

One or more saws adjustably mounted on drive shaft

Four clamp jaws adjustably mounted on each slotted crossbar spanning machine between two drive chains

Four spring-operated fingers pick up flat or flexed sheet metal or fiber blanks from magazine

FIG.3

Pat. No. 2,298,955

Rack

Rollers deliver blanks to reciprocating slide bars carrying dogs

Leaf springs lift fingers

Drive chain

Segment gear
Operating link

Eccentric

FIG.4

Pat. No. 2,270,871

FIG.5

Chain-tightening adjustment

Stock of varying thickness is grooved by cutter head

Drive chain

Cutterhead shaft

Fingers feed stock over cutterhead, while straightening and flattening warped stock

Solenoid circuit energized by cam-operated switch unless opened by electric eye

Fixed

Paper length adjustment

Latch

Paper

Silent ratchet

Paper-feed rolls

FIG.6

Correct adjustment

Spring is extended by crank on drive shaft when mechanism is latched

Drive shaft

Light source

Cell

When paper shuts off light, cell opens solenoid circuit, thus latching feed mechanism

19 teeth

Intermittent Feed Gearing

$10\frac{9}{16}$"

21 teeth

Drive gear

$6\frac{1}{2}$"

FIG.7

2"

$2\frac{7}{8}$"

# EIGHT PAPER-FEED MECHANISMS

In a world of reports, forms and memos, a prime need is to keep paper moving. Here are some ways that do the job for single sheets or continuous strip.

**FRANK WILLIAM WOOD JR,** president, Advanced Designs Inc, Vienna, Va

**VERNAL HUFFINES,** Lofstrand Corp, Rockville, Md

## SINGLE-SHEET FEEDERS

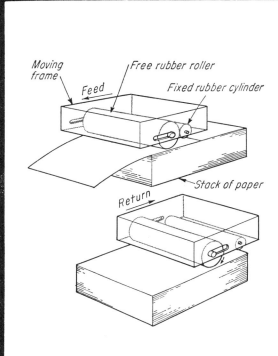

**1**

**FREE ROLLER** rides in slot. During feed it jams against the fixed cylinder and grips top sheet of paper. Return motion of frame transfers free roller to opposite end of slot, where it's free to roll back over paper.

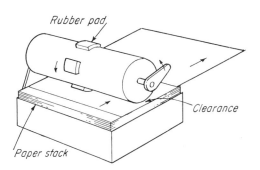

**2**

**RUBBER PADS** on rotating cylinder kick out one sheet per pad every revolution. Constant-force spring under paper-holder maintains proper clearance between paper and cylinder. Spacing of pads and the cylinder speed determine feed rate.

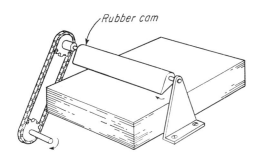

**3**

**RUBBER CAM** feeds one sheet each revolution. Constant-force spring under paper table keeps correct clearance. By correct timing, two or more cams in a stack will deliver different sheets in sequence. As with all single-sheet feeders, paper must be smooth enough to slide off pile.

# CONTINUOUS-STRIP FEEDERS

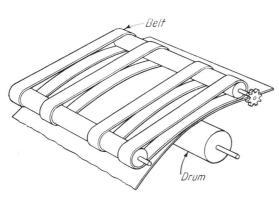

**4**

**BELTS** pressing against drum allow paper to slip and stay in alignment.

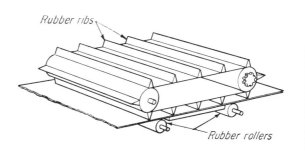

**5**

**RIBBED BELT** is another type of feed that allows paper to slip.

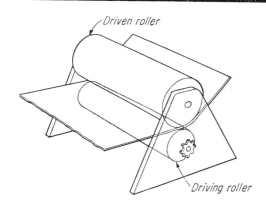

**6**

**FRICTION ROLLERS** are the commonest, cheapest way to feed paper in continuous strips.

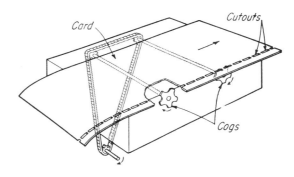

**7**

**COGS** fit in perforations to give positive feed with no slipping.

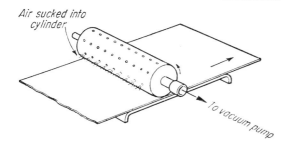

**8**

**VACUUM PUMP** sucks air in through the holes, holding paper against the cylinder. Intermittent operation of vacuum keeps paper from wrapping around cylinder.

# Typical Feeders, Take-Ups, Drives

Power required to operate a belt conveyor system is determined by movement of components, horizontal movement of material and lifting or lower-ing of material. Friction losses in idler bearings constitute a part of total power losses but are not as large as sometimes assumed. Idlers should be

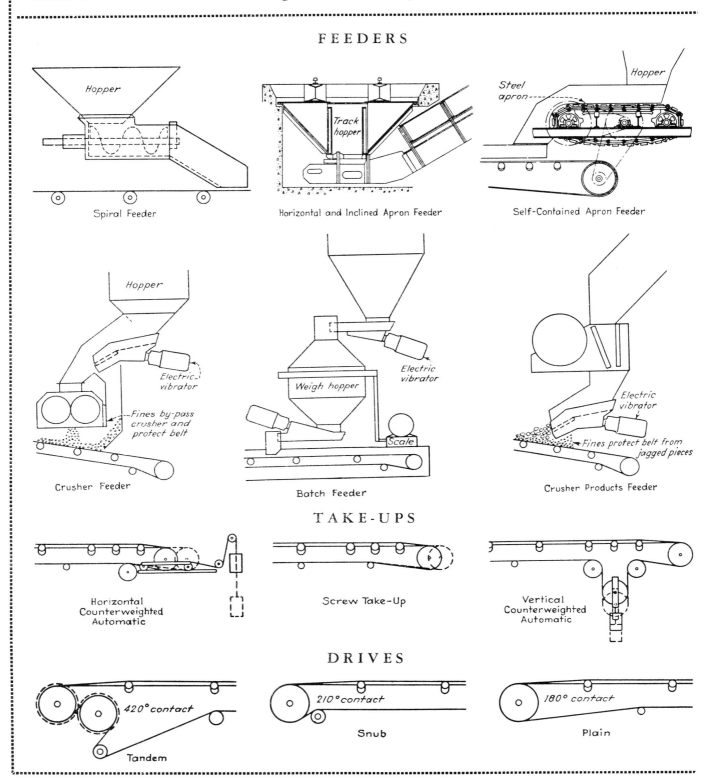

FEEDERS

Spiral Feeder

Horizontal and Inclined Apron Feeder

Self-Contained Apron Feeder

Crusher Feeder

Batch Feeder

Crusher Products Feeder

TAKE-UPS

Horizontal Counterweighted Automatic

Screw Take-Up

Vertical Counterweighted Automatic

DRIVES

Tandem

Snub

Plain

# and Idlers for Belt Conveyors

chosen carefully, with much thought to spacing. Largest single factor in power loss is the amount required in "working" the belt and forming the materials to belt shape. Different materials require different amounts of power for their forming. Sketches courtesy of the Jeffery Mfg. Co.

## IDLERS

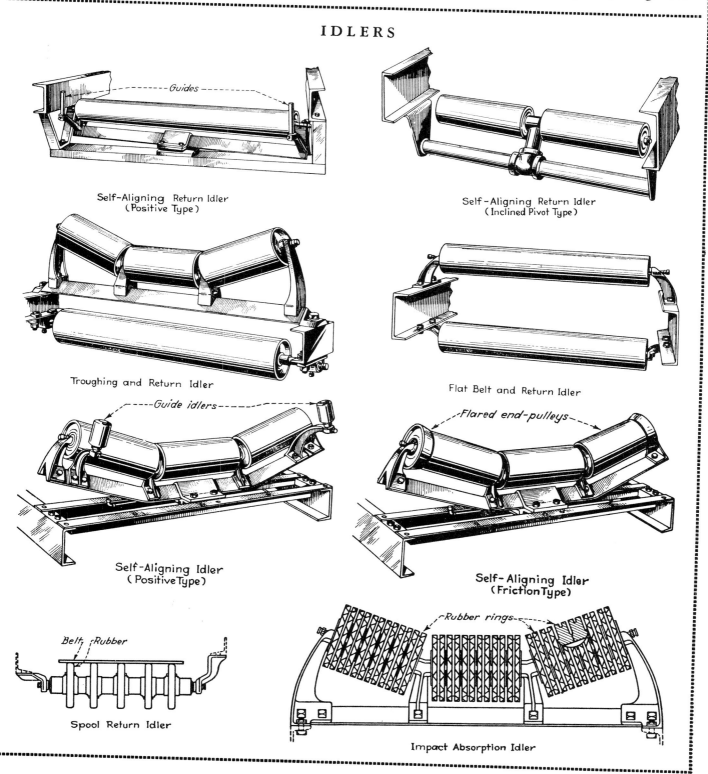

Self-Aligning Return Idler
(Positive Type)

Self-Aligning Return Idler
(Inclined Pivot Type)

Troughing and Return Idler

Flat Belt and Return Idler

Self-Aligning Idler
(Positive Type)

Self-Aligning Idler
(Friction Type)

Spool Return Idler

Impact Absorption Idler

# AUTOMATIC SAFETY MECHANISMS

THE most satisfactory automatic guard mechanisms for preventing injury to machine operators are those that have been designed with the machine. When properly designed they (1) do not reduce visibility, (2) do not impede the operator, (3) do not cause painful blows on the operator's hand in avoiding serious injury, (4) are safe with respect to wear in the safety mechanism, (5) are sensitive and instantaneous in operation, and (6) render the machine inoperative if tampered with or removed.

Safety devices range from those that keep both hands occupied with controls away from the work area to guards that completely inclose the work during operation of the machine and prevent operation of the machine unless so protected. The latter might include the "electric eye," which is the activating means of one of the mechanisms illustrated.

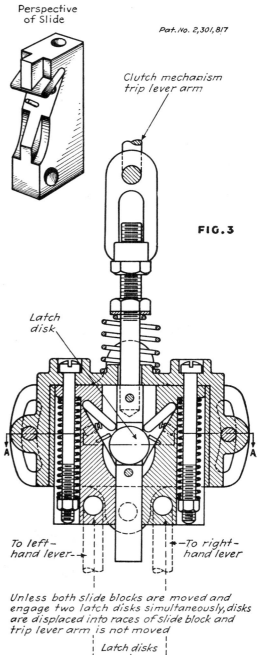

Perspective of Slide

Pat. No. 2,301,817

Clutch mechanism trip lever arm

FIG. 3

Latch disk

To left-hand lever

To right-hand lever

Unless both slide blocks are moved and engage two latch disks simultaneously, disks are displaced into races of slide block and trip lever arm is not moved

Latch disks

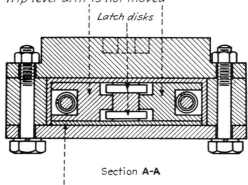

Section A-A

Box assembly slides in stationary housing when slide blocks move together

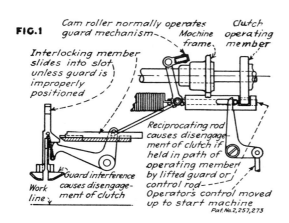

FIG. 1

Cam roller normally operates guard mechanism

Machine frame

Clutch operating member

Interlocking member slides into slot unless guard is improperly positioned

Reciprocating rod causes disengagement of clutch if held in path of operating member by lifted guard or control rod

Operators control moved up to start machine

Pat. No. 2,257,273

Work line

Guard interference causes disengagement of clutch

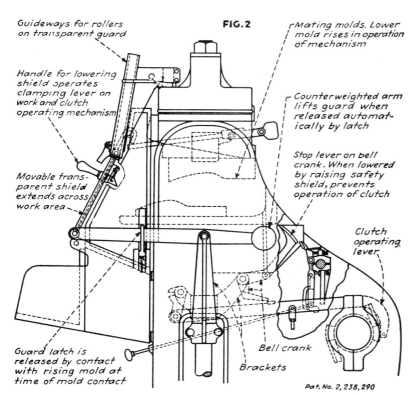

FIG. 2

Guideways for rollers on transparent guard

Handle for lowering shield operates clamping lever on work and clutch operating mechanism

Movable transparent shield extends across work area

Mating molds. Lower mold rises in operation of mechanism

Counterweighted arm lifts guard when released automatically by latch

Stop lever on bell crank. When lowered by raising safety shield, prevents operation of clutch

Clutch operating lever

Guard latch is released by contact with rising mold at time of mold contact

Bell crank

Brackets

Pat. No. 2,238,290

156

# FOR OPERATING MACHINES

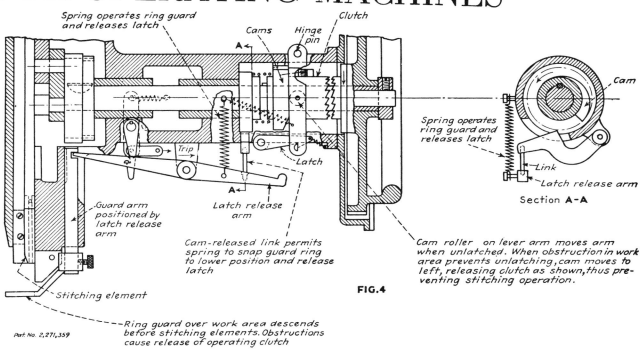

Spring operates ring guard and releases latch

Cams

Hinge pin

Clutch

Cam

A

Spring operates ring guard and releases latch

Link

Latch release arm

Section A-A

Trip

Latch

Guard arm positioned by latch release arm

Latch release arm

Cam-released link permits spring to snap guard ring to lower position and release latch

Cam roller on lever arm moves arm when unlatched. When obstruction in work area prevents unlatching, cam moves to left, releasing clutch as shown, thus preventing stitching operation.

Stitching element

**FIG.4**

Pat. No. 2,271,359

Ring guard over work area descends before stitching elements. Obstructions cause release of operating clutch

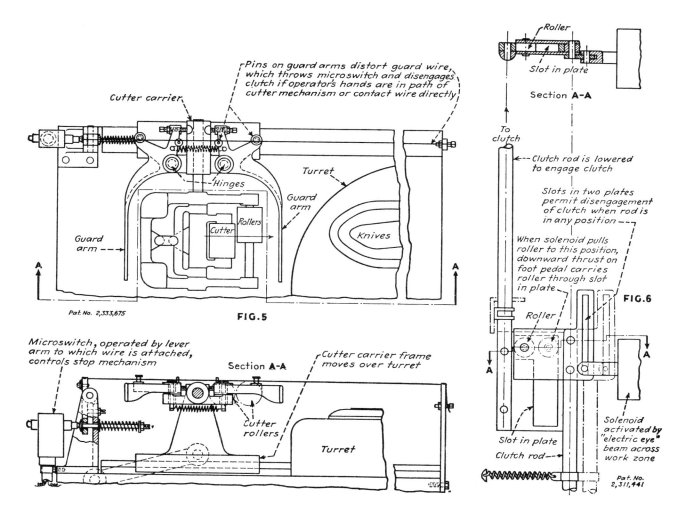

Roller

Slot in plate

Section A-A

Pins on guard arms distort guard wire, which throws microswitch and disengages clutch if operator's hands are in path of cutter mechanism or contact wire directly

Cutter carrier

Hinges

Turret

Guard arm

Guard arm

Rollers

Cutter

Knives

A

A

To clutch

Clutch rod is lowered to engage clutch

Slots in two plates permit disengagement of clutch when rod is in any position

When solenoid pulls roller to this position, downward thrust on foot pedal carries roller through slot in plate

**FIG.6**

Pat. No. 2,333,675

**FIG.5**

Microswitch, operated by lever arm to which wire is attached, controls stop mechanism

Section A-A

Cutter carrier frame moves over turret

Roller

A

A

Cutter rollers

Turret

Slot in plate

Clutch rod

Solenoid activated by "electric eye" beam across work zone

Pat. No. 2,311,441

157

# Speed control for

Friction devices, actuated by centrifugal force, automatically keep
speed constant regardless of
variation of load or driving force.

*FEDERICO STRASSER, Mankowitz & Strasser, Santiago, Chile*

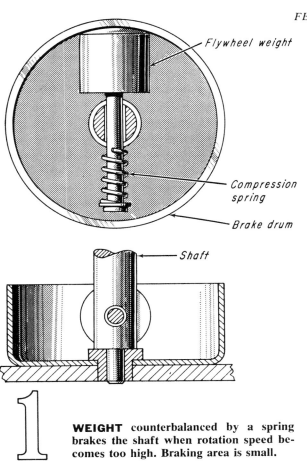

**1** **WEIGHT** counterbalanced by a spring
brakes the shaft when rotation speed becomes too high. Braking area is small.

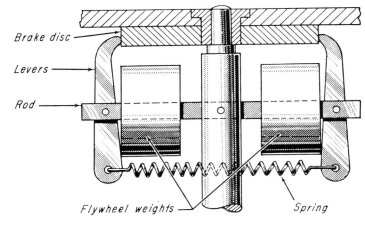

**2** **WEIGHT-ACTUATED LEVERS** make
this arrangement suitable where high braking moments are required.

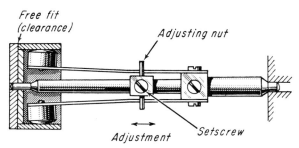

**5** **ADJUSTMENT** of speed at which this device starts to brake is quick and easy. Adjusting nut is locked in place with setscrew.

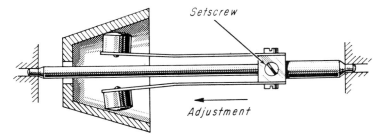

**6** **TAPERED BRAKE DRUM** is another
way of providing for varying speed-
control. The adjustment is again locked.

# small mechanisms

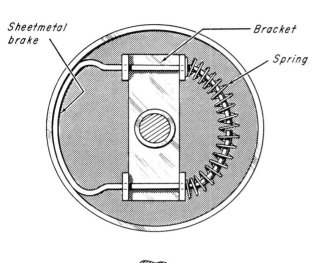

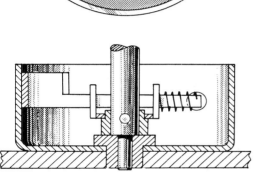

**SHEETMETAL BRAKE** provides larger braking area than previous design. Operation is thus more even and cooler.

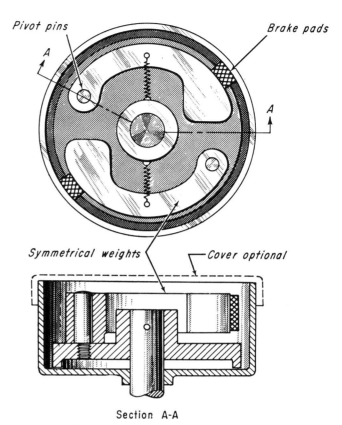

Section A-A

**SYMMETRICAL WEIGHTS** give even braking action when they pivot outward. Entire action can be enclosed.

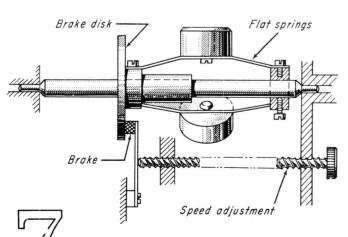

**THREE FLAT SPRINGS** carry weights that provide brake force upon rotation. Device can be provided with adjustment.

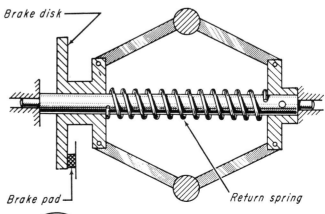

**TYPICAL GOVERNOR** action of swinging weights is utilized here. As in the previous device, adjustment is optional.

# How to damp axial and

Fluid-friction devices include two hydraulic and two pneumatic actions; swinging-vane arrangements dissipate energy and govern speed.

*FEDERICO STRASSER, Mankowitz & Strasser, Santiago, Chile*

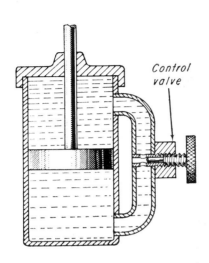

**ADJUSTABLE BYPASS** between the two sides of the piston controls speed at which fluid can flow when piston is moved.

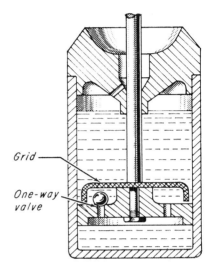

**CHECK VALVE** in piston lets speed be controlled so that the piston moves faster in one direction than in the other.

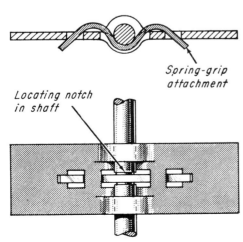

**ROTATING VANES** are resisted by the air as they revolve. Make allowance for sudden stops by providing a spring.

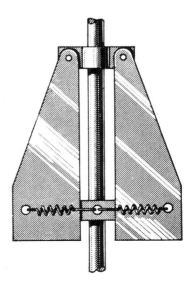

**SWINGING VANES** create increased wind drag as centrifugal force opens them to a larger radius.

# rotational motion

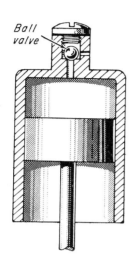

Ball valve

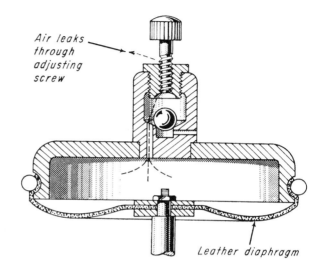

Air leaks through adjusting screw

Leather diaphragm

 **PNEUMATIC CHECK VALVE** acts in manner similar to that of previous device. Vertical position, of course, is necessary.

 **FLEXIBLE DIAPHRAGM** controls short movements. Speed is fast in one direction, but greatly slowed in return direction.

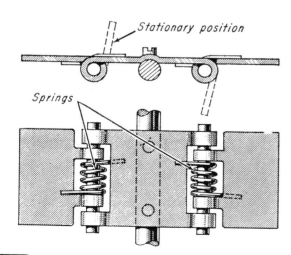

Stationary position

Springs

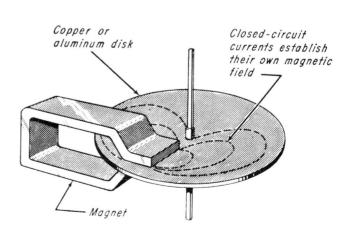

Copper or aluminum disk

Closed-circuit currents establish their own magnetic field

Magnet

 **VANE AREA INCREASES** when the spring-loaded vanes swing out. Forces differ for motion into or against the wind.

 **EDDY CURRENTS** are induced in disk when it is moved through a magnetic field. Braking is directly proportional to speed.

# AUTOMATIC STOPPING MECHANISMS

Many machines, particularly automatically operated production machines, may damage themselves or parts being processed unless they are equipped with devices that stop the machine or cause it to skip an operation when something goes wrong. The accompanying patented mechanisms show principles that can be employed to interrupt normal machine operations: Mechanical, electrical or electronic, hydraulic, pneumatic, or combinations of these means. Endless varieties of each method are in use.

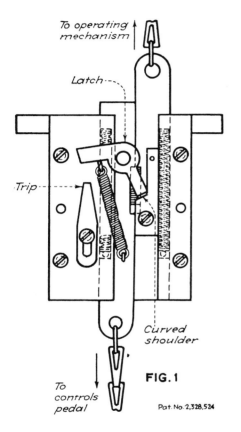

FIG. 1

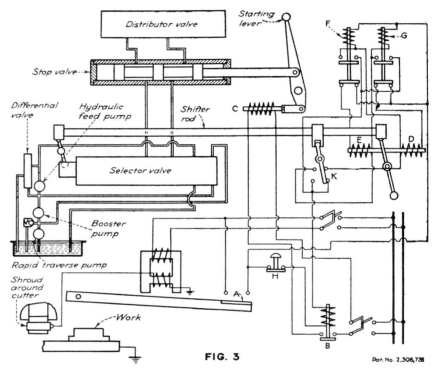

FIG. 3

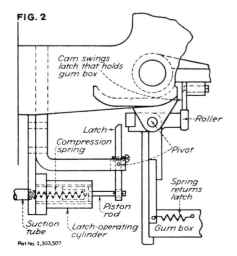

FIG. 2

**Fig. 1**—Repetition of machine cycle is prevented if pedal remains depressed. Latch carried by left slide pushes right slide downward by means of curved shoulder until latch is disengaged by trip member.

**Fig. 2**—Gumming of suction picker and label carrier when label is not picked up by the suction, is prevented by insufficient suction on latch-operating cylinder, caused by open suction holes on picker. When latch-operating cylinder does not operate, gum box holding latch returns to holding position after cyclic removal by cam and roller, thus preventing gum box and rolls from rocking to make contact with picker face.

**Fig. 3**—Damage to milling cutter, work or fixtures is prevented by shroud around cutter, which upon contact closes electric circuit through relay, thus closing contact A. This causes contact B to close, thus energizing relay C to operate stop valve, and closes circuit through relay D, thus reversing selector valve by means of shifter rod so that bed travel will reverse on starting. Simultaneously, relay F opens circuit of relay E and closes a holding circuit that was broken by the shifter lever at K. Relay G also closes a holding circuit and opens circuit through relay D. Starting lever, released by push button H, releases contact A and returns circuit to normal. If contact is made with shroud when bed travel is reversed, interchange D and E, and F and G in above sequence of operations.

162

# FOR FAULTY MACHINE OPERATION

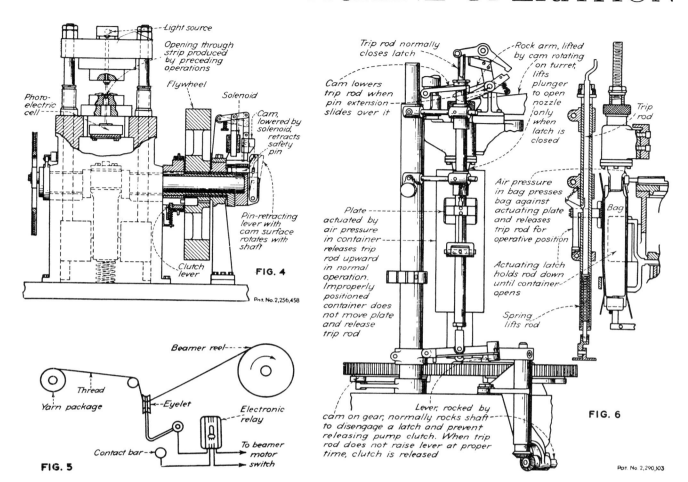

Photo-electric cell — Light source — Opening through strip produced by preceding operations — Flywheel — Solenoid — Cam, lowered by solenoid, retracts safety pin — Pin-retracting lever with cam surface rotates with shaft — Clutch lever — **FIG. 4** — Pat. No. 2,256,458

Beamer reel — Thread — Yarn package — Eyelet — Electronic relay — Contact bar — To beamer motor switch — **FIG. 5**

Trip rod normally closes latch — Rock arm, lifted by cam rotating on turret, lifts plunger to open nozzle only when latch is closed — Cam lowers trip rod when pin extension slides over it — Trip rod — Plate actuated by air pressure in container releases trip rod upward in normal operation. Improperly positioned container does not move plate and release trip rod — Air pressure in bag presses bag against actuating plate and releases trip rod for operative position — Bag — Actuating latch holds rod down until container opens — Spring lifts rod — Lever, rocked by cam on gear, normally rocks shaft to disengage a latch and prevent releasing pump clutch. When trip rod does not raise lever at proper time, clutch is released — **FIG. 6** — Pat. No. 2,290,103

**Fig. 4**—High-speed press is stopped when metal strip advances improperly so that hole punched in strip fails to match with opening in die block to permit passage of light beam. Intercepted light beam to photo-electric cell results in energizing solenoid and withdrawal of clutch pin.

**Fig. 5**—Broken thread permits contact bar to drop, thereby closing electronic relay circuit, which operates to stop beamer reeling equipment.

**Fig. 6**—Nozzle on packaging machine does not open when container is not in proper position.

**Fig. 7**—Obstruction under explorer foot of wire-stitching machine prevents damage to machine by raising a vertical plunger, which releases a latch lever so that rotary cam raises lever that retains clutch operating plunger.

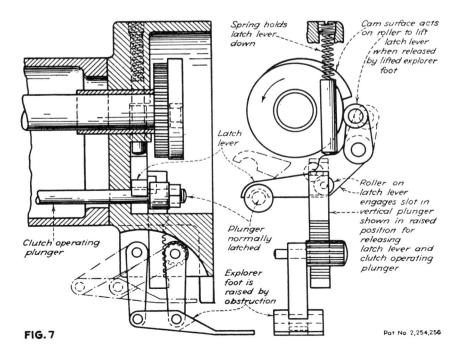

Spring holds latch lever down — Cam surface acts on roller to lift latch lever when released by lifted explorer foot — Latch lever — Roller on latch lever engages slot in vertical plunger shown in raised position for releasing latch lever and clutch operating plunger — Plunger normally latched — Clutch operating plunger — Explorer foot is raised by obstruction — **FIG. 7** — Pat. No. 2,254,256

# Thermostatic Mechanisms–I

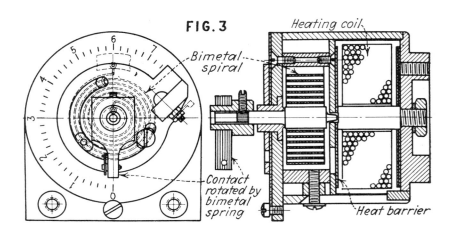

FIG. 1

IN THERMOSTATIC bimetals, the sensitivity or change in deflection for a given temperature change, depends upon the combination of metals selected to meet the operating temperature range as well as the dimensions of the bimetal element. Sensitivity increases with the square of the length and inversely with the thickness. The force developed for a given temperature change also depends on the type of bimetal, while the allowable working load for the thermostatic strip increases with the width and the square of the thickness. Thus, the design of bimetal elements depends upon the relative importance of sensitivity and working load.

**Fig. 1**—In the Taylor recording thermometer a pen is moved vertically across a revolving chart by a brass-invar bimetal element. To obtain sensitivity the long movement of the pen requires a long strip of bimetal, which is coiled into a helix to save space. For accuracy, a relatively large cross section gives stiffness, although the large thickness requires increased length to obtain the desired sensitivity.

**Fig. 2**—Room temperatures in summer as well as winter are controlled over a wide range by a single large-diameter coil of brass-invar in the Friez thermometer. To prevent chattering, a small permanent magnet is mounted on each side of the steel contact blade. The magnetic attraction on the blade, increasing inversely with the square of the distance from the magnet, gives a snap action to the contacts.

**Fig. 3**—In this Westinghouse overload relay for large motors, a portion of the motor current is passed through a heating coil within the relay. Heat from the coil raises the temperature of a bimetal spiral which rotates a shaft carrying an electrical contact. To withstand the operating temperature, a heat resistant bimetal is used, coiled into the spiral form for compactness. Because of the large deflection needed the spiral is long and thin, while the width is made large to provide the required contact pressure.

By the use of heat barriers between the bimetal spiral and the heating coil, temperature rise of the bimetal can be made to follow closely the increase in temperature within the motor. Thus, momentary overloads do not cause sufficient

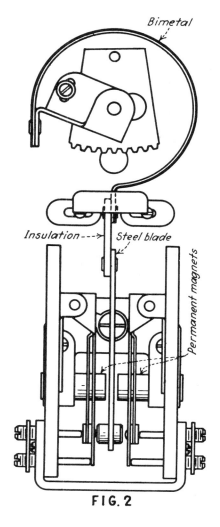

FIG. 2

FIG. 3

heating to close the contacts, while a continued overload will in time cause the bimetal to rotate the contact arm around to the adjustable stationary contact, causing a relay to shut down the motor.

**Fig. 4**—On the Dodge carburetor, when the engine is cold a vane in the exhaust passage to the "hot spot" is held open by a bimetal spring against the force of a small counterweight. When the thermostatic spiral is heated by the outside air or by the warm air stream from the radiator, the spring coils up allowing the weight to close the vane. Since high accuracy is not needed, a thin, flexible cross section is used with a long length to give the desired sensitivity.

**Fig. 5**—In the Friez relay a constant current through an electrical heating coil around a straight bimetal strip gives a time delay action. Since the temperature range is relatively large, high sensitivity is not necessary, hence a short, straight strip of bimetal is suitable. Because of the relatively heavy thickness used the strip is sufficiently stiff to close the contact firmly without chattering.

**Fig. 6**—A similar type of bimetal element is used in the Ward Leonard time delay relay for mercury vapor rectifiers. This relay closes the potential circuit to the mercury tube only after the filament has had time to reach its normal operating temperature. To eliminate the effect of changes in room temperature on the length of the contact gap, and

therefore the time interval, the stationary contact is carried by a second bimetal strip similar to the heated element. Barriers of laminated plastic on both sides of the active bimetal strip shield the compensating strip and prevent air currents from affecting the heating rate. The relatively high temperature range allows the use of a straight, thick strip, while the addition of the compensating strip makes accurate timing possible with a short travel.

**Fig. 7**—Oil pressure, engine temperature or gasoline level are indicated electrically on automobile dashboard instruments built by King-Seeley in which a bimetal element is used in both the sender and receiver. A grounded contact at the sender completes an electric circuit through heaters around two similar bimetal strips. Since the same current flows around the two bimetal elements, their deflections are the same. But the sender element when heated will bend away from the

grounded contact until the circuit is broken. Upon cooling, the bimetal again makes contact and the cycle continues, allowing the bimetal to follow the movement of the grounded contact. For the oil pressure gage, the grounded contact is attached to a diaphragm; for the temperature indicator, the contact is carried by another thermostatic bimetal strip; in the gasoline level device, the contact is shifted by a cam on a shaft rotated by a float. Deflections of the receiving bimetal are amplified through a linkage that operates a pointer over the scale of the receiving instrument. Since only small deflections are needed, the bimetal element is in the form of a short, stiff strip.

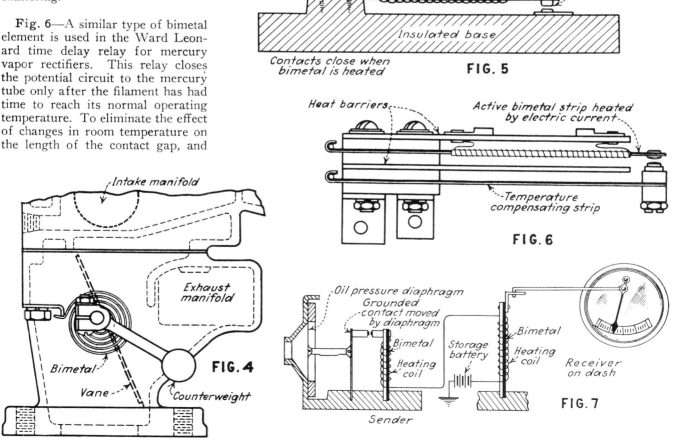

Insulated heater winding    Load contacts

Insulated base

Contacts close when bimetal is heated    **FIG. 5**

Heat barriers    Active bimetal strip heated by electric current

Temperature compensating strip

**FIG. 6**

Intake manifold

Exhaust manifold

Bimetal

Vane    Counterweight    **FIG. 4**

Oil pressure diaphragm
Grounded contact moved by diaphragm
Bimetal    Bimetal
Heating coil    Storage battery    Heating coil
Receiver on dash

Sender    **FIG. 7**

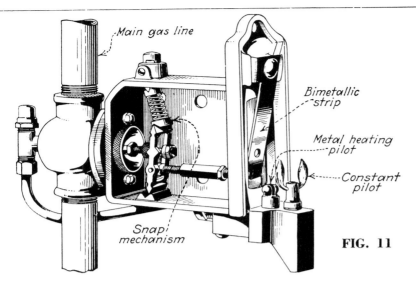

Main gas line

Bimetallic strip

Metal heating pilot

Constant pilot

Snap mechanism

**FIG. 11**

# Thermostatic

BIMETAL elements in thermometers, room thermostats, relays, carburetor heat controls and automobile instruments were shown in the first article. Additional mechanisms shown here are used to compensate for temperature errors in dashpots and thermometers, to control temperatures in automobile engines, hot water tanks and electric irons, and to operate pilot lights in gas burners.

Fig. 8—Oil dashpots used in heavy capacity Toledo scales have a thermostatic control to compensate for changes in oil viscosity with temperature. A rectangular orifice in the plunger is covered by a swaged projection on the bimetal element. With a decrease in oil temperature, the oil viscosity increases, tending to increase the damping effect; but the bimetal deflects upward, enlarging the orifice enough to keep the damping force constant. A wide bimetal strip is used for stiffness so that the orifice will not be altered by the force of the flowing oil.

Fig. 9—In mercury-filled indicating thermometers, expansion of the mercury in a bulb at the end of a capillary line causes the spiral tube in the gage to uncoil, moving the dial pointer by means of a linkage. However, changes in the temperature of the mercury in the capillary and spiral also affect the movement of the linkage introducing an error in the reading. In the Taylor indicating thermometer, compensation for changes in gage temperature is

obtained by a flat bimetal strip that forms a part of the pointer linkage. The strip is designed so that its deflections are equal but opposite to the effect caused by changes in gage temperature. Since little load is imposed on the thermostatic strip, the compensating action can be obtained with high accuracy.

Fig. 10—In cooling-water thermostats for automobile engines, the water flow imposes a load on the bimetal spiral, and in addition the over-travel caused by continued cooling after the valve is closed sets up stresses which increase as the temperature decreases. Sufficient strength and cross-section to safely withstand these stresses without permanent deformation requires a long flexible element. High accuracy is not obtainable, but in this application a relatively large variation in operating temperature is permissible. In the Chase thermostat, the bimetal element is in the form of a tapered spiral spring which is connected to a rotating valve by a simple linkage. To stabilize the bimetal element, it is subjected to a series of hot and cold treatments at temperatures beyond the normal temperature range.

Fig. 11—When the bimetal element in a gas pilot-light control is placed near the pilot flame, the bimetal is subjected to a temperature

**FIG. 8**

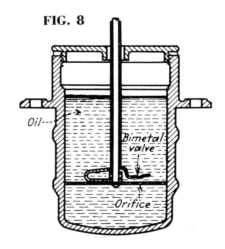

Oil

Bimetal valve

Orifice

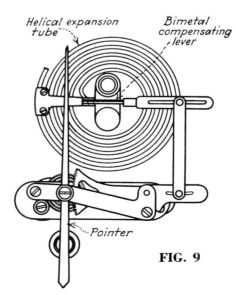

Helical expansion tube

Bimetal compensating lever

Pointer

**FIG. 9**

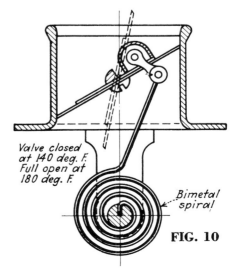

Valve closed at 140 deg. F. Full open at 180 deg. F.

Bimetal spiral

**FIG. 10**

# Mechanisms—II

near its maximum operating range, and in service over long periods of time the valve may become corroded and fail to function when an emergency arises. In the pilot control made by the Patrol Valve Company, operating temperature of the bimetal is reduced and distortion from overheating is prevented by a dual pilot construction. The constant-burning pilot ignites a second pilot which heats the bimetal strip when the thermostatic control calls for heat. The bimetal strip upon heating opens the toggle-operated main burner valve, which, by means of a double-seat construction, reduces the supply of gas to the second pilot, leaving just enough flame to keep the bimetal from closing the valve. Since relatively wide limits for temperature of operation are permissible, the bimetal element is designed to develop sufficient force to operate the toggle spring without the use of high working stresses.

**Fig. 12**—Toggle action, without separate springs, is obtained in the Spencer disk thermostat. The disk

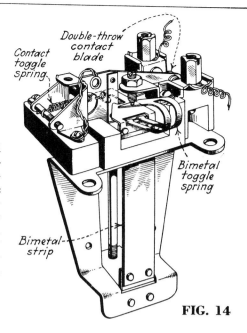

FIG. 14

is a saucer-shaped piece of bimetal sheet which snaps itself from a concave to a convex shape at a predetermined temperature. Both the amount of movement and the temperature differential between opening and closing temperature depend on the design of the disk. For greater sensitivity, smaller differential and a larger movement than can be obtained with the plain disk, the bimetal disk is corrugated. Since the disk is small and stores but little heat, it warms or cools rapidly.

When used as an electrical control device, insulated silver contacts are mounted on the bimetal disk. In the cold position shown, each of the contacts bridges a gap in insulated plates connected to the heavy terminals. When heated, the disk snaps to a convex shape, opening the circuit through the device at three points.

**Fig. 13**—Electric irons require a convenient adjustment for the temperature at which the bimetal element opens the circuit. In the mechanism designed by Proctor & Schwartz, a double lever not only permits adjustment of the operating temperature, but also relieves the bimetal strip of any restriction when it cools to room temperature. Since the operating temperature range is high, a heat resisting bimetal material is used in the form of a short, stiff strip. Current is conducted to the bimetal contact through a flexible silver ribbon,

eliminating the effect of heat caused by current passing through the bimetal strip.

**Fig. 14**—In the Westinghouse thermostat for electric hot water heaters, a small range of temperature difference between on and off is needed, and to eliminate the necessity for an intermediate relay, the contacts must break a relatively heavy current. These conflicting requirements are met by using a double-toggle mechanism. A light toggle spring on the contact blade keeps the contacts firmly seated until the stronger toggle on the bimetal strip comes into operation.

The bimetal blade is free to move nearly to the dead center position thereby storing energy in its toggle spring before any pressure is applied to the contact blade. Energy released by the toggle spring, when the bimetal blade passes dead center, delivers an impact to the contact blade, breaking loose any slight welding that may have occurred during the previous operation. This thermostat is used as a current-limiting switch, disconnecting one heater as another is connected. Because of the double-toggle design the thermostat contacts will safely interrupt 5 kw. at 220 volts a.c. with a temperature differential of 5 deg. F. or less.

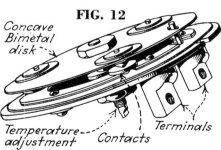

FIG. 12

Concave
Bimetal
disk

Temperature
adjustment

Contacts

Terminals

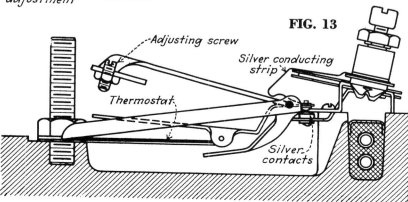

FIG. 13

Adjusting screw

Silver conducting
strip

Thermostat

Silver
contacts

# Thermostatic Mechanisms—III

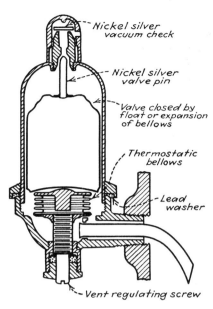

- Nickel silver vacuum check
- Nickel silver valve pin
- Valve closed by float or expansion of bellows
- Thermostatic bellows
- Lead washer
- Vent regulating screw

**FIG. 15**

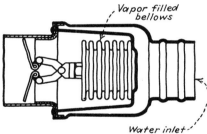

- Vapor filled bellows
- Water inlet

**FIG.16**

TWO PRECEDING articles, in this series of three, described thermostatic mechanisms operated by bimetal elements. The controls shown here are actuated by the expansion of vapor, gas or liquid contained in flexible bellows.

Fig. 15—In radiator air valves made by the Anderson Manufacturing Company, air forced into the valve passes around a small bellows partially filled with a liquid. When steam reaches the valve, the heat increases the vapor pressure within the bellows, and the resultant expansion raises the float, thereby closing the air vent orifice.

Fig. 16 — Automobile cooling water temperature is controlled by a self-contained bellows in the thermostat made by the Bridgeport Brass Company. As in the radiator air valve, the bellows itself is subjected to the temperature to be controlled. As the temperature of the water increases to about 140 deg. F., the valve starts to open; at approximately 180 deg. F. free flow is permitted. At intermediate temperatures the valve opening is in proportion to the temperature.

Fig. 17—In a throttling type of circulating water control valve made by C. J. Tagliabue Manufacturing Company for use in refrigeration plants, the valve opening varies with the pressure on the bellows. This valve controls the rate of flow of the cooling water through the condenser, a greater amount of water being required when the temperature, and therefore the pressure, increases. The pressure in the condenser is transmitted through a pipe to the valve bellows thereby adjusting the flow of cooling water. The bronze bellows is protected from contact with the water by a rubber diaphragm.

Fig. 18—An automatic gas range control made by the Wilcolator Company has a sealed thermostatic element consisting of a bulb, capillary tube and bellows. As food is often placed near the bulb, a non-toxic liquid, chlorinated diphenyl, is used in the liquid expansion system. The liquid is also non-inflammable and has no corrosive effect upon the phosphor bronze bellows. By placing the liquid outside instead of inside the bellows, the working stresses are maximum at normal temperatures when the bellows bottoms on the cup. At elevated working temperatures, the expansion of the liquid compresses the bellows against the action of the extended spring which in turn, is adjusted by the knob. Changes in calibration caused by variations in ambient temperature are compensated by making the rocker arm of bimetal suitable for high temperature service.

Fig. 19—For electric ranges the Wilcolator thermostat has the same bellows unit as is used on the gas-type control. But, instead of a

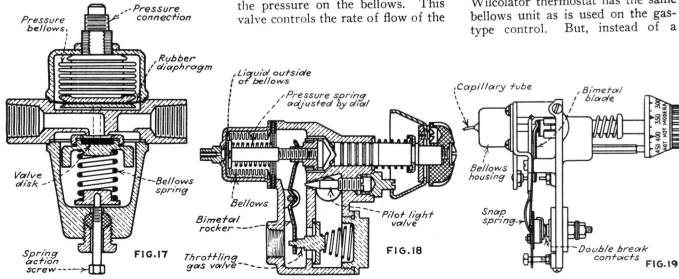

- Pressure bellows
- Pressure connection
- Rubber diaphragm
- Valve disk
- Bellows spring
- Spring action screw

**FIG.17**

- Liquid outside of bellows
- Pressure spring adjusted by dial
- Bellows
- Bimetal rocker
- Throttling gas valve
- Pilot light valve

**FIG.18**

- Capillary tube
- Bimetal blade
- Bellows housing
- Snap spring
- Double break contacts

**FIG.19**

throttling action, the thermostat opens and closes the electrical contacts with a snap action. To obtain sufficient force for the snap action the control requires a temperature difference between "on" and "off" positions. For a control range from room temperature to 550 deg. F., the differential in this device is plus or minus 10 deg. F.; with a smaller control range, the differential is proportionately less. The snap action switch is made of beryllium copper, giving high strength, better snap action and longer life than obtainable with phosphor bronze, and because of its corrosion resistance the beryllium-copper blade requires no protective finish.

Fig. 20—For heavy duty room temperature controls, the Penn thermostat uses a bellows mechanism that develops a high force with small changes in temperature. The bronze bellows is partially filled with butane, a liquid having a large change in vapor pressure with changes in temperature in the range of room temperatures. Snap action of the electrical contact is obtained from a small permanent magnet that pulls the steel contact blade into firm contact when the bellows cools. Because of the firm contact, the device is rated at 20 amp. for non-inductive loads. To avoid chattering or bounce under the impact delivered by the rapid magnetic closing action, small auxiliary contacts are carried on light spring blades. With the large force developed by the bellows, a temperature differential of only 2 deg. F. is obtained.

Fig. 21—Snap action in the Tagliabue refrigerator control is obtained from a bowed flat spring. The silver contacts carried on an extended end of the spring open or close rapidly when movement of the bellows actuates the spring. With this snap action the contacts can control an a.c. motor as large as 1½ hp. without the use of auxiliary relays. Temperature differential is adjusted by changing the spacing between two collars on the bellows shaft passing through the contact spring. For temperatures used in freezing ice, the bellows system is partially filled with butane.

Fig. 22—In the General Electric refrigerator control, the necessary snap action is obtained from a toggle spring supported from a long arm moved by the bellows. With this type of toggle action the contact pressure is a maximum at the instant the contacts start to open. Thermostatic action is obtained from a vapor-filled system using sulphur dioxide for usual refrigerating service or methyl chloride where lower temperatures are required. To reduce friction, the bellows makes point contact with the bellows cup. Operating temperature is adjusted by changing the initial compression in the bellows spring. For resistance to corrosion, levers and blades are stainless steel with bronze pin bearings.

Fig. 23—Two bellows units are used in the Fedders thermostatic expansion valve for controlling large refrigeration systems. A removable power bellows unit is operated by vapor pressure in a bulb attached to the evaporator output line. The second bellows serves as a flexible, gas-tight seal for the gas valve. A stainless steel spring holds the valve closed until opened by pressure transmitted from the thermostatic bellows through a molded push pin.

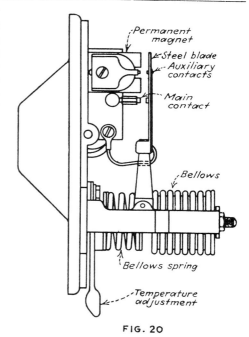

FIG. 20

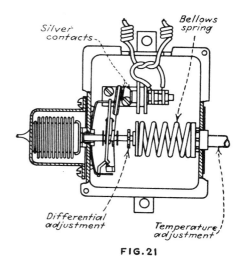

FIG. 21

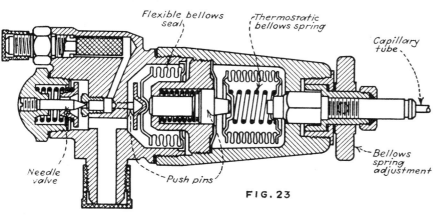

FIG. 23

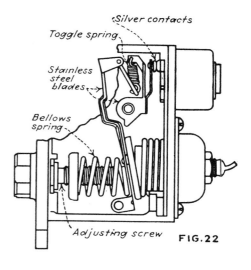

FIG. 22

# Applications of Differential

Known for its mechanical advantage, the differential winch is a control mechanism that can supplement the gear and rack and four-bar linkage systems in changing rotary mo-

ALEXANDER B. HULSE, JR. and ROBERT AYMAR
Factoring Instruments & Devices, Inc., Brooklyn, N. Y.

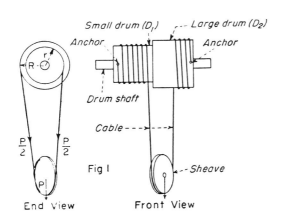

FIG. 1—Standard Differential Winch; consists of two drums $D_1$ and $D_2$ and a cable or chain which is anchored on both ends and wound clockwise around one drum and counterclockwise around the other. The cable supports a load carrying sheave and if the shaft is rotated clockwise, the cable, which unwinds from $D_1$ on to $D_2$, will raise the sheave a distance

$$\text{Sheave rise/rev} = \frac{2\pi R - 2\pi r}{2} = \pi(R - r)$$

The winch, which is not in equilibrium, exerts a counterclockwise torque.

$$\text{Unbalanced torque} = \frac{P}{2}(R - r)$$

FIG. 2(A)—Hulse Differential Winch*. Two drums, which are in the form of worm threads contoured to guide the cables, concentrically occupy the same longitudinal space. This keeps the cables approximately at right angles to the shaft and eliminates cable shifting and rubbing especially when used with variable cross sections as in Fig. 2(B) where any equation of motion can be satisfied by choosing suitable cross sections for the drums.

The axial thrust is equal to

$$\text{Pitch} \times \text{Load}$$

Fig. 2(C) shows typical reductions in displacement.          *Pat. No. 2,590,623

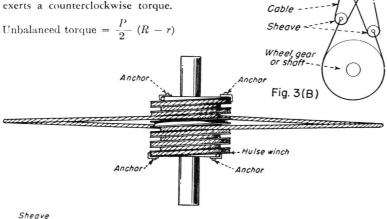

Fig. 3(B)

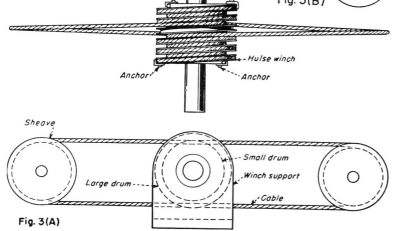

Fig. 3(A)

FIG. 3(A) Hulse Winch with Opposing Sheaves. This arrangement which uses two separate cables and four anchor points can be considered as two winches back-to-back using one common set of drums. Variations in motion can be obtained by: (1) restraining the sheaves so that when the system is rotated the drums will travel toward one of the sheaves; (2) restraining the drums and allowing the sheaves to travel. The distance between the sheaves will remain constant and are usually connected by a bar; (3) permitting the drums to move axially while restraining them transversely. When the system is rotated, drums will travel axially one pitch per revolution, and sheaves remain in same plane perpendicular to drum axis. This variation can

# Winch to Control Systems

tion into linear. It can magnify displacement to meet the requirements of delicate instruments or be varied almost at which to fulfill uncommon equations of motion.

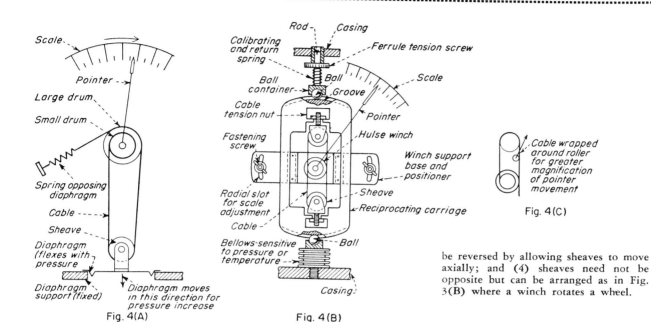

Fig. 4(A)

Fig. 4(B)

Fig. 4(C)

be reversed by allowing sheaves to move axially; and (4) sheaves need not be opposite but can be arranged as in Fig. 3(B) where a winch rotates a wheel.

FIG. 4(A)—Pressure and Temperature Indicators. A pressure change causes the diaphragm and sheave to move vertically and the pointer radially. Equilibrium occurs when spring force balances actuating torque. Replacing diaphragm with a thermal element changes instrument into a temperature indicator. Two sheaves and a reciprocating carriage, Fig. 4(B), are based on the principal shown in Fig. 3(A). Carriage is activated by pressure or temperature and is balanced by a spring force in opposite end. Further magnification can be obtained, Fig. 4(C), by wrapping cable around a roller to which pointer is attached.

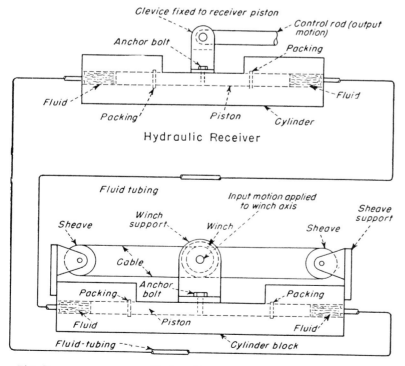

Hydraulic Receiver

Hydraulic Sender

Fig. 5

FIG. 5—Hydraulic Control System Actuated by a Differential Winch. Used for remote precision positioning of a control rod with a minimum of applied torque. The sending piston, retained in a cylinder block, reciprocates back and forth by a torque applied to the winch shaft. Fluid is forced out from one end of the cylinder through the pipe lines to displace the receiving piston which in turn activates a control rod. The receiver simultaneously displaces a similar amount of fluid from the opposite end back to the sender. By suitable valving the sender may be used as a double-acting pump.

# Chapter 5

# FASTENING AND JOINING

# How to design for better

Small but important details of mechanical parts make all the difference between mediocre and superior design.

*FEDERICO STRASSER, Mankowitz and Strasser, Santiago, Chile*

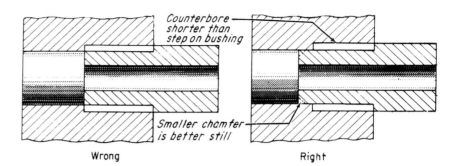

**1** **LONG BUSHINGS** are easier to assemble when they have different OD's, but make sure the counterbore is shorter than the step.

Counterbore shorter than step on bushing

Smaller chamfer is better still

Wrong — Right

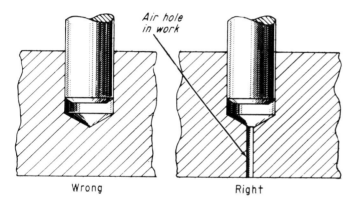

Air hole in work

Wrong — Right

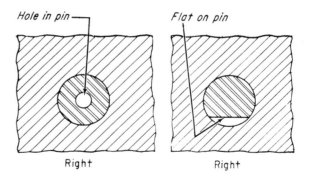

Hole in pin — Flat on pin

Right — Right

**3** **AIR-RELIEF HOLES** and channels in dowels prevent air compression from hindering assembly. Also hole allows entry for extraction punch.

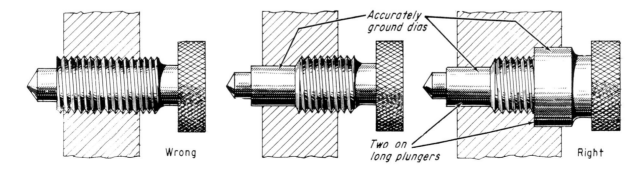

Accurately ground dias

Two on long plungers

Wrong — Right

**6** **ALIGNING DIAMETERS** should be provided on threaded plungers. Never rely on the thread for accurate concentric alignment of plunger.

# assembly

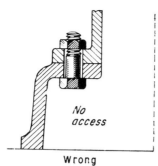

No access

Wrong

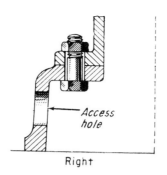

Access hole

Right

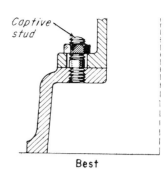

Captive stud

Best

**2** **ACCESS HOLES** or studs should always be provided in assemblies where bolt heads would be impossible or difficult to reach with a wrench.

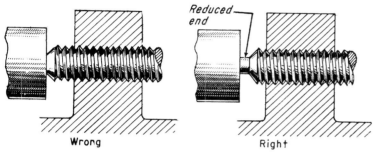

Reduced end

Wrong

Right

**4** **PRESSURE SCREWS** should have reduced ends to prevent expansion of the threads, which would make removal of the screws difficult.

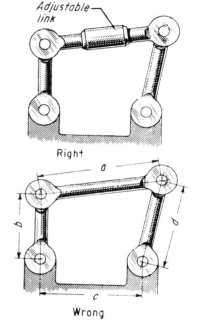

Adjustable link

Right

Wrong

**5** **ADJUSTABLE LINK** is necessary here where dimension *a* must be exact; otherwise dimensions *b*, *c*, *d* must have excessively close tolerances.

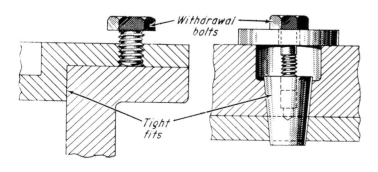

Withdrawal bolts

Tight fits

**7** **WITHDRAWAL BOLTS** make disassembly easier when tight fits are required between two parts that can not otherwise be separated safely.

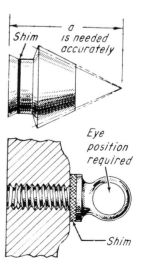

*a* is needed accurately

Shim

Eye position required

Shim

**8** **SHIMS** for bevel gears or threaded eyebolts are necessary where dimension *a* and the angular position of the eye are important to the design.

# Assemble sheetmetal with

These eight sheetmetal parts join sheetmetal
quickly with the simplest of tools, few screws or bolts.

*L KASPER, design consultant, Philadelphia*

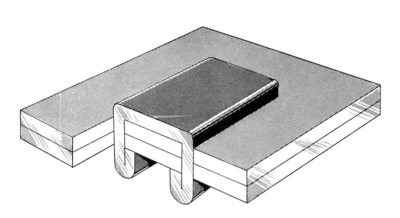

**1** **SQUEEZE CLIP** holds two overlapping sheets together. The ends of the clip are pushed through parallel slots, then bent over much like a staple.

**2** **ALIGNING PIECE** slides up out of the way in long slot while butting sheets are being positioned. Afterwards it slips down over lower sheet.

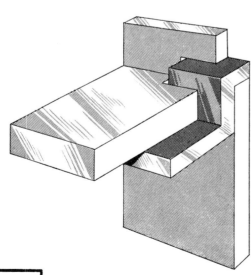

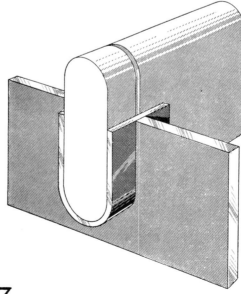

**5** **ESS** supports shelf between uprights. By mating with notched edge it acts as a key to keep shelf from sliding back and forth. and provides positive location.

**6** **CUP** carries a bar on both sides of divider. Here bars stick up above the top, but deeper cutout will lower them until they are flush or sunk.

# 8 interlocking fasteners

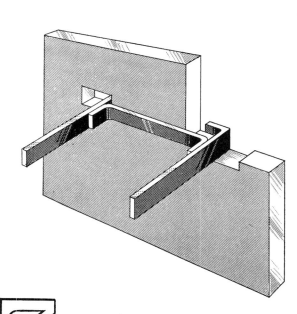

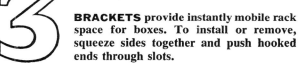

**3** **BRACKETS** provide instantly mobile rack space for boxes. To install or remove, squeeze sides together and push hooked ends through slots.

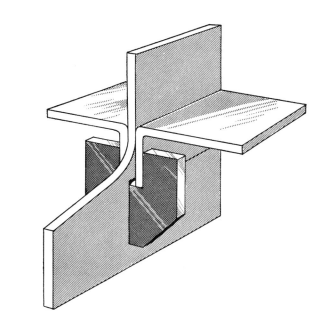

**4** **FLANGE HOLDER** does double duty by holding up shelves on both sides of a partition. Angular corners allow it to fit through small slit when tilted.

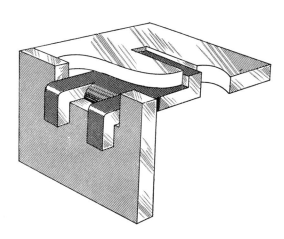

**7** **CLAW** holds top sheet between two end pieces. Tail snaps into slot, then claw is hammered over edge. With notched edge, top is even with sides.

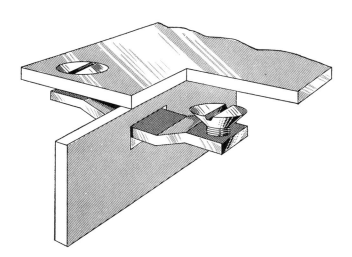

**8** **BAR** clamps divider in place. Extruded holes provide a recess for screws so that they stay flush with upper surface of horizontal sheet.

# 7 ways to assemble

Adhesives have come into their own now, so
why not use them to greater advantage
in mechanical and electrical assemblies?

*EUGENE J. AMITRANI, Technical Associate, IBM, Poughkeepsie, NY*

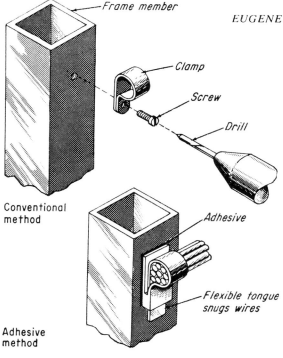

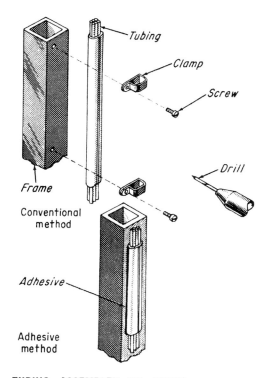

**1** CABLE CLAMP OF NEW DESIGN
uses adhesive as a fastening method. Conventional clamps can be
fastened in the same manner.

**2** TUBING ASSEMBLED TO FRAME
members does not require the use
of screws and clamps when adhesive is used for the job.

 **5** PANEL FINISH IS NOT MARRED by
using adhesive to mount studs.
Welded studs spoil finish on panel
outer surface.

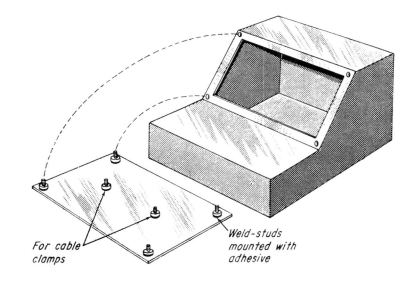

# with adhesives

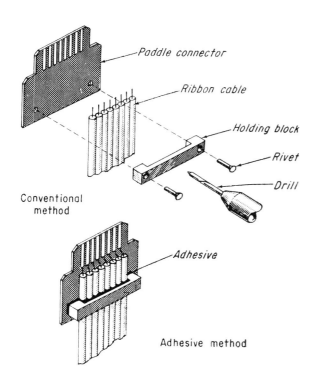

Conventional method

Paddle connector

Ribbon cable

Holding block

Rivet

Drill

Adhesive

Adhesive method

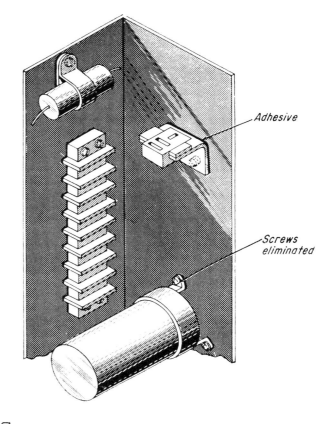

Adhesive

Screws eliminated

**SAVE RIVETS AND TIME** by using adhesive to fasten ribbon cable to connector-board. Dissassembly is not easy, though.

**SCREWS AND LOCKWASHERS** shown by dotted lines in sketch can be eliminated by using adhesive to attach components.

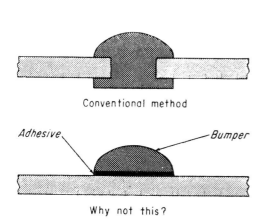

Conventional method

Adhesive

Bumper

Why not this?

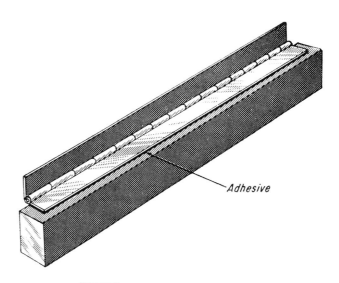

Adhesive

**RUBBER BUMPERS** usually need to be specially shaped and fitted into a hole in the component. Adhesive can simplify such assemblies.

**PIANO HINGES** are frequently used in instrument cases. Adhesive saves both hardware and time spent in making sure alignment is accurate.

# ATTACHING HUBLESS GEARS TO SHAFTS

*Thin gears and cams save space—but how to fasten them to their shafts? These illustrated methods give simple, effective answers.*

**L KASPER,** consultant
Philadelphia

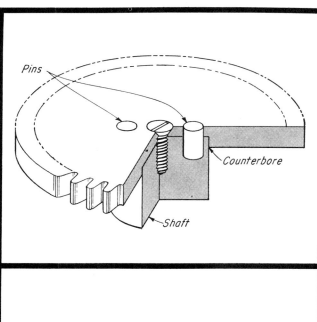

**1 COUNTERBORE** with close fit on shaft ensures concentric mounting. Torque is transmitted by pins; positive fastening is provided by flathead screw.

**2 TIGHT-FITTING** washer in counterbored hole carries the radial load; its shear area is large enough to ensure ample strength.

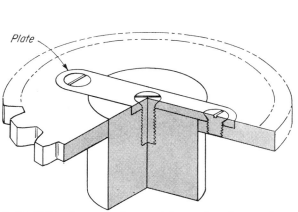

**3 PLATE** gives greater resistance to shear when radial loads are likely to be heavy. When the gear is mounted, the plate becomes the driver; the center screw merely acts as a retainer.

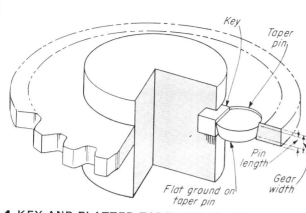

**4 KEY AND FLATTED TAPER-PIN** should not protrude above surface of gear; pin length should be slightly shorter than gear width. Note that this attachment is not positive—gear retention is by friction only.

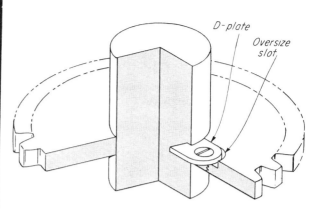

**5 D-PLATE** keys gear to shaft; optimum slot depth in shaft will depend upon torque forces and stop-and-start requirements—low, constant torque requires only minimum depth and groove length; heavy-duty operation requires enough depth to provide longer bearing surface.

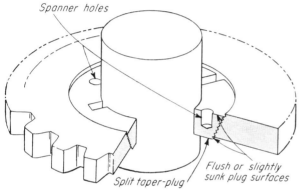

**6 TAPERED PLUG** is another friction holding device. This type mounting should be used so that the radial load will tend to tighten rather than loosen the thread. For added security, thread can be lefthand to reduce tampering risk.

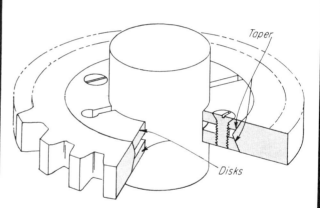

**7 TWO FRICTION DISKS,** tapered to about 5° included angle on their rims, are bored to fit the shaft. Flathead screws provide clamping force, which can be quickly eased to allow axial or radial adjustment of gear.

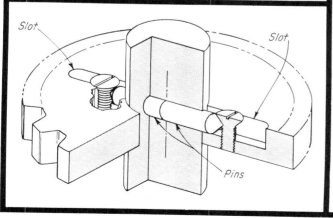

**8 TWO PINS** in radial hole of shaft provide positive drive that can be easily disassembled. Pins with conical end are forced tightly together by flathead screws. Slot length should be sufficient to allow pins to be withdrawn while gear is in place if backside of gear is "tight" against housing.

# design guide:

# ATTACHING MOTORS
# TO INSTRUMENT GEARHEADS

### Methods include servoclamps, screws, pins, adapter plates and half-rings, plus an eccentric mounting.

**FRANK WILLIAM WOOD JR**
*Systems Development Dept*
*Vitro Labs, Silver Spring, Md*

Instrument gearheads are increasingly useful in complex servo equipment where space is at a premium. Motors to drive the gearheads are usually mounted in line with them and must be reliably and economically attached. Sketches show some of the various methods possible. The method chosen for a particular design is determined by configuration of the motor, the type of input plate on the gearhead, or a combination of both.

Installation should be simple—it should not require disassembly of gearhead; connection should not loosen under vibration or shock, should not increase diameter of gearhead, should provide adjustment in high-precision requirements, and should provide necessary environmental protection at point of attachment (keep dust, moisture, etc., from entering gearhead). Backlash adjustment is also a desirable feature to include.

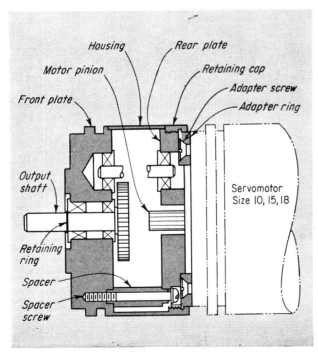

**1 TYPICAL GEARHEAD** and motor using "plate construction" gearhead.

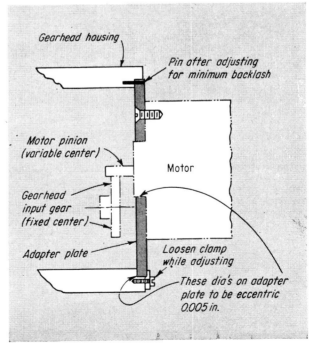

**2 MOTOR IS MOUNTED** on eccentrically bored adapter plate to permit backlash adjustment. By rotating adapter plate, backlash can be reduced to minimum between motor pinion and gearhead input gear.

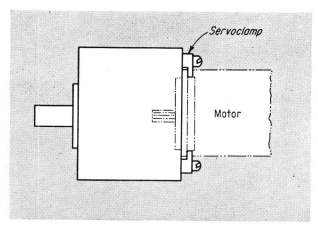

**3** STANDARD SERVOCLAMP

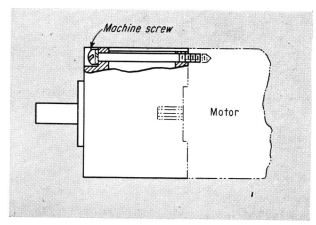

**4** BOLT THROUGH GEARHEAD INTO MOTOR

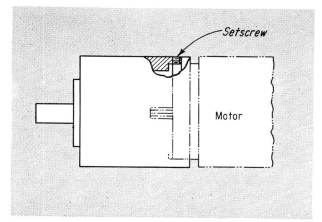

**5** SETSCREW THROUGH HOUSING SIDE-CLAMP TO MOTOR

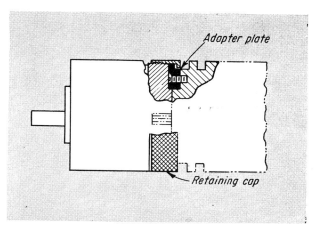

**6** ADAPTER PLATE AND RETAINING CAP

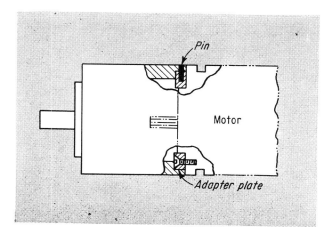

**7** PIN THROUGH HOUSING SIDE INTO ADAPTER PLATE

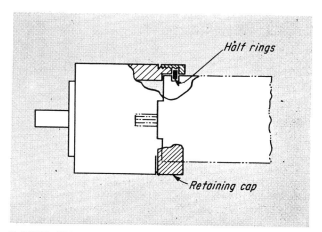

**8** TWO HALF-RINGS AND RETAINING CAP

# Fifteen Types of Mechanical

Constructions of tubing butt joints not requiring welding are shown. Most of these, Figs. 1 to 10, can be assembled and disassembled without damaging any of the component parts of the joint. Others, Figs. 11 to 15, are either detachable or permanent, depending on some of the details of the construction. This data has been prepared by the Product Development Committee of the Formed Steel Tube Institute, Cleveland, Ohio.

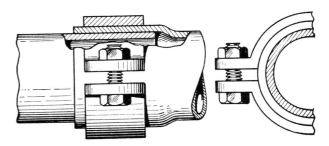

Fig. 1—Telescoping clamp fastening. There is no reduction in the inside diameter of the tube.

Fig. 2—Threaded sleeve fastening. This joint can be used either in structural members or in piping systems.

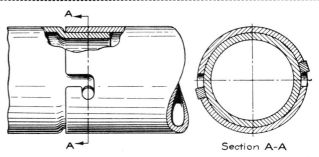

Fig. 3—Bayonet type fastening. This is an easily assembled joint of fixed length for attaching two tubes.

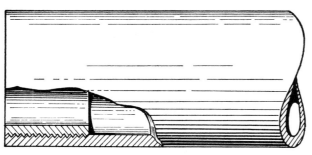

Fig. 4—Standard inside diameter thread connection. This type of joint is usually used in piping systems.

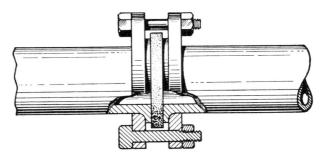

Fig. 5—Square flange gasket. This can be used as a fastening for pipes or ducts carrying liquid, air or gas.

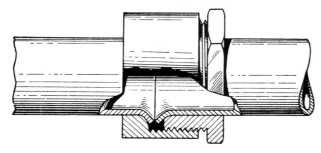

Fig. 6—Stuffing box type connecting clamp and 45 deg flange. This joint is used for pipes carrying liquids.

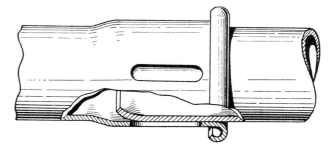

Fig. 7—Friction type joint. This easily assembled and disassembled joint is often used in vacuum cleaners.

# Joints for Tubing

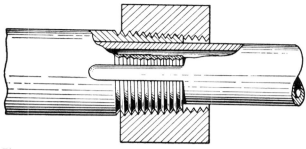

Fig. 8—Tapered locknut type joint is advantageous when adjustments in overall length are often required.

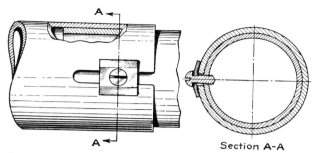

Section A-A

Fig. 9—Clip type joint. The clip curves away from the tube. Its flexibility facilitates longitudinal adjustment.

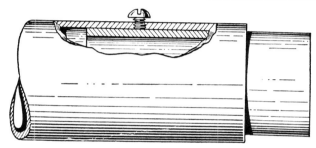

Fig. 10—Set screw. This fastening is a simple, inexpensive method of joining where adjustment is necessary.

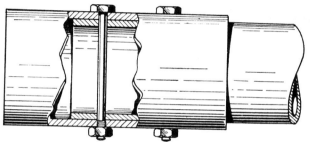

Fig. 11—Riveted or bolted joint. The bolted construction facilitates frequent assembly and disassembly.

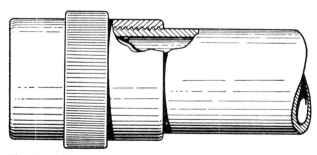

Fig. 12—Self-tapping threaded coupling. Thin walled tubing can be used. Occasional disassembly is possible.

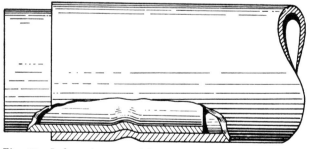

Fig. 13—Indentation type joint. The depth of the dimple determines whether or not it is detachable.

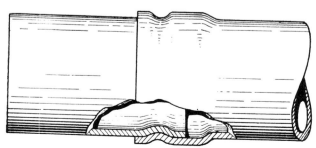

Fig. 14—Beaded joint assembly. The inside bead is preformed, and the outside bead is made after assembly.

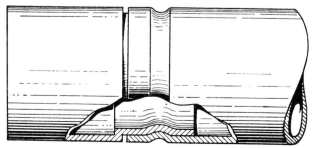

Fig. 15—Beaded assembly. This is like the assembly of Fig. 14 except that the outside diameters are matched.

# 8 Detents for clevis

When handles are mounted in clevises they often need to be held in one or more positions by detents. Here are ways to do this.

*IRWIN N. SCHUSTER, Design Consultant, Secane, Pa.*

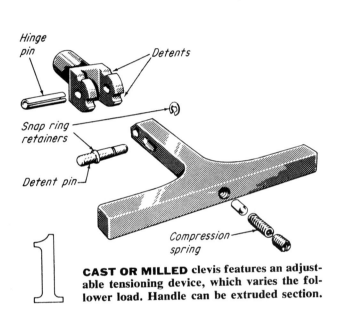

**CAST OR MILLED** clevis features an adjustable tensioning device, which varies the follower load. Handle can be extruded section.

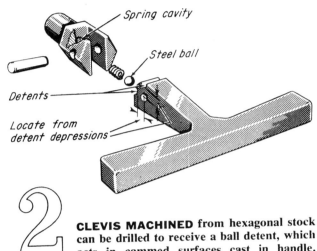

**CLEVIS MACHINED** from hexagonal stock can be drilled to receive a ball detent, which acts in cammed surfaces cast in handle.

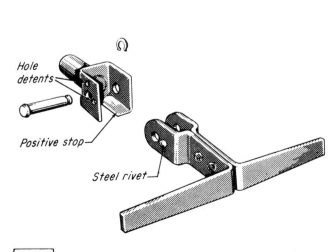

**WELDED CLEVIS** is relieved to improve spring characteristics. Punched holes receive steel rivet head which acts as the detent.

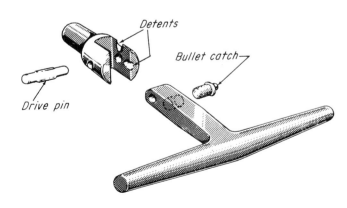

**CAST HANDLE** is drilled to accept a commercial "bullet" catch, which detents in the milled internal surface of the clevis flanges.

186

# mountings

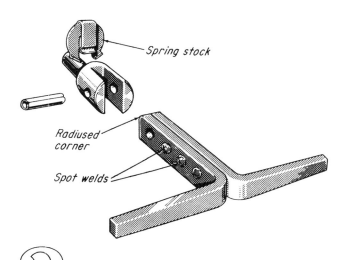

Spring stock

Radiused corner

Spot welds

**3** **STAMPED SPRING** snaps onto clevis before final assembly and acts as detent against the flat end and top surfaces of metal handle.

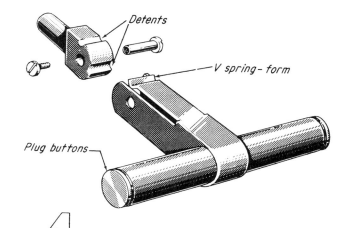

Detents

V spring-form

Plug buttons

**4** **TUBE AND SHEETMETAL** clevis handle has integral leaf spring which detents in cammed surface of machined shaft head.

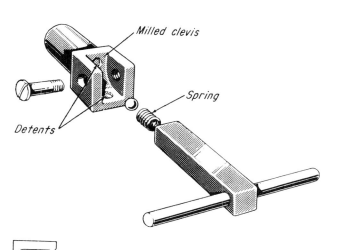

Milled clevis

Spring

Detents

**7** **MILLED CLEVIS** accepts ball-bearing follower, actuated by a spring, which seats against a pivot pin in the bar and rod handle.

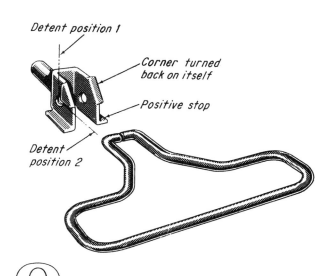

Detent position 1

Corner turned back on itself

Positive stop

Detent position 2

**8** **WIRE HANDLE** acts as spring and follower in sheetmetal clevis, in which cammed surfaces and positive stops are made by bending.

# 10 ways to CONCEAL FASTENERS

How to improve appearance of instrument panels by
hiding screw heads.

**FRANK WILLIAM WOOD JR**
*design engineer*
*Vitro Laboratories, Silver Spring, Md*

The appearance of an otherwise good-looking instrument panel is often spoiled by screw heads distributed in an uneven pattern across the panel surface. The following designs illustrate methods of improving appearance by subduing and concealing fasteners. In some cases, applications of these designs will not only improve appearance but also will reduce fabricating and assembly costs. Sometimes you get tamper protection as well.

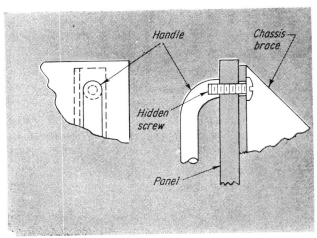

**1 DOUBLE-DUTY SCREW** attaches chassis to panel, is concealed by handle . A bonus is reduced fabrication and assembly time.

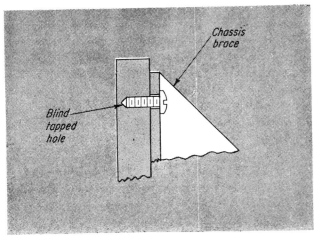

**2 BLIND HOLE** in panel conceals screw. This method is best suited for thicker panels, when adequate depth can be obtained without close tolerances.

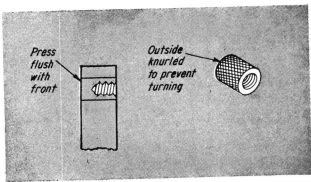

**3 TAPPED INSERT** pressed into panel is sometimes more economical than blind-tapped panel.

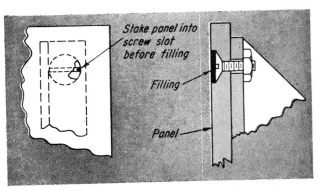

**4 RECESSED SCREW HEAD** is concealed with an epoxy resin before panel finish is applied. To prevent loosening of screw, the panel should be threaded. This thread, in conjunction with staking, locks the screw securely in position.

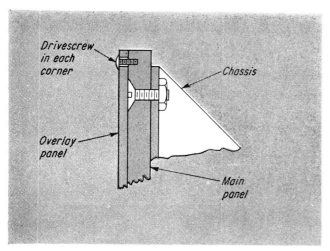

**5** "OVERLAY" PANEL conceals all front-panel hardware. Overlay panel offers no support for components and in many cases is attached with pressure-sensitive adhesive. All markings and nomenclature for controls can be carried by this panel.

**6** ORIENT SCREW-HEAD SLOTS in same direction to subdue detracting appearance of screw heads.

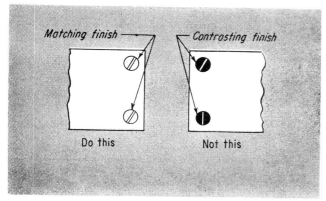

**7** MATCHING HARDWARE FINISH to that of the panel effectively subdues hardware appearance. A familiar example of this is the black oxide finish commonly used on panel-meter screws.

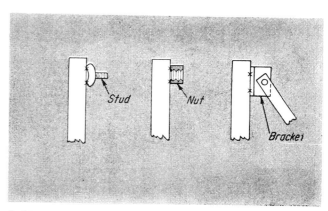

**8** SPOT-WELDED STUDS AND NUTS are commercially available for use on steel panels. Or, alternatively, special brackets can be used.

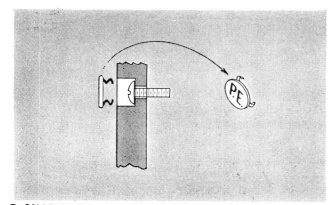

**9** SNAP-IN "PLUG BUTTON" fits into counterbored recess to conceal screw head and also provide corporate or product identity.

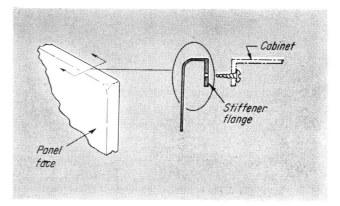

**10** SHEETMETAL STIFFENER FLANGES can be integral, as shown here, or separate when panel material cannot be formed. Sheetmetal screws hold panel.

# These alternates for

Some simple ways to fasten or locate round or flat parts without having to use dowels or other pins.

*FEDERICO STRASSER, Mankowitz & Strasser, Santiago, Chile*

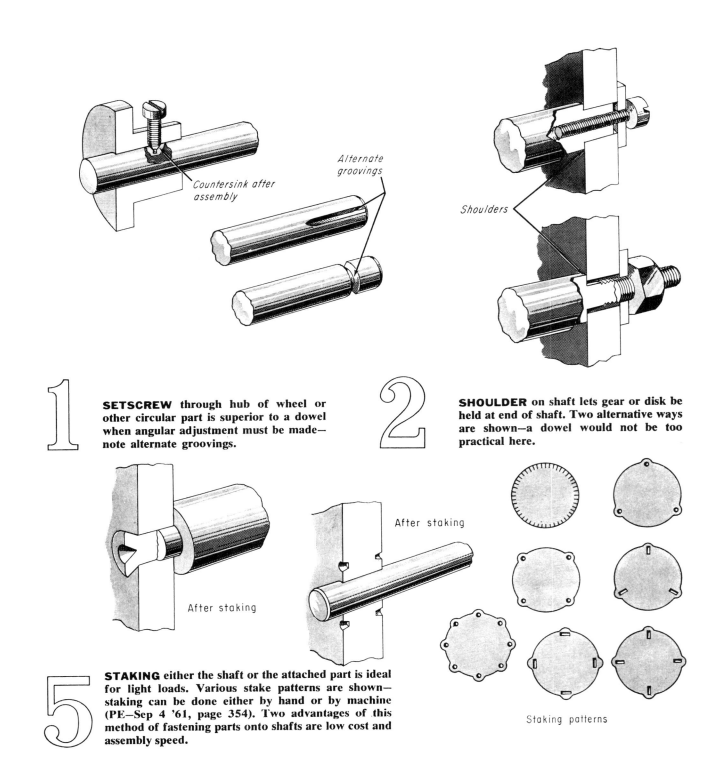

Countersink after assembly

Alternate groovings

Shoulders

After staking

After staking

After staking

Staking patterns

**1** **SETSCREW** through hub of wheel or other circular part is superior to a dowel when angular adjustment must be made—note alternate groovings.

**2** **SHOULDER** on shaft lets gear or disk be held at end of shaft. Two alternative ways are shown—a dowel would not be too practical here.

**5** **STAKING** either the shaft or the attached part is ideal for light loads. Various stake patterns are shown—staking can be done either by hand or by machine (PE—Sep 4 '61, page 354). Two advantages of this method of fastening parts onto shafts are low cost and assembly speed.

# doweled fastenings

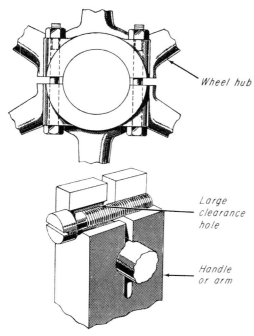

Wheel hub

Large clearance hole

Handle or arm

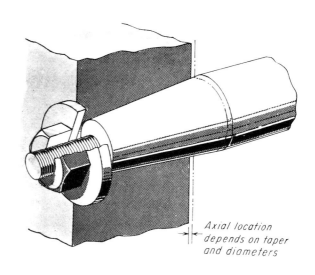

Axial location depends on taper and diameters

**PRESSURE JOINTS** are best when large composite wheels or similar parts are to be fastened to their shafts with only one or two screws.

**TAPERED JOINTS** are ideal when no clearance can be allowed between hub and shaft. Dowelling would be impracticable because of fit.

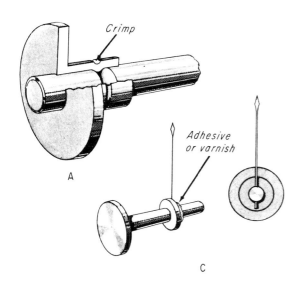

Crimp

Adhesive or varnish

A

C

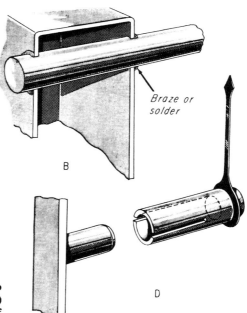

Braze or solder

B

D

**PERMANENT FASTENINGS** of parts assembled to shafts are crimped (A); soldered, brazed or welded (B) or adhesive-held (C). Non-permanent fastening of small indicator-pointer is best achieved by providing simple push fit (D). If positive location is required here, dimple hub after assembly.

# 6 More alternates for

These simple but effective methods fasten or locate
round and flat plates without dowels or other pins.

*FEDERICO STRASSER, Mankowitz & Strasser, Santiago, Chile*

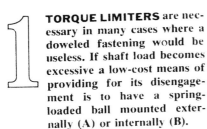

**1** **TORQUE LIMITERS** are necessary in many cases where a doweled fastening would be useless. If shaft load becomes excessive a low-cost means of providing for its disengagement is to have a spring-loaded ball mounted externally (A) or internally (B).

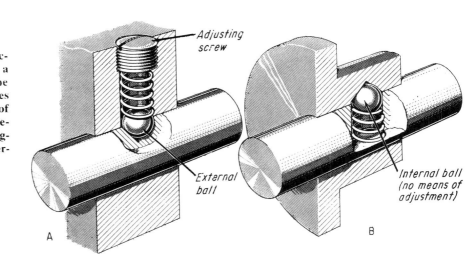

*Adjusting screw*

*External ball*

*Internal ball (no means of adjustment)*

A

B

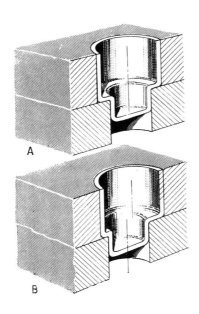

A

B

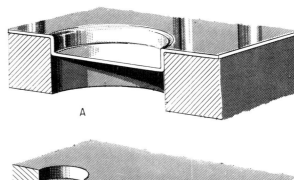

A

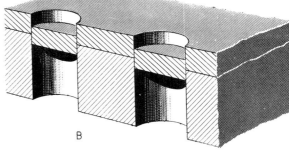

B

**3** **SHEET METAL "DOWELS"** can be used where location of two parts is needed without precise hole location. Cup is drawn after assembly.

**4** **SELF-DOWELING** part can be sheet metal (A) or other thin-material part (B). Merely emboss or punch slug halfway through to locate in hole.

# doweled fastenings

**BASIC FRICTION-CLUTCH** can also provide for disengagement when torque exceeds a safe value. There is basically no difference between collared shaft (A) and ringed shaft (B), but adjustment of tension in collared shaft is limited by amount of threading on end of shaft.

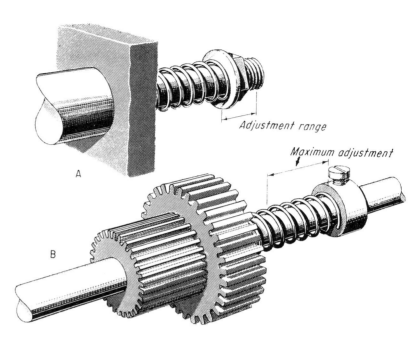

*Adjustment range*

*Maximum adjustment*

A

B

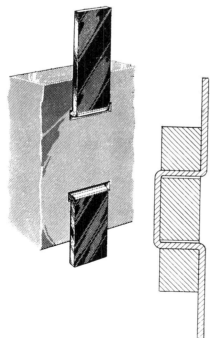

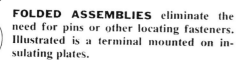

**FOLDED ASSEMBLIES** eliminate the need for pins or other locating fasteners. Illustrated is a terminal mounted on insulating plates.

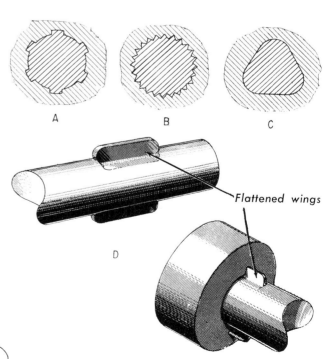

A  B  C

*Flattened wings*

D

**SPLINES** such as square (A) and involute (B) are often the best way to locate and hold hubs. Don't overlook simpler methods shown at C and D.

# Hangers put up by hand

No tools needed to install these hangers made of wire, rod or bar-stock.

*L KASPER, design consultant, Philadelphia*

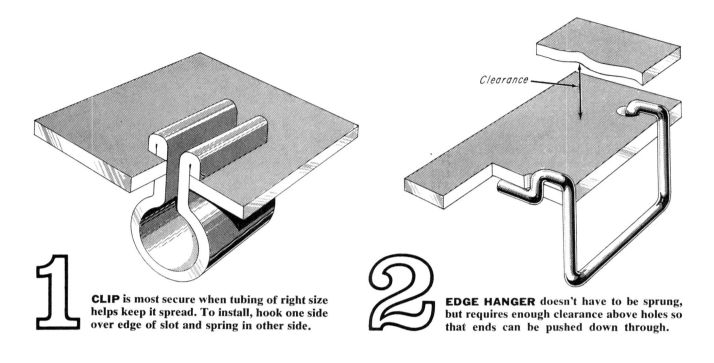

**1** **CLIP** is most secure when tubing of right size helps keep it spread. To install, hook one side over edge of slot and spring in other side.

**2** **EDGE HANGER** doesn't have to be sprung, but requires enough clearance above holes so that ends can be pushed down through.

Clearance

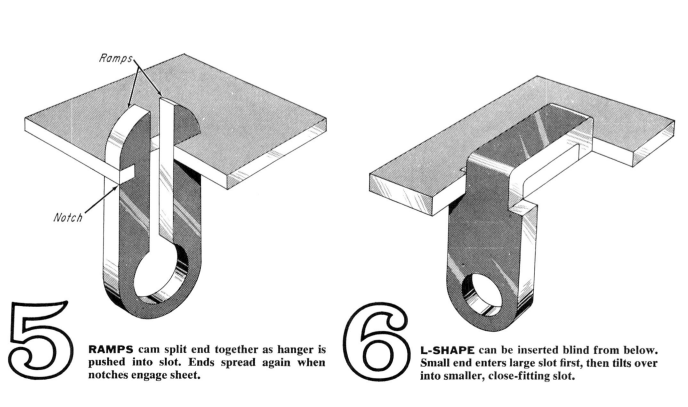

Ramps

Notch

**5** **RAMPS** cam split end together as hanger is pushed into slot. Ends spread again when notches engage sheet.

**6** **L-SHAPE** can be inserted blind from below. Small end enters large slot first, then tilts over into smaller, close-fitting slot.

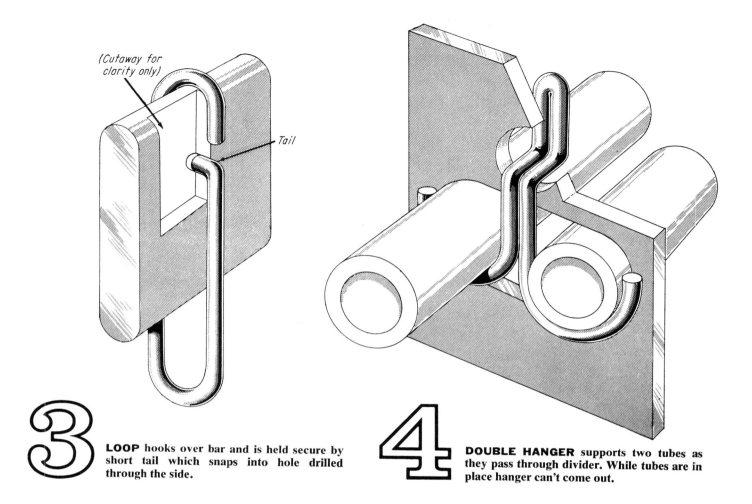

**3** **LOOP** hooks over bar and is held secure by short tail which snaps into hole drilled through the side.

*(Cutaway for clarity only)*

*Tail*

**4** **DOUBLE HANGER** supports two tubes as they pass through divider. While tubes are in place hanger can't come out.

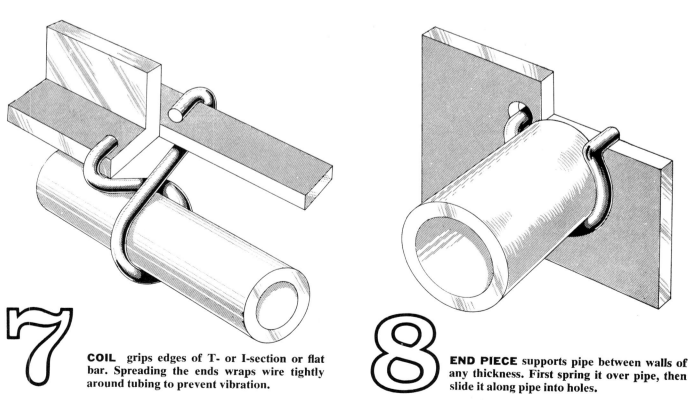

**7** **COIL** grips edges of T- or I-section or flat bar. Spreading the ends wraps wire tightly around tubing to prevent vibration.

**8** **END PIECE** supports pipe between walls of any thickness. First spring it over pipe, then slide it along pipe into holes.

# Fasteners that disconnect

Ideal for linkages, these quick-disconnect designs can simplify installation and maintenance because no tools are needed.

FRANK W. WOOD JR, Senior Engineer, General Precision Inc — Link Div, Binghamton, NY

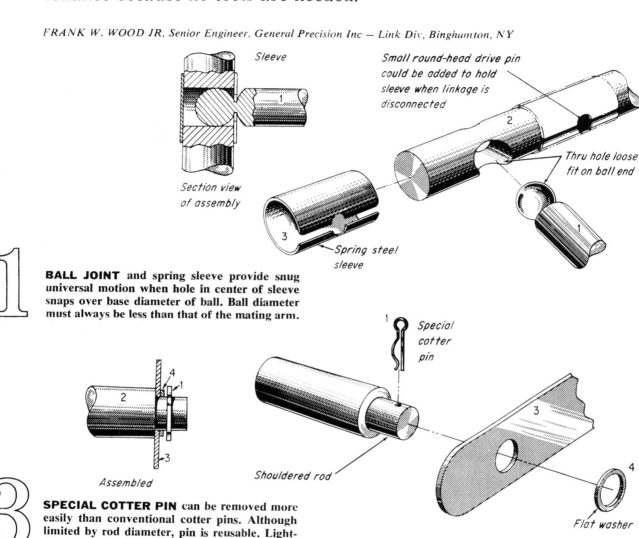

**1** **BALL JOINT** and spring sleeve provide snug universal motion when hole in center of sleeve snaps over base diameter of ball. Ball diameter must always be less than that of the mating arm.

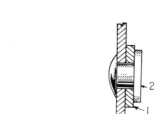

**3** **SPECIAL COTTER PIN** can be removed more easily than conventional cotter pins. Although limited by rod diameter, pin is reusable. Light-duty applications only are recommended.

**5** **ELONGATED FASTENER HEAD** and slot can be disconnected only when head and slot are aligned. Phase the linkage to avoid alignment of slot and head; otherwise it may work free.

# quickly

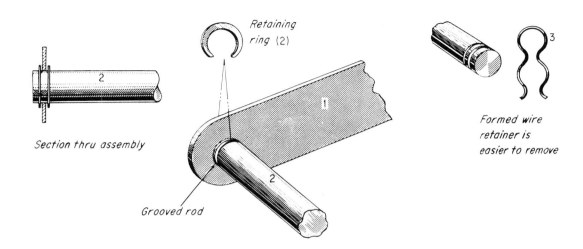

*Section thru assembly*

Retaining ring (2)

*Grooved rod*

Formed wire retainer is easier to remove

**GROOVED ROD** and retaining rings, while not having the freedom of motion of previous design, are simple and inexpensive to make. Double grooves are usually necessary.

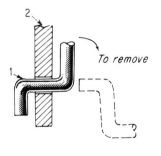

*To remove*

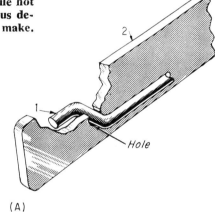

*Hole*

(A)

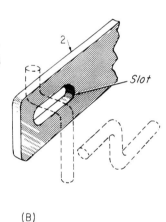

*Slot*

(B)

**FORMED ROD** in hole or slot allows disassembly only when the rod is free to be manipulated out of the arm. Slot design has play, which may or may not be advantageous.

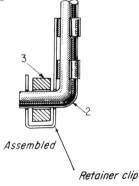

*Assembled*

*Retainer clip*

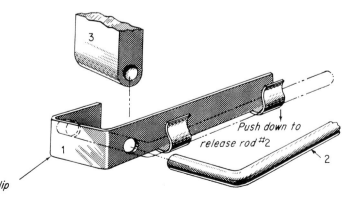

*Push down to release rod #2*

**RETAINER CLIP** and formed rod are ideal when production quantities are high enough to warrant tooling costs necessary for clip. But the clip is relatively easy to make.

# More quick-disconnect

These methods of fastening linkage arms
allow them to be disassembled without tools. Snap
slides, springs, pins, etc, are featured.

*FRANK W. WOOD JR, Senior Engineer, General Precision Inc — Link Div, Binghamton, NY*

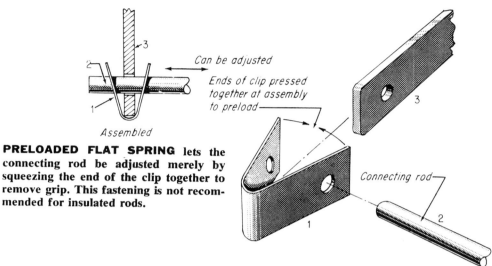

**1** **PRELOADED FLAT SPRING** lets the
connecting rod be adjusted merely by
squeezing the end of the clip together to
remove grip. This fastening is not recommended for insulated rods.

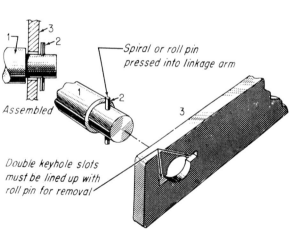

**3** **SPECIAL PIN AND DOUBLE KEYHOLE**
comprise a bayonet type of fastening —
reliable only when pinned rod won't turn
during operation, when alignment may
let pinned arm work free.

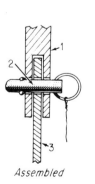

**5** **YOKE AND SPRING DETENT PIN** together make a common fastening method
for many mechanisms. It's sometimes wise
to tie pin to a member so that the pin will
not be lost.

# linkages

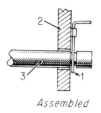

*Assembled*

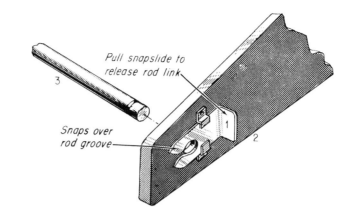

Pull snapslide to
release rod link

Snaps over
rod groove

**SNAP SLIDE AND GROOVED ROD**
provide a fastening method with no loose
parts to handle. Snap slide is commercially
available, or can be easily fashioned in the
model room.

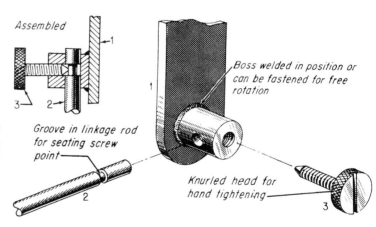

*Assembled*

Boss welded in position or
can be fastened for free
rotation

Groove in linkage rod
for seating screw
point

Knurled head for
hand tightening

**GROOVED ROD AND CLAMP SCREW**
will not allow relative, movement between
rod and other linkage member unless the
boss is free to rotate on its arm.

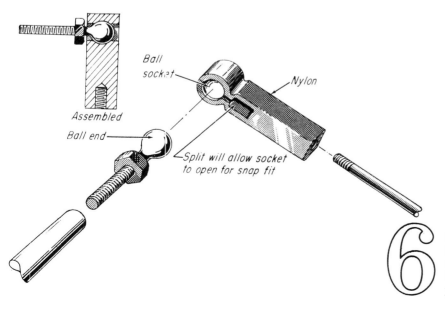

Ball
socket

Nylon

*Assembled*

Ball end

Split will allow socket
to open for snap fit

**NYLON ROD COUPLER** allows typical
ball-and-socket freedom combined with
the self-lubricating properties of nylon.
If load becomes excessive, the nylon will
yield, preventing damage to linkage.

# 8 Fastener comparisons

## A variety of basic applications show how these rings simplify design and cut costs.

*HOWARD ROBERTS, manager, engineering services, Truarc Retaining Rings Div, Waldes-Kohinoor Inc, Long Island City 1, NY*

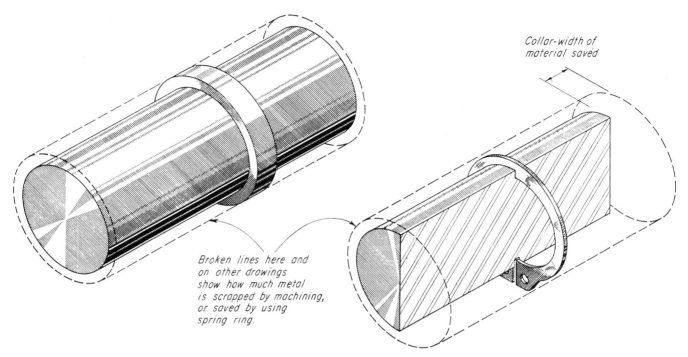

*Collar-width of material saved*

*Broken lines here and on other drawings show how much metal is scrapped by machining, or saved by using spring ring.*

 **MACHINED SHOULDERS** are replaced with savings in material, tools and time. Grooving for ring can be done during a cut-off, or other machining operation.

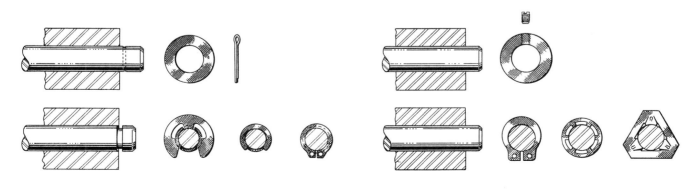

 **RINGS THAT CAN REPLACE** cotter pin and washer are economical since only one part is required and pin-spreading operation is not needed thus cutting time and costs.

 **WHEN COLLAR AND SETSCREW** are substituted by ring, risk of screw vibrating loose is avoided. Also, no damage to shaft by screw point occurs — a frequent cause of trouble.

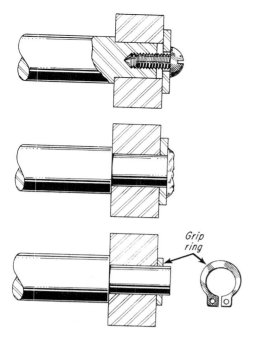

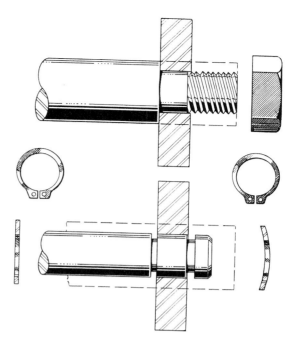

 **RETAIN COMPONENTS** on diecastings with a simple-to-use grip ring. Slipped over the end of the shaft, the ring exerts a frictional hold against axial displacement of the shaft.

 **SHOULDER AND NUT** are replaced by two retaining rings. A flat ring replaces the shoulder, while a bowed ring holds the component on shaft for resilient end-play take-up.

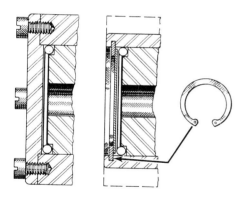

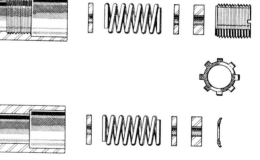

 **COVER-PLATE ASSEMBLY** has been re-designed (lower drawing) to avoid use of screws and machined cover-plate. Much thinner wall can be used—no drilling or tapping.

 **THREADED INTERNAL FASTENERS** are costly because of expensive internal threading operation. Simplify by substituting a self-locking retaining ring—see lower drawing.

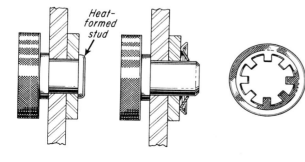

 **HEAT-FORMED STUD** provides a shoulder against retained parts but must be scrapped if the parts must be disassembled for service. Self-locking ring can be easily removed.

# More work for round

Try this low-cost fastener for locking shafts and other parts. It will also work as a shaft step for bearings and an actuating ring for switches.

DOMINIC J. LAPERA  Design Engineer, Marotta Valve Corp., N. J.

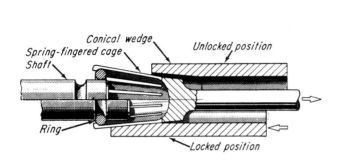

**1** **LOCK A SHAFT** by forcing a retaining ring over the groove in the shaft. In locking position, the spring-fingered cage is actuated by the conical wedge.

**2** **PISTON IS LOCKED** in place on the rod when drawn into place by means of a setscrew. To remove, slide the piston away from the ring, then remove the ring.

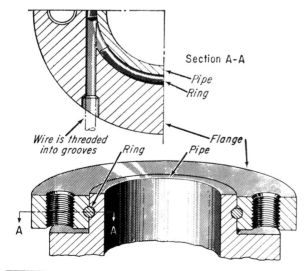

**5** **FLANGE ASSEMBLY** is permanently fastened by threading the wire into the mating grooves through the flange. Flange can rotate if wire doesn't protrude.

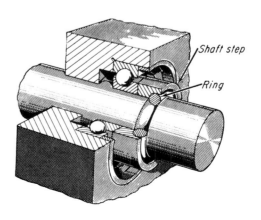

**6** **THIS SHAFT STEP** for a rotating bearing is quickly and simply made by grooving the shaft to accept a spring ring. Counterbore the shaft step to mate.

# retaining rings

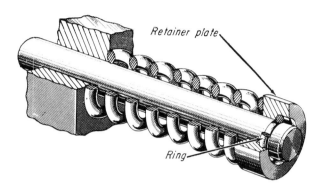

Retainer plate

Ring

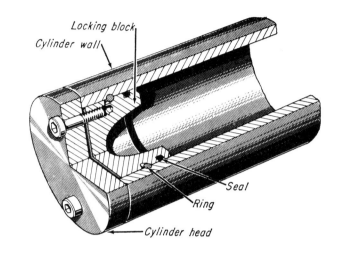

Locking block

Cylinder wall

Seal

Ring

Cylinder head

**3** **THIS SPRING-HELD** shaft lock is a basic application for retaining rings. The best groove dimensions for round spring rings are readily available from suppliers.

**4** **ASSEMBLE CYLINDER HEADS** and similar parts to thin walls by means of a retaining ring and a locking block. Tightening the screws expands the ring.

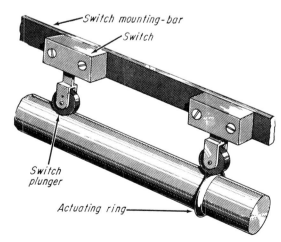

Switch mounting-bar

Switch

Switch plunger

Actuating ring

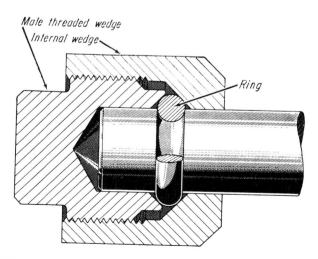

Male threaded wedge

Internal wedge

Ring

**7** **SWITCH ACTUATORS** of round retaining rings offer a simple solution when permanent shaft steps would present assembly problems. Close the ring gap.

**8** **THREE-PIECE WEDGE** lets the shaft move freely until the wedge is tightened by screwing it in. The round retaining ring is then forced into the groove.

# Getting the most

Special jobs often call for special screw
arrangements; here are some examples of
how this busy fastener can perform.

*FEDERICO STRASSER Rome, Italy*

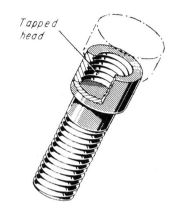

**1** TAPPED HEAD LETS EXTENSIONS BE ADDED.

Tapped head

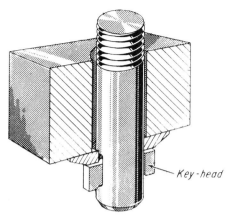

Key-head

**2** KEY-TYPE HEAD PROVIDES QUICK-RELEASE FEATURE.

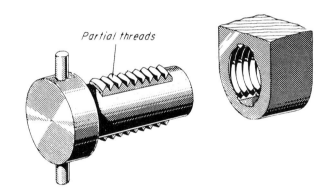

Partial threads

**4** PARTIAL THREADS ASSEMBLE FAST, DON'T WORK LOOSE.

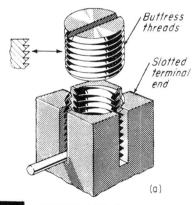

Buttress threads

Slotted terminal end

(a)

**5** BUTTRESS THREADS PREVENT (a) radial
forces from opening slotted ends;
otherwise (b) a reinforcing sleeve is
needed.

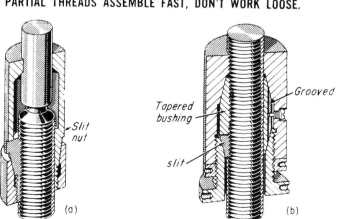

Slit nut

Tapered bushing

Grooved

slit

(a)                    (b)

**7** SLIT NUT (a) and tapered bushing (also slit) (b)
allows backlash-free adjustment.

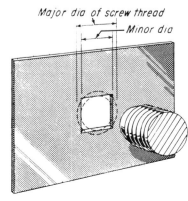

Major dia of screw thread

Minor dia

**8** SQUARE HOLE for light metal or plastic sub-
stitutes well for threaded holes.

# from screws

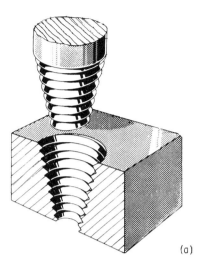

(a)

**3** TAPERED SCREWS ASSEMBLE AND RELEASE FAST, BUT WORK LOOSE EASILY.

Coupling solid rods

(b)

Reinforcing sleeve

(b)

Coarse thread

Fine thread

(a)

Knob

X tpi

Y tpi

$\delta$

(b)

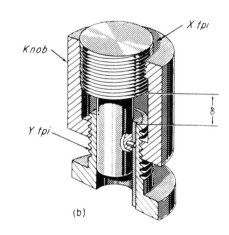

**6** DIFFERENTIAL THREADS PROVIDE (a) extra tight fastening or (b) extra small relative movement, $\delta$, per revolution of knob.

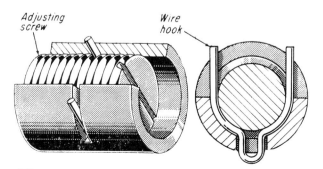

Adjusting screw

Wire hook

**9** WIRE HOOK provides single-thread grip for low-cost device.

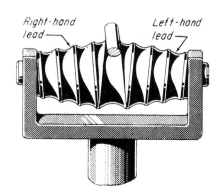

Right-hand lead

Left-hand lead

**10** DOUBLE SCREW for wire guide or follower always leads wire to center.

# Snap fasteners for

It's difficult to cement polyethylene parts together, so eliminate extra cost of separate fasteners with these snap-together designs.

*EDGER BURNS, Project Engineer, Eldon Industries, L.A.*

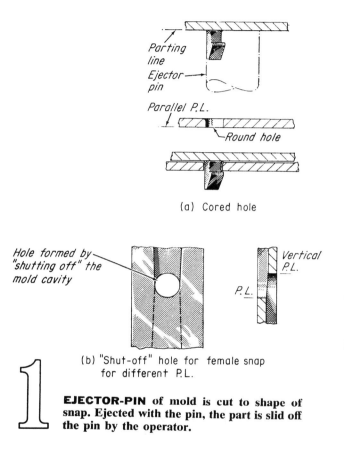

(a) Cored hole

Parting line
Ejector pin
Parallel P.L.
Round hole

Hole formed by "shutting off" the mold cavity

Vertical P.L.

P.L.

(b) "Shut-off" hole for female snap for different P.L.

## 1

**EJECTOR-PIN** of mold is cut to shape of snap. Ejected with the pin, the part is slid off the pin by the operator.

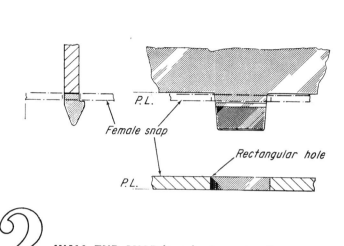

P.L.

Female snap

Rectangular hole

P.L.

## 2

**WALL-END SNAP** is easier to remove from the mold than the ejector-pin snap. The best length for this snap is ¼ to ½ in.

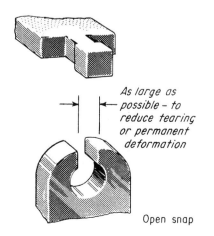

As large as possible – to reduce tearing or permanent deformation

Open snap

## 5

**OPEN SNAP** relies on an undercut in the mold and on the ability of the polyethylene to deform and then spring back on ejection.

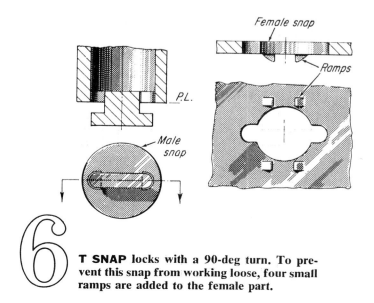

Female snap

Ramps

P.L.

Male snap

## 6

**T SNAP** locks with a 90-deg turn. To prevent this snap from working loose, four small ramps are added to the female part.

# polyethylene

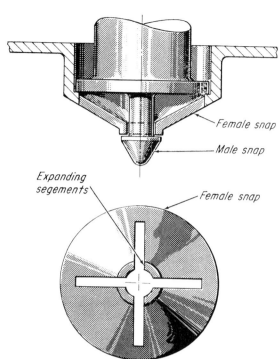

Female snap

Male snap

Expanding segements

Female snap

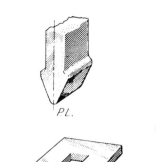

P.L.

Spear snap

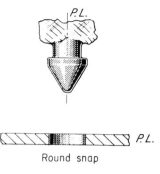

P.L.

P.L.

Round snap

**3**

**SEGMENTED WALL** of female snap allows a large-headed male snap to enter easily. The snap can not be pulled apart with light loads.

**4** **SPEAR AND ROUND** snaps are similar in design to the wall-end snap, but are ideal for assembling small parts to larger ones.

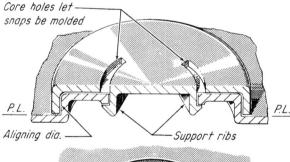

Core holes let snaps be molded

P.L.

P.L.

Aligning dia.

Support ribs

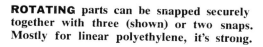

**7** **ROTATING** parts can be snapped securely together with three (shown) or two snaps. Mostly for linear polyethylene, it's strong.

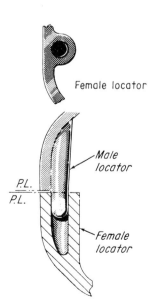

Female locator

Male locator

P.L.

P.L.

Female locator

**8** **LOCATORS** are not really snaps, but align parts for subsequent eyeleting or riveting or in conjunction with other snaps.

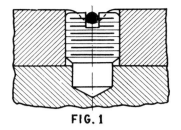

**FIG. 1**

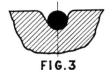

**FIG. 3**

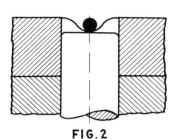

**FIG. 2**

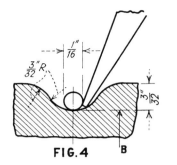

**FIG. 4**

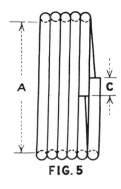

**FIG. 5**

# Wire Locks and Snap

### ADAM FREDERICKS

Frequently considerable savings can be made by the substitution of wire locks or snap rings in place of expensive tapping operations, or to eliminate the necessity of boring holes to two different diameters and grinding shafts to shoulders. Often, screws and lock nuts can also be eliminated.

Wire locks and snap rings can be used only where the loads are radial and thrust loads are light. Spring steel or music wire is usually used for the material. Usually, $\frac{1}{16}$-in. diameter wire is sufficiently large. In nearly all of the accompanying illustrations the wire size is shown exaggerated.

**Figs. 1 and 2**—Two common applications for wire locks to a screw or a pin.

**Fig. 3**—The two forms of grooves shown here should be avoided, as each offers too much difficulty in snapping off the ring, particularly when the outside or outermost diameter of the wire ring is below the surface of the work.

**Fig. 4**—Enlarged view of a successful type of groove, the rounded edges permitting the wire to be snapped out with greater facility.

**Fig. 5**—Wire locks may be made in the form of a close wound spring and successive coils cut off to suit. Diameter $A$ should be $\frac{1}{16}$-in. smaller than the diameter $B$ indicated in Fig. 4. Lap $C$ should be $\frac{1}{16}$ in. for each $\frac{1}{16}$-in. difference between diameters $A$ and $B$.

**Figs. 6 to 8**—Three typical applications of snap rings.

**Fig. 9**—Spring lock of $\frac{3}{64}$-in. wire on a $\frac{1}{4}$-in. diameter pin, as used in a well-known universal joint. Once assembled, the spring lock cannot snap out.

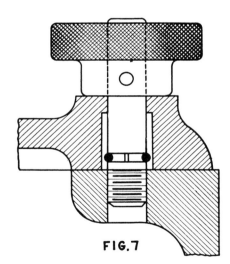

**FIG. 6**

**FIG. 7**

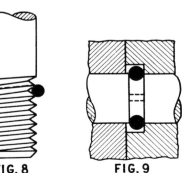

**FIG. 8**          **FIG. 9**

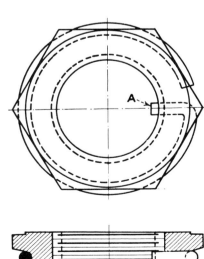

**FIG.10**

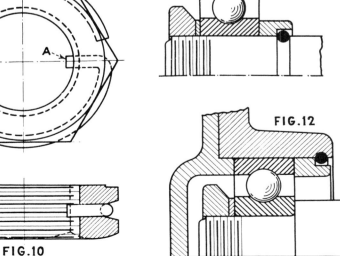

**FIG.11**

**FIG.12**

# Rings for Fastenings

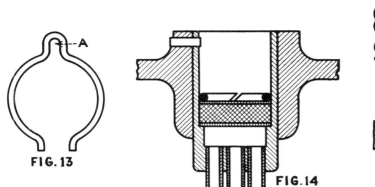

FIG. 13

FIG. 14

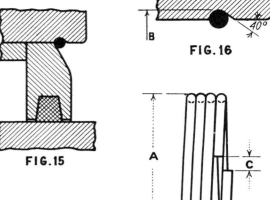

FIG. 15

FIG. 16

FIG. 17

Fig. 10—A hole in the shaft receives the end *A* of the spring lock. When the position of the nut is changed a new hole must be drilled in the shaft.

Figs. 11 and 12—Typical applications of wire locks.

Fig. 13—Press-formed external wire lock. Loop *A* allows insertion of a wire puller when disassembling.

Fig. 14—Application of a wire lock in a lubricating device to hold the wire mesh screen and felt in place.

Fig. 15 and 16—Felt seal housing held in place by a wire lock, and enlarged view of groove.

Fig. 17—Method of cutting internal lock rings from a close wound spring. Diameter *A* should be $\frac{1}{16}$-in. larger than diameter *B* and gap *C* is $\frac{1}{2}$ in. for each $\frac{1}{16}$-in. difference between diameters *A* and *B*.

Figs. 18 and 19—Wire locks for the felt seal housing of a tapered roller bearing. In Fig. 19 is shown the enlarged view showing the different positions taken by the wire lock for a various of plus or minus $\frac{1}{32}$ in. axially.

Fig. 20—Wire lock, internal, applied to a sheet metal stamping.

Fig. 21—Wire lock in the outer race of an open-end bearing to make it integral.

Fig. 22 to 26—Typical snap ring made of rectangular spring and various applications of snap rings made of rectangular stock, as applied to roller bearings and ball bearings.

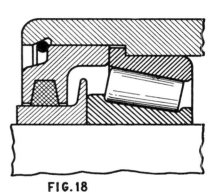

FIG. 18

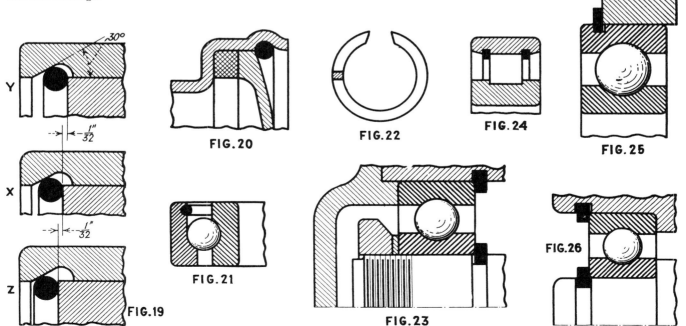

FIG. 20

FIG. 22

FIG. 24

FIG. 25

FIG. 19

FIG. 21

FIG. 23

FIG. 26

# Chapter 6

# HYDRAULICS AND PNEUMATICS

# Air-Operated Chucking Devices

### UNIVERSAL POWER CHUCK

Single rotating cylinder-piston assembly controls clamping pressure of step-cut false jaws. General usage is for external gripping of round pieces; internal gripping can be achieved by reversing the jaws. By utilizing a plug-type hand-control valve, the jaws can be eased against the work piece, thereby facilitating exact positioning.

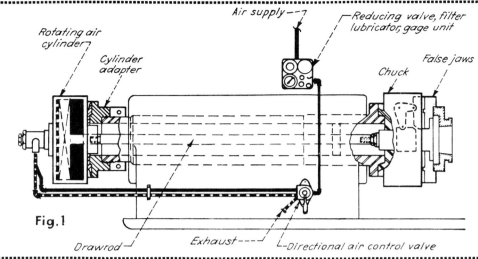

Fig. 1

### COMPENSATING AIR CHUCK

Similar to Fig. 1, except tail stock center is utilized. Since floating jaws are centered automatically before full gripping pressure is applied, irregularities in the work piece up to $\frac{1}{4}$ in. can be handled. Used for "second" operation when piece must be located from a previously machined surface.

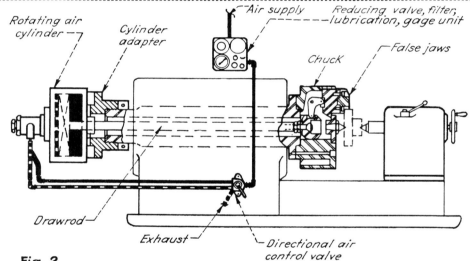

Fig. 2

### AIR-OPERATED CHUCK AND TAILSTOCK

Non-rotating cylinder piston advances tailstock center, thus positioning work in chuck operated by rotating cylinder. Pressing push button A causes air-hydraulic cylinder to feed tool into work at a speed regulated by oil chamber valve. Limit switch B causes tool to retract. This arrangement enables one person to operate several lathes.

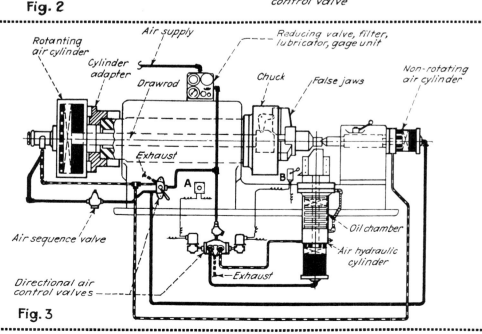

Fig. 3

# for Lathe Applications

HARRY L. STEWART
Logansport Machine Company, Inc.

## COLLET-TYPE CHUCK

Electrically operated valve controls rotating cylinder assembly that locks bar stock fed through the hollow spindle. Pressure angle of chuck affords high gripping pressure. Hollow cylinder airshaft is water cooled if surface speed is more than 400 feet per minute.

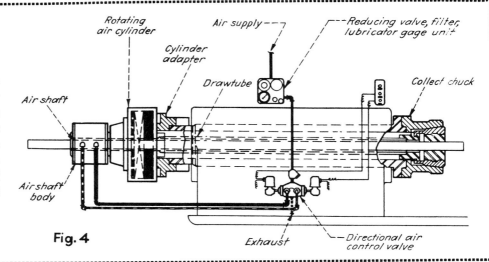

**Fig. 4**

## MANDREL-TYPE CHUCK

Hand-operated air valves control movement of tail stock and locking of mandrel jaws. Used when high pressure gripping is desired and when work piece has long overhang. Non-rotating cylinder tailstock assembly provides fast, positive positioning of piece to be machined.

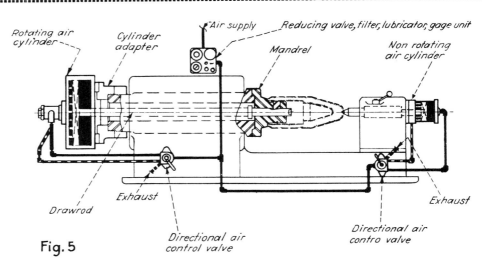

**Fig. 5**

## DOUBLE-JAW MANDREL CHUCK

Expanding-type mandrel is equipped with an adjustable work-locator nose for positioning the work piece. Used for long pieces and on which heavy cuts are to be taken. Foot-operated control valve permits operator to use both hands for adjusting the work piece or preparing the next part for insertion.

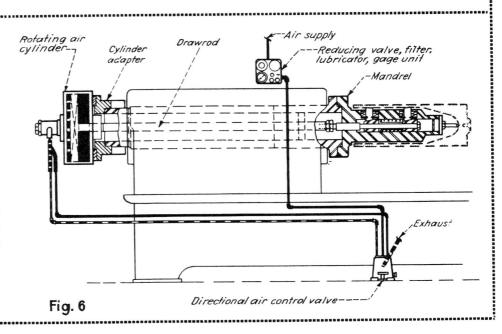

**Fig. 6**

# Hydraulic Chucking Devices

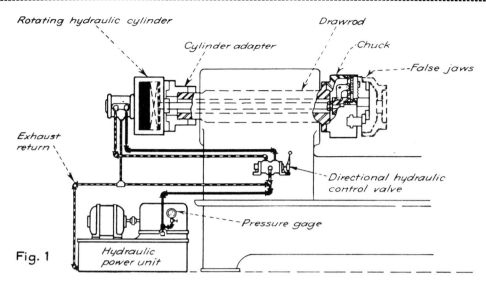

### INTERNAL HYDRAULIC CHUCKING

Hydraulic fluid enters rotating cylinder when directional hydraulic control valve is shifted. Rotating cylinder piston then pushes on bell crank of chuck through drawrod. False jaws operated by bell crank then grip work. To release grip, drawrod is pulled back when control valve lever is reversed.

Fig. 1

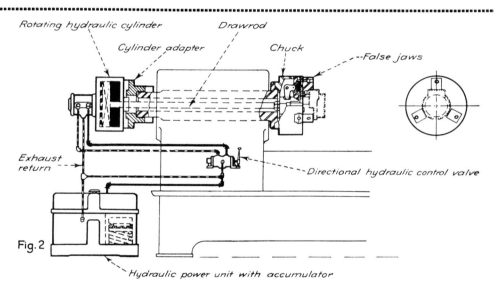

### EXTERNAL HYDRAULIC CHUCKING

After operation of directional hydraulic control valve, pull on bell crank through drawrod closes false jaws on work. Upon reversal of control valve, jaws are opened and work is released. Hydraulic accumulator in power unit maintains pressure for relatively long periods of chuck operation.

Fig. 2

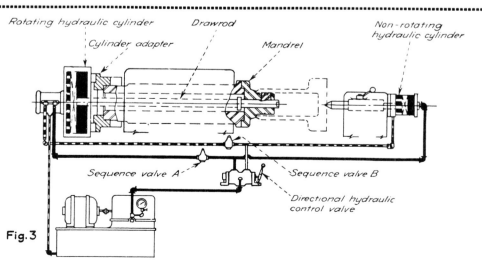

### HYDRAULIC CHUCK AND TAILSTOCK

After operation of directional hydraulic control valve, fluid enters non-rotating cylinder, and tailstock moves into position, and sequence valve *A* opens. Hydraulic fluid then admitted to rotating cylinder causes mandrel to grip work. When machine operation is completed, control valve is reversed. Tailstock retracts and sequence valve *B* opens, causing mandrel to release work.

Fig. 3

# for Lathe Applications

HARRY L. STEWART
Logansport Machine Company, Inc.

## HYDRAULIC CHUCK AND FEED

After directional control valve is shifted, mandrel grips work. Push button operated solenoid valve admits hydraulic fluid to tool feed cylinder at a rate regulated by flow control valve. Completion of tool travel trips limit switch reversing solenoid valve. Tool then returns to original position. Reversing directional control valve then causes mandrel to release work.

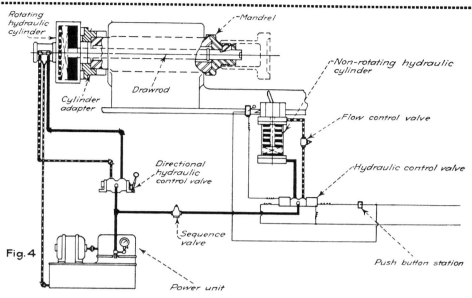

Fig. 4

## HYDRAULIC CHUCK AND AUTOMATIC FEED

Shifting hand operated hydraulic pilot valve causes push type mandrels to grip work. Gripping work automatically trips sequence valve, opening control valve for non-rotating hydraulic cylinder. Tool is then fed hydraulically until hydraulic pilot valve is tripped. This reverses righthand control valve to return tool feed cylinder. Shifting hand operated pilot valve releases work.

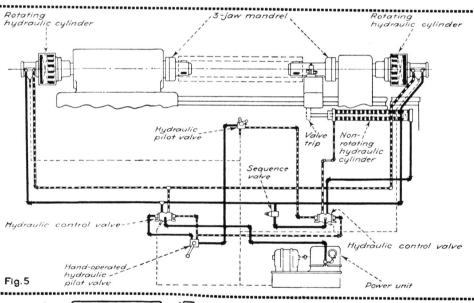

Fig. 5

## HYDRAULIC CHUCK WITH ELECTRIC CONTROLS

Electric controls replace the pilot valves shown in Fig. 5. Pressing push button causes mandrels to grip work. This trips the pressure switch causing non-rotating hydraulic cylinder to feed cylinder. At the end of the tool travel, tripping the left hand limit switch returns tool to original position. This trips righthand limit switch, which initiates release of work.

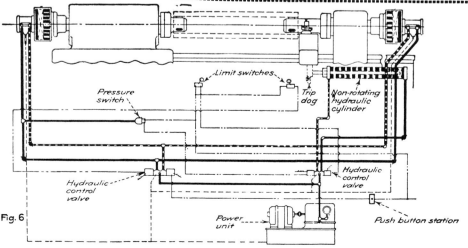

Fig. 6

# HYDRAULIC CIRCUITS AND

Versatility in hydraulic operation of machine tools, special machines, and for other purposes such as pressure test equipment has resulted in many ingenious applications and designs of hydraulic circuits, often in combination with electrically controlled valves, to produce a sequence of operations. Hydraulic circuits also operate automatically through a series of operations by fully hydraulic means, such as pressure activated valves, or by mechanically operated valves. Both types of automatic operation are illustrated here, as well as other ways of using hydraulic equipment.

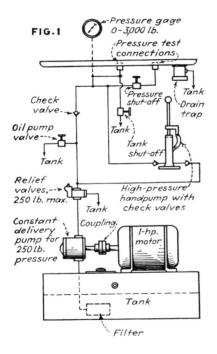

Fig. 1—Test part is subjected to 250 lb. per sq. in. pressure by opening pressure shut-off valve and closing oil pump and tank shut-off valves. Full test pressure is applied by hand pump after opening oil pump valve. Opening tank shut-off valve relieves pressure for removal of the part subjected to test.

Fig. 2—Holding pushbutton on riveting gun energizes Hi-Lo panel solenoid, applying low pressure to gun cylinder. Rivet resistance builds pressure in pressure switch, causing shift in panel to high-pressure line. Rivet compression pressure finally causes pressure switch to de-energize panel solenoid, thus reversing gun piston with low pressure. Return of gun piston causes panel shift which blocks both high and low pressure until pushbutton is released and pressed again.

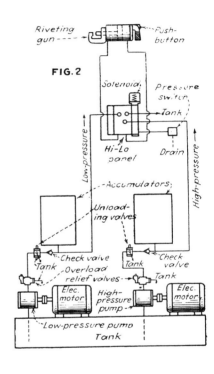

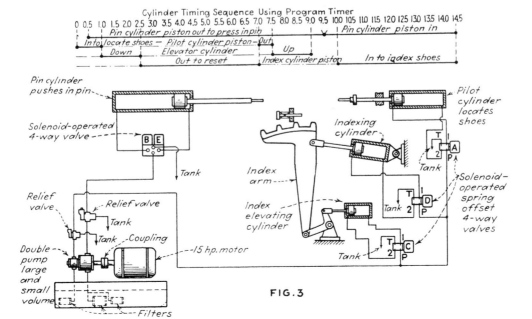

FIG. 3

Fig. 3—Tank track shoes are pinned together by automatic machine with electric program timer and individual solenoid operated spring offset 4 way valves for each of the 4 hydraulic operating cylinders. Sequence of operations is indicated by chart. Absence of pin on either shoe leaves electric circuits open, thus stopping operation of machine automatically.

# THEIR OPERATION—I

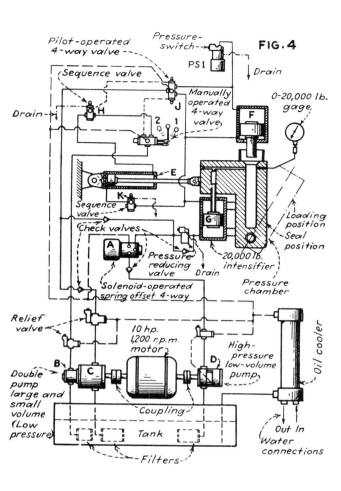

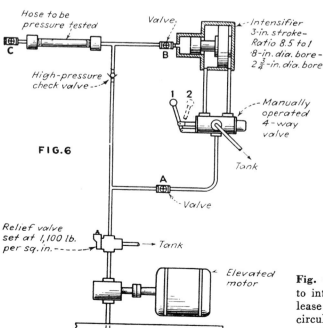

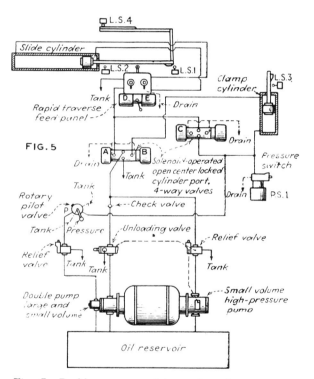

**Fig. 4**—Pressure chamber moves from loading to seal position when hand lever at 1 admits oil from pump B to cylinder E. Pressure build-up opens valve H to valve J, which permits oil from pump C to force piston F down to seal position. Pressure build-up in P.S.1 energizes solenoid A permitting oil from pump D upward to force piston G up, thus boosting pressure in pressure chamber. This pressure is released by moving hand lever to 2, thus shifting valve J and reversing pistons F and G by means of pump C. Pressure build-up opens valve K in line to head end of cylinder E, thus returning chamber to loading position.

**Fig. 5**—Pushbutton energizing solenoid A operates clamp cylinder, then pressure switch P.S.1, which energizes solenoids C and E. Solenoid C blocks main oil volume from clamp cylinder, which is then held by small volume pump, while E opens main flow to piston end of slide cylinder. Solenoid E is de-energized by L.S.4 just before cam actuation of panel reduces rapid forward traverse to coarse and fine feeds. Solenoid D, energized by L.S.1, causes rapid return of slide until L.S.2 de-energizes solenoids D, C, and A, and energizes solenoid B, which releases clamp cylinder. When L.S.3 is contacted solenoid B is de-energized.

**Fig. 6**—Hand lever held at 2 admits pump pressure to intensifier, thus multiplying pressure on hose. Release of hand lever to 1 returns intensifier piston and circulates oil through 4-way valve to tank. Valve C is opened before removing hose.

# HYDRAULIC CIRCUITS AND

JAMES A. LEONARD, *Hydraulic Machinery Inc.*

Hydraulic operation of machines, sequencing of processing operations, and pressure testing have been developed to meet a wide range of conditions, often with interlocked timing of several operations. Automatic operation is often produced by electric solenoids activated by switches whose contacts are opened and closed by moving machine elements. Such operation is possible hydraulically also as shown in Fig. 4. These hydraulic operations, together with those presented last month indicate the possibilities of hydraulics for complicated operations.

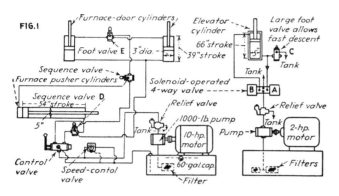

**Fig. 1**—Furnace doors are opened when control valve is at position 1. Pressure build-up then opens sequence valve to pusher cylinder, which pushes new tray into furnace and heated tray onto elevator where it contacts a limit switch that energizes solenoid *A*. This causes elevator to lower tray into quench tank and contact a limit switch that de-energizes solenoid *A* and starts a timer, which eventually energizes solenoid *B*. Tray moving off elevator contacts a limit switch that energizes solenoid *A* thus lowering elevator for loading unless held at *C*. A limit switch at loading position de-energizes solenoid *A*. During these operations control valve is put in position 2, causing pusher cylinder to retract, then open sequence valve *D* to close furnace door unless held by foot valve *E*.

**Fig. 2**—Fluid motor on boring mill runs when solenoid *A* is energized and solenoid *B* is de-energized, and stops when the reverse is true. Push-buttons on panel control speed. Horizontal and vertical cylinder direction and speed are controlled by four 2-position pilot valves. Feed rate is regulated by a control valve.

**Fig. 3**—End of part to be pressure tested is held in seal chamber by seal fixture when rotary valve *A* is in position shown. Pressure build-up opens sequence valve *B*, causing cylinder *C* to submerge test set-up. Air is admitted by moving valve lever *D* to position shown. Energizing solenoid *A* builds pressure in booster cylinder from 100 to 250 lb. Air pressure is released by reversing lever *D* and test set-up is raised by reversing valve *A*. Pressure build-up opens sequence valve *F*, thus releasing seal fixture.

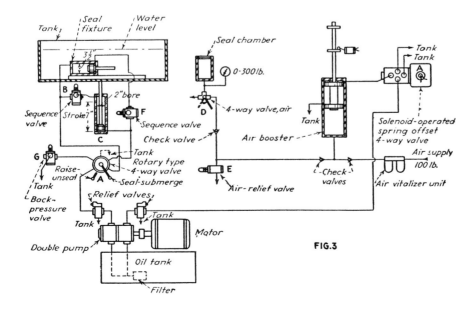

# THEIR OPERATION—II

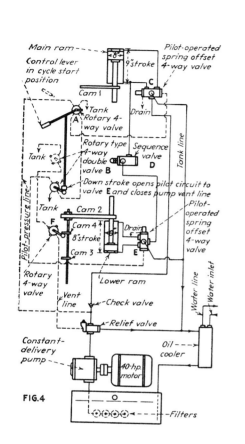

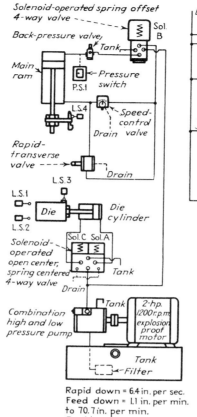

Rapid down = 6.4 in. per sec.
Feed down = 1.1 in. per min.
to 70.7 in. per min.
Rapid up = 8.1 in. per sec.

**Fig. 4**—Main ram of press is started downward by moving lever of valve *A* to position shown, causing pilot pressure to shift valve *C*. Cam 1 reverses valve *A*, thus retracting ram and opening sequence valve *D* to valve *E*, which causes lower ram to eject work from die until cam 2 reverses valve *B* and cam 3 reverses valve *F*. Valve *F*, reversed slightly before *B*, keeps vent line closed. Valve *B* removes pressure from valve *E*, which allows lower ram to retract until valve *F* is reversed by cam 4, thus opening vent line to tank.

Electrical Circuit

**FIG.5**

**Fig. 5**—Start button energizes solenoid *A*, causing die piston to close and contact switches P.S. 1 and 2. This energizes solenoid *B* through L.S. 3, which closed when cam moved with die, and causes main ram of press to move down on work until oil pressure opens P.S. 1, de-energizing solenoid *A* and energizing solenoid *C*. This causes die to retract, opening L.S. 3 and thus de-energizing solenoid *B*, which causes main ram to rise. Opening of L.S. 4 by ram de-energizes solenoid *C*, venting pump to the oil storage tank.

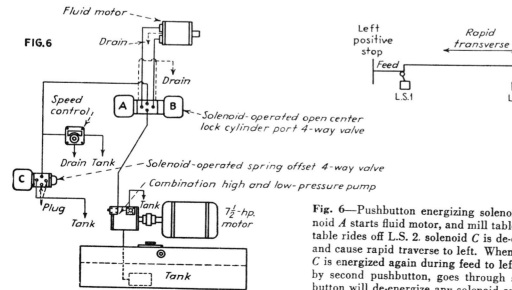

**Fig. 6**—Pushbutton energizing solenoid *B* and de-energizing solenoid *A* starts fluid motor, and mill table moves to left. When cam on table rides off L.S. 2. solenoid *C* is de-energized to close oil by-pass and cause rapid traverse to left. When L.S. 2 is contacted, solenoid *C* is energized again during feed to left stop. Return stroke, **started** by second pushbutton, goes through same cycle in reverse. Stop button will de-energize any solenoid and stop table in any position.

HYDRAULIC CIRCUITS are but combinations of pumps and valves designed to apply pressure at regulated intervals. There are countless possible combinations of pumps and valves for controlling such pressure to the operating cylinders.

Hydraulic transmissions in machine tools may include slides, clamps, interlock and safety devices, all properly timed with relation to each other.

The circuit also consists of combinations of stop valves, reversing valves, pilot valves for controlling larger valves such as the main reversing valve, throttling or dwell valves for slowing motion or delaying action, sequence valves to hold back certain motions until others are completed, and relief valves to maintain a uniform pressure in the system.

Where required oil pressure is not high, or where lightweight machine parts are to be accelerated and decelerated, constant-volume pumps such as gear and vane pumps are used.

The variable-volume system is used where there must be close control, where the pump delivers a variable and metered volume of oil, and where heavy machine parts and work are to be accelerated or decelerated without shock. It uses a plunger pump in which the length of stroke can be controlled.

Data and illustrations of hydraulically controlled machine tools supplied from Socony-Vacuum Oil Company publication "Hydraulic Systems."

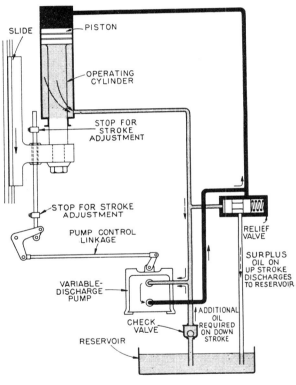

*Fig. 1—Circuit of a vertical broaching machine using a variable-volume pump. Difference between areas on top and bottom faces of piston gives slow down stroke and rapid return for a given pump discharge. Check valve allows additional oil required on the down stroke to be drawn from the reservoir. At the end of the down stroke, a slide engages an adjustable stop and controls the reversing valve in the pump. On up stroke, relief valve permits excess oil to enter reservoir.*

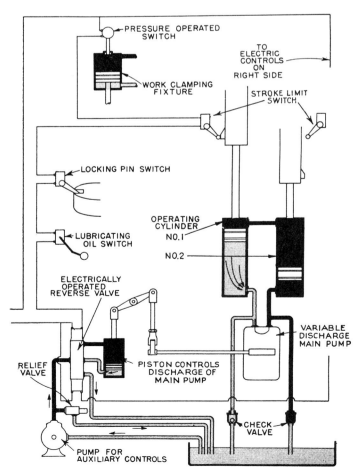

*Fig. 2—Variable-volume hydraulic system of a double broaching machine. Two interconnected operating cylinders can be supplied with oil in either direction. As No. 2 piston moves up, the oil moves to the top of No. 1, pushing No. 1 piston down, and expelling oil to the pump suction. If, due to leakage above pistons, the operating cylinders get out of step, there are valves and connections, not shown, for manually refilling upper ends of cylinders. Oil flow to main pump control is regulated by an electrically operated reversing valve the solenoid of which is in series with the lubricating oil switch, locking pin switch, stroke limit switch, and the pressure switch on the work clamping fixture.*

# HYDRAULIC TRANSMISSIONS

 OIL UNDER PRESSURE SHOWN

 OIL IN THE RETURN CIRCUIT

Fig. 3—Lock feed hydraulic system of a milling machine. Table travel speed is controlled by a variable discharge metering pump which removes measured amounts of oil from the front of the advancing piston. The positive flow of oil to and from the operating cylinder accurately controls working piston motion. When the reversing valve is thrown to the position shown by the dotted lines, the booster pump discharges entirely through the relief valve, and the gear pump supplies low-pressure oil for a quick return stroke.

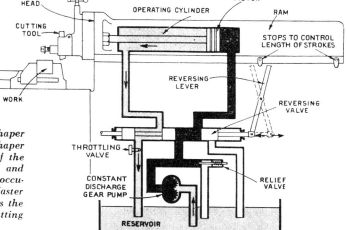

Fig. 4—Constant-volume hydraulic circuit for a shaper drive. Forward motion of the piston moves the shaper head forward for the cutting stroke. At the end of the working stroke, a stop throws the reversing valve and the shaper head starts on the return stroke. Space occupied by the piston rod makes the return stroke faster than the working stroke. The return stroke is always the same for a given pump discharge rate but the cutting stroke can be adjusted by the throttling valve.

Illustrations © Socony-Vacuum Oil Company

Fig. 5—Hydraulic system of a horizontal honing machine. When start and stop valve is in start position, oil is sent to either end of a reversing valve. Electrical contact points are set for the desired spindle head travel. A hydraulic motor, through gears and a cable, reciprocates the spindle head. Dwell valve between pilot and reversing valve, causes dwell at end of working stroke. A hydraulic indexing cylinder and ratchet mechanism advances spindle each time the hydraulic motor reverses for a working stroke.

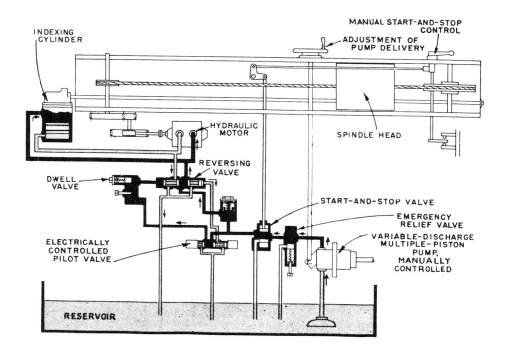

# PNEUMATIC CIRCUITS AND

PROPERLY controlled compressed air is a good medium for automatic and sequence operations where clean, dry, non-hazardous conditions must prevail. Processing, mixing, packaging, marking of foodstuffs, explosives, textiles, fragile materials, and other machine operations are being controlled quickly and efficiently by pneumatic cylinders. The accompanying diagrams illustrate various types of air controls on double-acting cylinders. The exhaust-type of control system requires no return piping. Master valves are mounted near cylinders and pilot valves are convenient for hand or foot operation at a distance. These and additional illustrations in subsequent issues will give an idea of the scope of applications. Air pressure, speed, duty cycle of operations and general conditions are factors capable of being varied to suit individual requirements. Layouts are typical of possible applications encountered by Ross Operating Valve Company. Advantages and limitations of pneumatic circuits were given in further detail on pages 255-7 and 318-21 June and July, 1940, and pages 174-7 March, 1944, PRODUCT ENGINEERING.

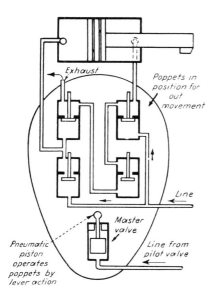

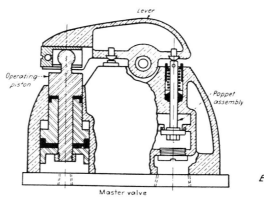

Fig. 1—Master valves MV consist of 4 poppet valves, which can all be closed or are opened by pairs for out and back strokes in cylinder, and a pneumatic piston for operating poppets by lever action. Some master valves are designed for manual and electrical operation.

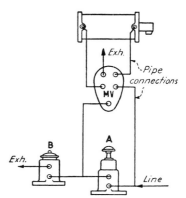

Fig. 2—Simplest piping layout for controlling out and back strokes of a pneumatic cylinder. Pilot valve A supplies air pressure to master valve operating piston, which opens air circuit for out stroke. Pilot valve B releases air in the operating piston, which opens the air circuit for return stroke. These two pilot valves may be combined in one three-way valve if desired. Convenience of valve locations is the determining consideration in valve selection.

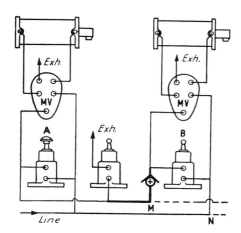

Fig. 3—Two pneumatic cylinders may be operated in various combinations of movements. Simultaneous strokes, either in the same or reverse directions, can be handled by one master valve. Independent operation requires two master valves. This circuit gives independent out strokes by means of pilot valves A and B, and simultaneous back strokes by pilot exhaust valve releasing air pressure in both master valve operating pistons. Valve B will also give simultaneous out strokes if A has not been operated.

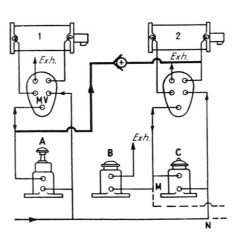

Fig. 4—Another combination of two pneumatic cylinders employs the same valves as in Fig. 3 with a slightly different piping layout as indicated by the heavy lines in each diagram. Valve A controls the out stroke of cylinder 1, valve B returns No. 1 and makes an out stroke in cylinder 2, and valve C returns No. 2 cylinder.

# TYPICAL APPLICATIONS

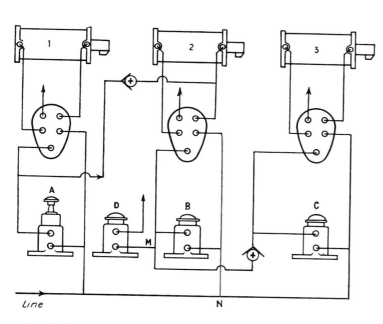

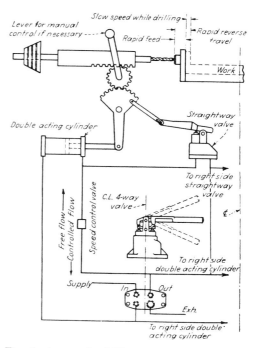

Fig. 5—Increase to three cylinders further increases possible combinations of operation. One or more units can be added to Fig. 3 layout merely by opening the line at points *M* and *N*. Fig. 5 duplicates Fig. 4 with an added unit and check valve connected at points *M* and *N*. In this layout *A* puts No. 1 out, *B* puts No. 1 back and No. 2 out, *C* puts No. 3 out, and *D* puts Nos. 2 and 3 back.

Fig. 6—Automatic drilling operation has three speeds: (1) Rapid feed of drills to points of contact with work; (2) slower speed during drilling as the result of straightway valves mechanically operated at the point of contact, which close bypasses around speed control valves; and (3) rapid reverse stroke. Right half is duplicate of left except for 4-way valve.

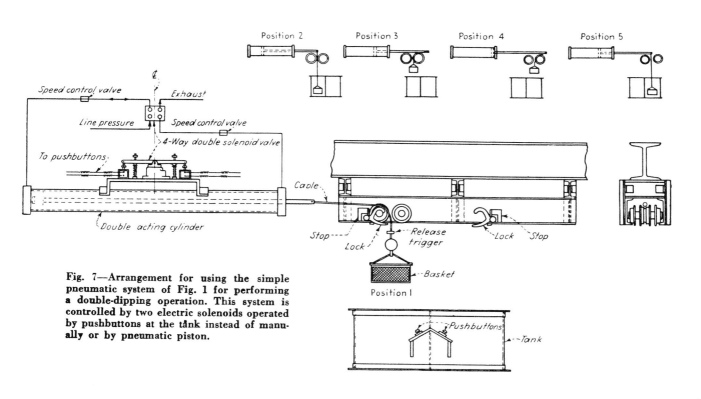

Fig. 7—Arrangement for using the simple pneumatic system of Fig. 1 for performing a double-dipping operation. This system is controlled by two electric solenoids operated by pushbuttons at the tank instead of manually or by pneumatic piston.

# Designs and Operating Principles of

### Types of pumps used to transfer liquids and to supply

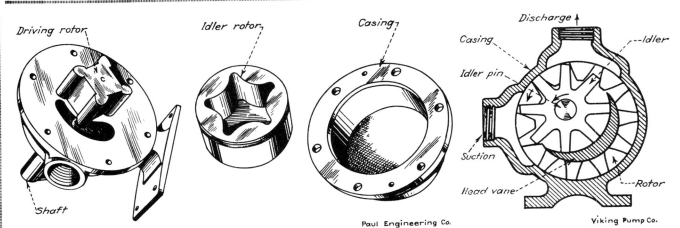

Paul Engineering Co.

Viking Pump Co.

**1** WITH BUT TWO MOVING PARTS, the rotors that turn in the same direction, the Sundberg Rotary Pump has reduced friction to a minimum. The rotors rotate against flexible synthetic rubber cushions that allow sand, grit and other abrasives to flow freely through the pump without damage. It is a positive displacement pump that develops a constant pressure and will deliver a uniform flow at any given speed. The pump is reversible and can be driven by a gasoline engine or electric motor. The rubber cushions withstand the action of oil, kerosene and gasoline and the pump operates at any angle. It has been used in circulating water systems, cutting tool coolant oil systems and general service applications.

**2** PUMPING ACTION is produced by the meshing of the idler and rotor teeth in the Viking Rotary Pump. Idler is pin-mounted to the head. Rotor operates in either direction. Pump will not splash, foam, churn or cause pounding. Liquids of any viscosity, which do not contain grit, can be transferred by this pump made of combinations of iron and bronze parts.

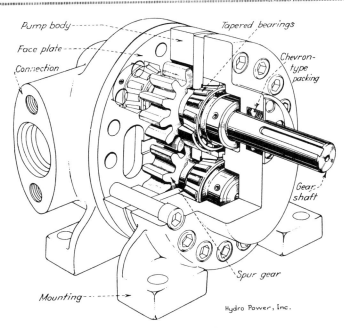

Hydro Power, Inc.

**5** THE GEAR SHAFTS of this hydraulic gear pump are mounted on tapered roller bearings that accurately position the gears, decrease end play and reduce wear to a minimum. The heavy duty construction of the Hydro-Power Gear Pump is designed for use with pressures up to 1,000 psi. These pumps are available with either single or double end shaft design and can be foot or flange mounted. The drive shaft entrance packing is constructed of oil resistant material. Gear shafts are made of hardened molybdenum steel.

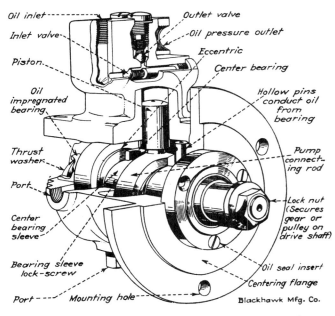

Blackhawk Mfg. Co.

**6** THIS HIGH PRESSURE hydraulic pump has twin pistons that build pressures from 100 to 4,000 psi at speeds from 600 to 1,200 rev per minute. The Blackhawk P-104 can be used continuously at 900 rpm and 2,500 psi with 1.37 gpm delivered. Because it can be mounted at any angle, and because it is used with small oil lines, small diameter rams and compact valves, the P-104 is practical for building into new equipment. This pump contains a pressure adjusting valve that is factory set to by-pass at a predetermined pressure.

# Typical Pumps Used in Industry—I

hydraulic power, with a discussion of design features and uses.

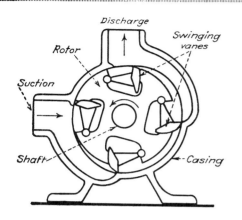

Blackmer Pump Co.

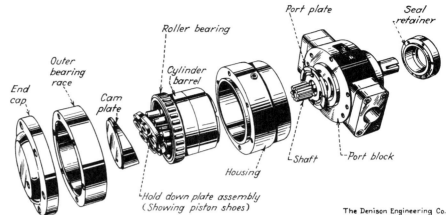

The Denison Engineering Co.

**3** BASED on the swinging vane principle, the Blackmer Rotary Pump maintains its volumetric efficiency automatically. The action of the buckets, fitted loosely into recesses in the rotor, compensates for wear. In operation, the tip of the bucket is in light contact with the casing wall. Liquids are moved by sucking and pushing actions and are not churned or foamed.

**4** HIGH PRESSURE, high volume pumps of the axial piston, constant displacement type are rated at 3,500 psi for continuous duty operation; higher pressure is permissible for intermittent operation. A pressure-balanced piston shoe lubricates the cam plate and prevents direct contact between the shoe and cam plate. The use of the pressure balanced system removes the need for thrust bearings. The two-piece shaft absorbs deflection and minimizes bearing wear. The pump and electric driving motor are connected by a flexible coupling. The revolving cylinder barrel causes the axial reciprocation of the pumping pistons. The Denison 3500 Series pumps are only used to pump hydraulic fluids.

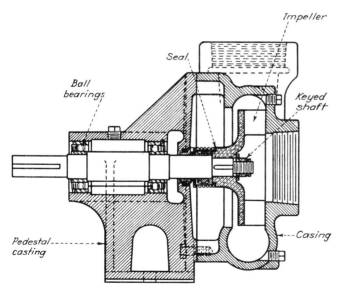

Allis-Chalmers Mfg. Co.

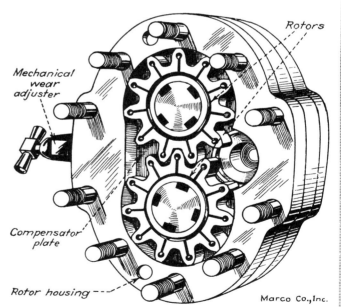

Marco Co., Inc.

**7** AS ITS NAME IMPLIES, the Pedrifugal pump is characterized by its pedestal mounting. The only fit, not a critical one, is between the pedestal casting and the casing. Positive alignment is obtained because the sealed ball bearings and the shaft are supported in the single casting. The 5-vaned, open, bronze impeller will move liquids with a considerable volume of solids. The pump is not for use with corrosive liquids. The five sizes of this pump, up to 500 gpm, are identical except for the impeller and the casing.

**8** USED TO TRANSFER, meter or proportion liquids of high or low viscosity, the Flowmaster Victor is a positive displacement gear pump. It is made of stainless metal or stainless steel with a stainless steel armored, automatic take-up, shaft seal of the single-gland type. Automatic wear control compensates for normal wear and maintains volumetric efficiency. The Victor will handle 5 to 300 gal per hour without churning or foaming. This pump needs no lubrication and operates against high or low pressure.

225

# Designs and Operating Principles of

The field of pump design is being bettered and broadened by the use

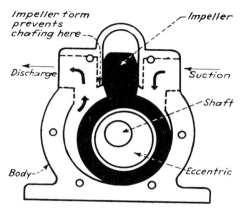

Eco Engineering Co.

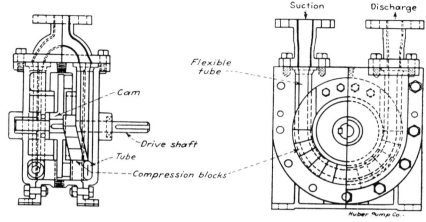

Huber Pump Co.

**9** ORIGINALLY DESIGNED for water use in the marine field, this gearless pump is now available in stainless steel, monel and bronze for handling acids, oils and solvents. The impeller is made of pressure-vulcanized laminated layers of Hycar, 85 to 90 percent hard. Sand, grit, scale and fibrous materials will pass through. With capacities from 1 to 12 gpm and speeds from 200 to 3,500 rpm, pumps will deliver against pressures up to 60 psi. Not self-priming, it can be installed with a reservoir. Operates in either direction and is self-lubricating. Wearing parts replaceable.

**10** THE SQUEEGEE PUMP consists of a U-shaped flexible tube made of rubber or other flexible material. Acids and corrosive liquids or gases pass through the tube and do not contact working parts or lubricating oil. This prevents contamination of the liquid and avoids corrosion of metal parts. In operation, the tube is compressed progressively from the intake side to the discharge side by cams mounted on a driven shaft. Compression blocks move against the tube, closing the tube gradually and firmly from block to block, which forces the liquid out. As the cam passes the compression blocks, the tube returns to its original diameter. This creates a high vacuum on the intake side and causes the tube to be filled rapidly. The pump can be driven clockwise or counter-clockwise. The tube is completely incased and cannot expand beyond its original diameter. The standard pump is made of bronze and will handle volumes to 15 gpm. The Squeegee develops a vacuum of 25 in. of mercury and will work against pressures of 50 lb per sq inch.

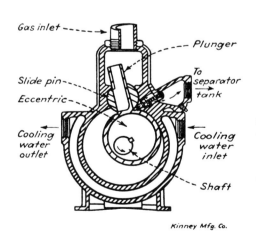

Kinney Mfg. Co.

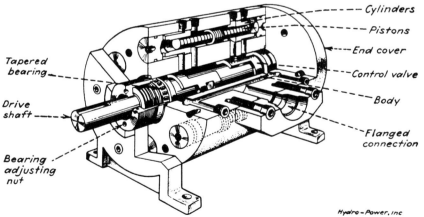

Hydro-Power, Inc.

**13** HIGH VACUUM PUMPS operate with rotating plunger action of liquid pumps. Sealing oil lubricates the three moving parts. Parts are accessible without disturbing piping. They are used to rough out system before connecting diffusion pump; to evacuate light bulbs and electronic tubes, and to vacuum dry and distill. Single pumps draw vacuum from 2 to 5 microns; in series to 0.5 micron, and compound pumps draw to 0.1 micron. Pumps can be run in reverse for transferring liquids. Diagonal cored slots, closed by slide pin, form passageway and inlet valve. Poppet or feather outlet valves are used.

**14** A COMPACT MULTI-PLUNGER INTENSIFIER, this hydraulic booster is designed to convert low pressure to high pressure in any oil-hydraulic circuit. No additional pumps are required. Because of the six plungers, the pressure flow from the booster is both smooth and uninterrupted. Many savings in cost are claimed for this booster: First costs are low since high pressure pumps are not required; no operating valves are needed to control the high pressure system, and small cylinder and ram assemblies can be used on operating equipment because the pressure is high. Operating costs can also be low because of efficient use of connected horsepower. The inertia effects of the small operating rams are low so high speed operations can be attained. Hydro-power boosters are built in two standard sizes, each of which is available in two pressure ranges: 2 to 1 and 3 to 1. Volumetric output is in inverse proportion to the pressure ratio. All units have a maximum 7,500 psi discharge pressure. Pistons are double-acting and the central valve admits oil to pistons in sequence and is always hydraulically balanced. Drive shaft integral with valve.

# Typical Pumps Used in Industry—II

of new ideas and the application of new materials.

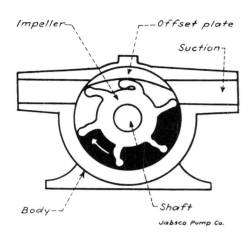

Impeller — Offset plate — Suction — Body — Shaft

Jabsco Pump Co.

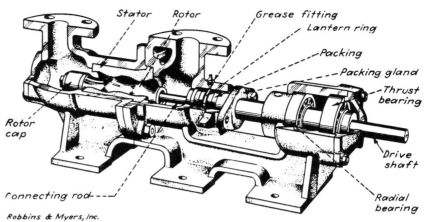

Stator — Rotor — Grease fitting — Lantern ring — Packing — Packing gland — Thrust bearing — Rotor cap — Connecting rod — Drive shaft — Radial bearing

Robbins & Myers, Inc.

**11** DEFLECTED BLADES of flexible neoprene impeller straighten as they leave contact with offset plate. High suction created draws fluid into pump, filling space between blades. Handles animal, vegetable and mineral oils but not napthas, gasoline, ordinary cleaning solvents or paint thinners. Pump operates in either direction and can be mounted at any angle. Pumps run at 100 to 2,000 rpm, can deliver up to 55 gpm, and will operate against 25 psi. Operates at temperatures between 0 and 160 F. Replaceable impeller floats on splined shaft and is not restrained.

**12** FOR PUMPING ALMOST ANYTHING from free-flowing liquids to non-pourable pastes, clean or contaminated with abrasives, chemically inert or active, homogeneous or containing solids in suspension, the Moyno is a positive displacement pump that delivers continuous, uniform flow. The one moving part, the low alloy or tool steel rotor, is a single helix and the Hycar or natural rubber stator is a double internal helix. Pumping action is similar to that of a piston moving through a cylinder of infinite length. Containing no valves, this pump will self-prime at 28 ft suction lift. Head developed is independent of speed; capacity is proportional to speed. Slippage is a function of viscosity and pressure and is predictable for any operating condition. The Moyno passes particles up to $\frac{7}{8}$ in. diameter through its largest pump. Pumping action can be in either direction. Largest standard pump, with two continuous seal lines, handles 150 gpm up to 200 psi; multi-stage pumps can pump against higher pressures because there are more seal lines.

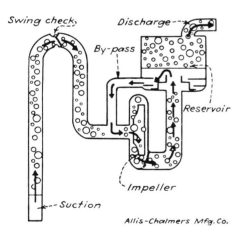

Swing check — Discharge — By-pass — Reservoir — Impeller — Suction

Allis-Chalmers Mfg. Co.

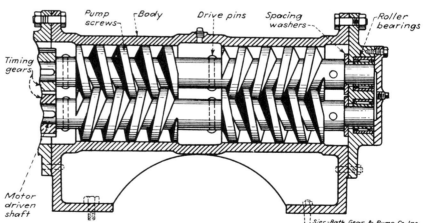

Pump screws — Body — Drive pins — Spacing washers — Roller bearings — Timing gears — Motor driven shaft

Sier-Bath Gear & Pump Co., Inc.

**15** SELF-PRIMING PUMP that gives rapid and smooth transition from priming cycle to centrifugal pumping. Pump starts with priming chamber full. Liquid is recirculated through impeller until pump is primed. As priming liquid circulates, air is drawn through impeller and expelled through discharge. When all air is evacuated, discharge velocity closes priming valve completely. Pumps can be supplied with open or closed impellers. Solids up to 1 in. can be passed through 3 in. size pump with open impeller. Self-priming pumps are equipped with a mechanical shaft seal, factory installed and tested.

**16** INTERNAL SCREW PUMPS are very successful for transferring high viscosity petroleum products. They can be used as boiler fuel pumps since they deliver a pulseless flow of oil. For marine or stationary systems, the characteristic low vibration of screw pumps has allowed them to be mounted on light foundations. The absence of vibration and pulsing flow reduces strain on pipes, hose and fittings. The pumping screws are mounted on shafts and take in liquid at both ends of the pump body and move the liquid to the center for discharge. This balanced pumping action makes it unnecessary to use thrust bearings except in installations where the pump is mounted at a high angle. The pumps can be used at any angle up to vertical. Where thrust bearings are needed, anti-friction bearings capable of supporting the load of shaft and screws are used. The intermeshing pumping screws are timed through a pair of precision-cut herringbone gears, which are self-centering, and do not allow side wear of screws while pumping. Pump is designed to give best efficiency under 1,200 rpm for electric motor and 1,300 rpm for steam turbine drives.

# FORMS OF PUMPS USED

Many types of pumps are available for delivering hydraulic power for control circuits. They fall into two groupings, constant discharge, without change of speed, and variable discharge pumps. Gear pumps and most vane pumps come within the first group. Data and illustrations supplied from Socony-Vacuum Oil Company publication "Hydraulic Systems."

Fig. 1—Northern Internal Gear Pump. A driving pinion meshes with and rotates a larger internal gear that fits snugly in the pump housing. The space unswept by the moving teeth is filled by a stationary crescent which is part of the housing. Oilways from the inner to outer periphery of the internal gear exist between each pair of teeth. Oil is carried through the pump by the pockets between the teeth of both gears. Oilways at the bases of internal gear teeth are sealed by the outer casing, and the tops of the teeth are sealed by the crescent.

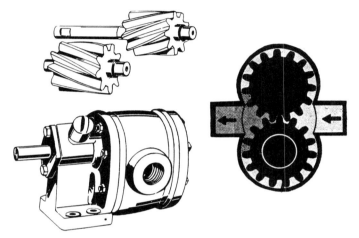

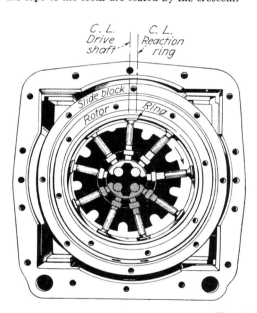

Fig. 2—Constant-Discharge Gear Pump. This type normally operates at a maximum pressure of a few hundred lb. per sq. in., but is sometimes designed for higher pressures. As gears revolve, oil is trapped in pockets formed between the pump case and teeth of the gears. Oil travels from the suction side of the pump, around the teeth of both gears to the discharge side. Meshing of the teeth prevents return of oil to the suction side. The pump shown has helical gears, but it can also have spur, herringbone or special form gears.

Fig. 3—Oilgear Radial-Piston Pump. This pump is designed for several thousand lb. per sq. in. Hub and ring revolve and a mushroom head on the end of each piston makes the driving connection with the ring. More than one set of cylinders may be located side by side in the same hub to give increased capacity and flexibility.

Fig. 4—Northern Radial-Piston Pump. Pistons of this pump are moved in and out of the cylinders by rollers which make contact with the outer ring.

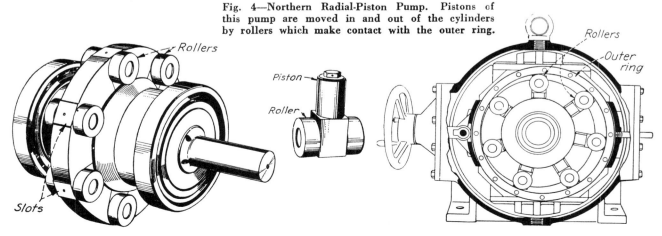

# IN HYDRAULIC CIRCUITS

OIL UNDER PRESSURE SHOWN

OIL IN THE RETURN CIRCUIT

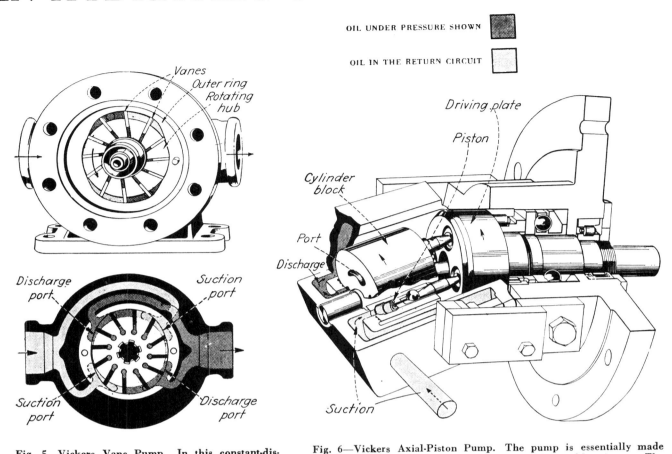

Fig. 5—Vickers Vane Pump. In this constant-discharge pump, pumping is produced by radial vanes which are free to slide in and out of a rotating hub thereby maintaining contact with the outer ring. That this contact will be maintained at all times, there are oilways from the high pressure side of the pump to the spaces behind the vanes. Suction ports are located where the housing recedes from the rotating hub; discharge ports where the housing again approaches the hub. The rotor is hydraulically balanced by double sets of ports diametrically opposite to each other. Because of close tolerances between vanes, hubs and case, high pressures can be developed by this constant-discharge pump.

Fig. 6—Vickers Axial-Piston Pump. The pump is essentially made up of a driving plate, a cylinder block, and suitable pistons. The pistons are actuated by the driving plate through connecting rods. Variable discharge from this type pump is obtained by adjusting the angularity between the driving plate and the cylinder block so that the length of strokes of the piston can be varied.

Fig. 7—Gerotor Pump. In this special form of internal gear pump, an inner gear rotates with the driving shaft. An outer gear, driven by the inner gear, is free to rotate with a snug fit in a recess in one end of the housing. Teeth of the two gears are shaped to be in sliding contact with each other. When gears are enclosed by the housing, oil tight pockets are formed between the teeth of the gears. Because of the off-center location of the gears, the volume of these oil pockets changes from zero to maximum and again to zero during each revolution. Oil is drawn into the pockets from the suction port, during one-half of each gear revolution. During the other half of the revolution, oil is forced out through the discharge port.

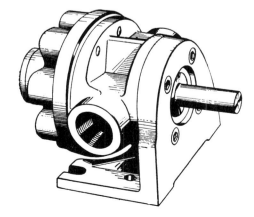

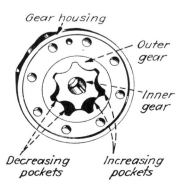

# *Applications of Electrically*

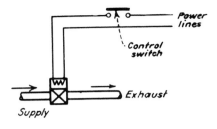

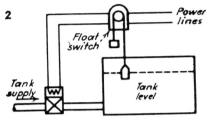

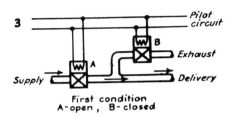

First condition
A-open, B-closed

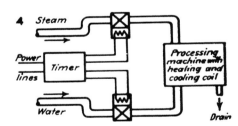

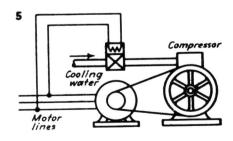

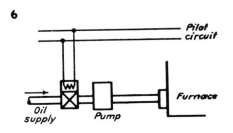

Solenoid valves can be used in many different ways, this presentation being limited to a selected group of typical applications of the several different types of the valves. This is therefore not intended as a comprehensive list but rather as a digest of the more generally applicable methods of employing such devices, with the purpose of suggesting the numerous other ways in which it is possible to use electrically operated valves for both machine-control and industrial applications

Fig. 1—Straight-way solenoid valve as commonly connected for simple fluid control. Control switch energizes solenoid, opening valve and permitting flow to begin.

Fig. 2—Straight-way valve applied to automatically control liquid level. Float switch used as pilot control device for valve.

Fig. 3—Two straight-way valves, *A* normally open and *B* normally closed, provide two-way fluid control. Energizing solenoids cuts off supply and vents delivery through exhaust.

Fig. 4—Two straight-way valves offer means of automatically controlling cycle of processing machine, such as plastic molding press, having heating and cooling coils.

Fig. 5—Single straight-way valve can be connected across one phase of motor winding to start flow of cooling water to compressor whenever motor starts.

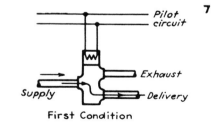

First Condition

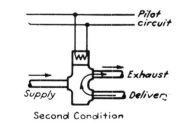

Second Condition

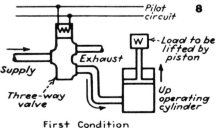

First Condition

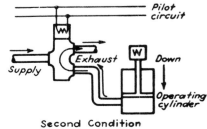

Second Condition

# Operated Valves

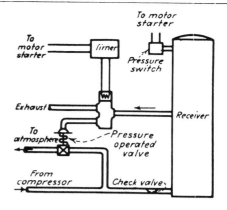

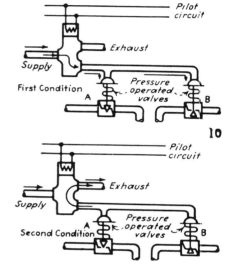

Fig. 6—Straight-way valve of trip type interlocked with oil-furnace control system to cut off oil supply upon loss of current to motor-driven pump or to atomizing equipment and upon occurrence of low water, low stack temperature, or similar conditions.

Fig. 7—Single three-way solenoid valve cuts off supply and vents delivery through exhaust. Application similar to that, shown in Fig. 3, using two straight-way valves.

Fig. 8—Three-way valve provides convenient means of controlling single-acting cylinders or diaphragms. Utilizing principle shown in Fig. 7, valve cuts off supply and vents delivery through exhaust, thus permitting return stroke of piston to take place.

Fig. 9—Three-way valve, used in manner similar to that shown in Fig. 8, unloads compressor until motor has time to come up to speed.

Fig. 10—Three-way valve arranged for multiple control of pressure-operated valves. In the first condition, Valve *A* is closed and Valve *B* open. In the second condition, the reverse is true, with Valve *A* open and Valve *B* closed.

Fig. 11—Three-way valve applied as convenient means of transferring one supply to either of two deliveries.

Fig. 12—Three-way valve, utilizing inversion of principle shown in Fig. 11, offers means of transferring either of two supplies to a common delivery. Useful in applications where an emergency supply is provided.

Fig. 13—Four-way valve arranged to control double-acting cylinder. Upon energization of solenoid, operating rod of cylinder reverses direction.

Fig. 14—Four-way valve arrangement, employing principle shown in Fig. 13, provides automatic control of tank level through pressure-operated valve.

*Courtesy General Electric Co.*

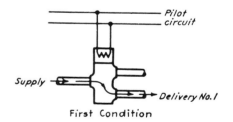

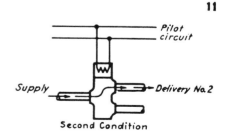

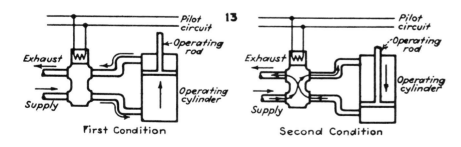

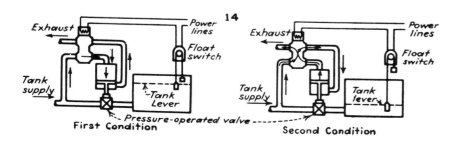

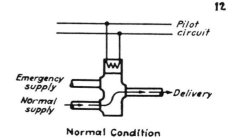

# AUTOMATIC CONTROLLING MECHANISMS

Automatic valve operators, designed to control valves remotely and automatically, generally depend upon electricity or fluid pressure for their actuation. The valves themselves may be of either the single or double-seat type depending upon conditions of line-pressure fluctuation, pressure drop and duration of shut-off periods. Some of the operators utilizing pressure and electricity for actuation are described and illustrated below.

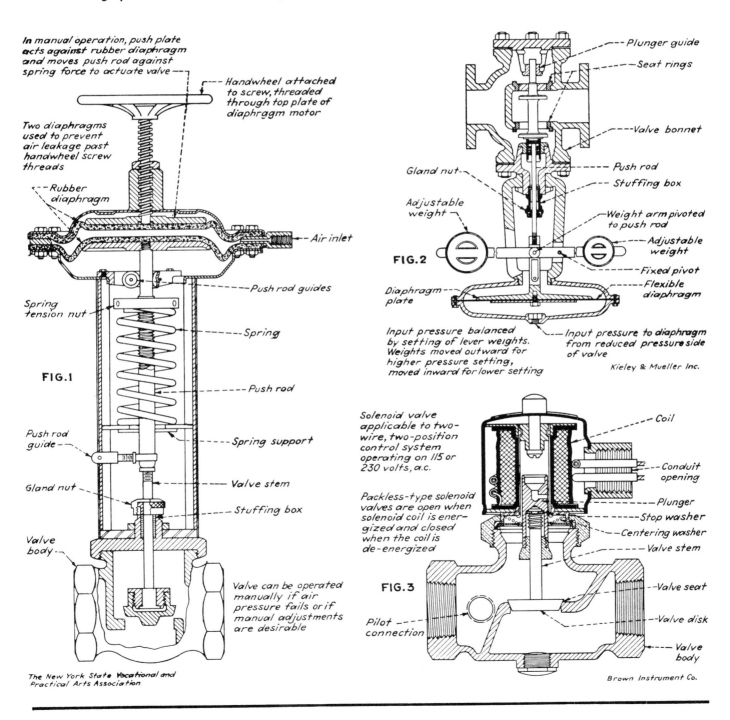

In manual operation, push plate acts against rubber diaphragm and moves push rod against spring force to actuate valve

Handwheel attached to screw, threaded through top plate of diaphragm motor

Two diaphragms used to prevent air leakage past handwheel screw threads

Rubber diaphragm

Air inlet

Push rod guides

Spring tension nut

Spring

FIG. 1

Push rod

Push rod guide

Spring support

Gland nut

Valve stem

Stuffing box

Valve body

Valve can be operated manually if air pressure fails or if manual adjustments are desirable

The New York State Vocational and Practical Arts Association

Plunger guide

Seat rings

Valve bonnet

Gland nut

Push rod

Adjustable weight

Stuffing box

Weight arm pivoted to push rod

FIG. 2

Adjustable weight

Fixed pivot

Flexible diaphragm

Diaphragm plate

Input pressure balanced by setting of lever weights. Weights moved outward for higher pressure setting, moved inward for lower setting

Input pressure to diaphragm from reduced pressure side of valve

Kieley & Mueller Inc.

Solenoid valve applicable to two-wire, two-position control system operating on 115 or 230 volts, a.c.

Packless-type solenoid valves are open when solenoid coil is energized and closed when the coil is de-energized

Coil

Conduit opening

Plunger

Stop washer

Centering washer

Valve stem

FIG. 3

Valve seat

Valve disk

Pilot connection

Valve body

Brown Instrument Co.

# FOR VALVE OPERATION—I

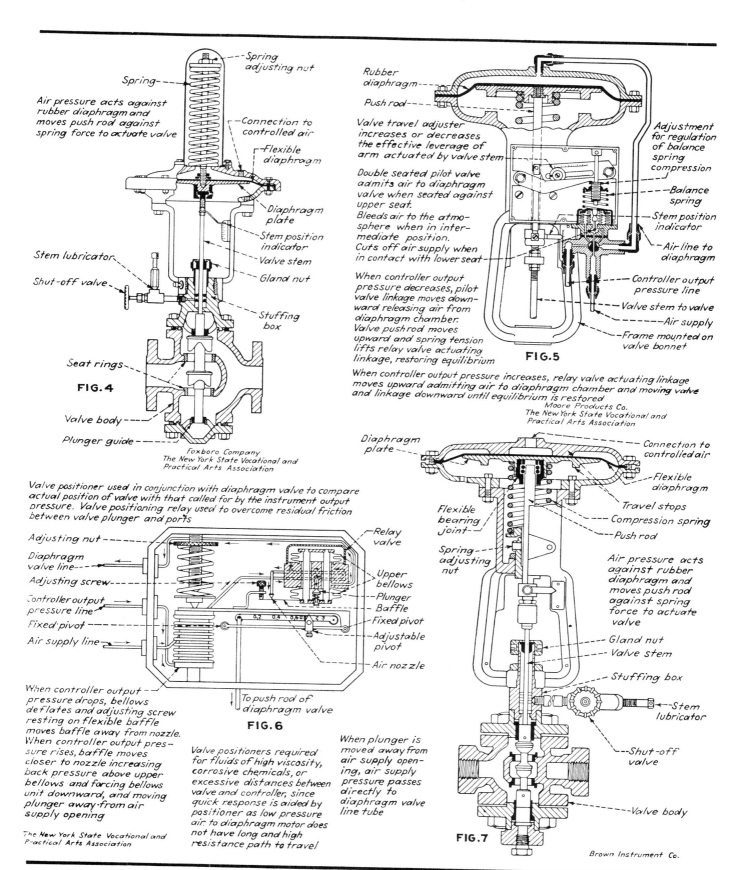

Air pressure acts against rubber diaphragm and moves push rod against spring force to actuate valve

Spring —

Spring adjusting nut

Connection to controlled air

Flexible diaphragm

Diaphragm plate

Stem position indicator

Valve stem

Gland nut

Stuffing box

Stem lubricator

Shut-off valve

Seat rings

**FIG. 4**

Valve body

Plunger guide

Foxboro Company
The New York State Vocational and
Practical Arts Association

Rubber diaphragm

Push rod

Valve travel adjuster increases or decreases the effective leverage of arm actuated by valve stem

Double seated pilot valve admits air to diaphragm valve when seated against upper seat.
Bleeds air to the atmosphere when in intermediate position.
Cuts off air supply when in contact with lower seat

When controller output pressure decreases, pilot valve linkage moves downward releasing air from diaphragm chamber. Valve pushrod moves upward and spring tension lifts relay valve actuating linkage, restoring equilibrium

Adjustment for regulation of balance spring compression

Balance spring

Stem position indicator

Air line to diaphragm

Controller output pressure line

Valve stem to valve

Air supply

Frame mounted on valve bonnet

**FIG. 5**

When controller output pressure increases, relay valve actuating linkage moves upward admitting air to diaphragm chamber and moving valve and linkage downward until equilibrium is restored

Moore Products Co.
The New York State Vocational and
Practical Arts Association

Valve positioner used in conjunction with diaphragm valve to compare actual position of valve with that called for by the instrument output pressure. Valve positioning relay used to overcome residual friction between valve plunger and ports

Adjusting nut

Diaphragm valve line

Adjusting screw

Controller output pressure line

Fixed pivot

Air supply line

Relay valve

Upper bellows

Plunger

Baffle

Fixed pivot

Adjustable pivot

Air nozzle

0.2  0.4  0.60  0.8  2  3

To push rod of diaphragm valve

**FIG. 6**

When controller output pressure drops, bellows deflates and adjusting screw resting on flexible baffle moves baffle away from nozzle. When controller output pressure rises, baffle moves closer to nozzle increasing back pressure above upper bellows and forcing bellows unit downward, and moving plunger away from air supply opening

The New York State Vocational and
Practical Arts Association

Valve positioners required for fluids of high viscosity, corrosive chemicals, or excessive distances between valve and controller, since quick response is aided by positioner as low pressure air to diaphragm motor does not have long and high resistance path to travel

When plunger is moved away from air supply opening, air supply pressure passes directly to diaphragm valve line tube

Diaphragm plate

Connection to controlled air

Flexible diaphragm

Travel stops

Compression spring

Push rod

Flexible bearing joint

Spring adjusting nut

Air pressure acts against rubber diaphragm and moves push rod against spring force to actuate valve

Gland nut

Valve stem

Stuffing box

Stem lubricator

Shut-off valve

Valve body

**FIG. 7**

Brown Instrument Co.

233

# AUTOMATIC CONTROLLING MECHANISMS

In addition to the pressure-operated valve controllers presented in the June issue, other types, utilizing electricity for their actuation are available. These may be used to control valves individually or in gangs, and provisions for manual control are often included. Some of these are described and illustrated below.

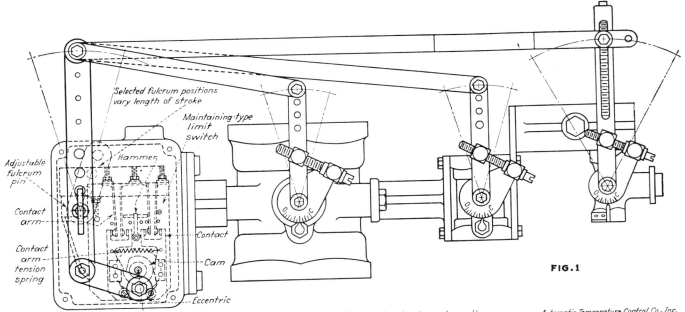

Selected fulcrum positions vary length of stroke

Maintaining-type limit switch

Adjustable fulcrum pin

Hammer

Contact arm

Contact

Contact arm tension spring

Cam

Eccentric

Input from uni-directional motor and reduction gearing to give reciprocating controlled movement to valve assembly by use of eccentric

FIG.1

Automatic Temperature Control Co., Inc.

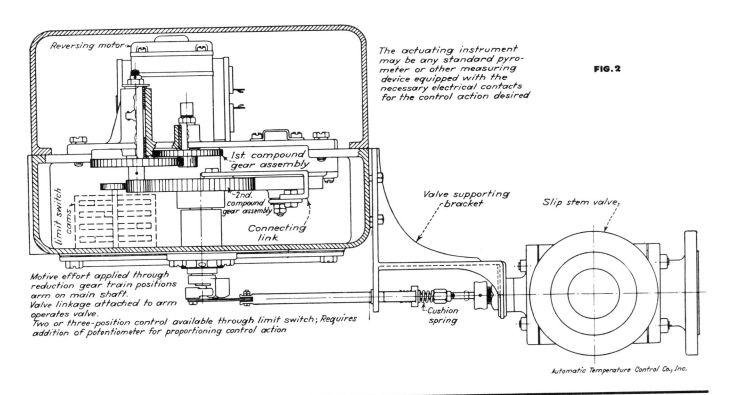

Reversing motor

The actuating instrument may be any standard pyrometer or other measuring device equipped with the necessary electrical contacts for the control action desired

FIG.2

1st compound gear assembly

2nd. compound gear assembly

Limit switch cams

Connecting link

Valve supporting bracket

Slip stem valve

Motive effort applied through reduction gear train positions arm on main shaft.
Valve linkage attached to arm operates valve.
Two or three-position control available through limit switch; Requires addition of potentiometer for proportioning control action

Cushion spring

Automatic Temperature Control Co., Inc.

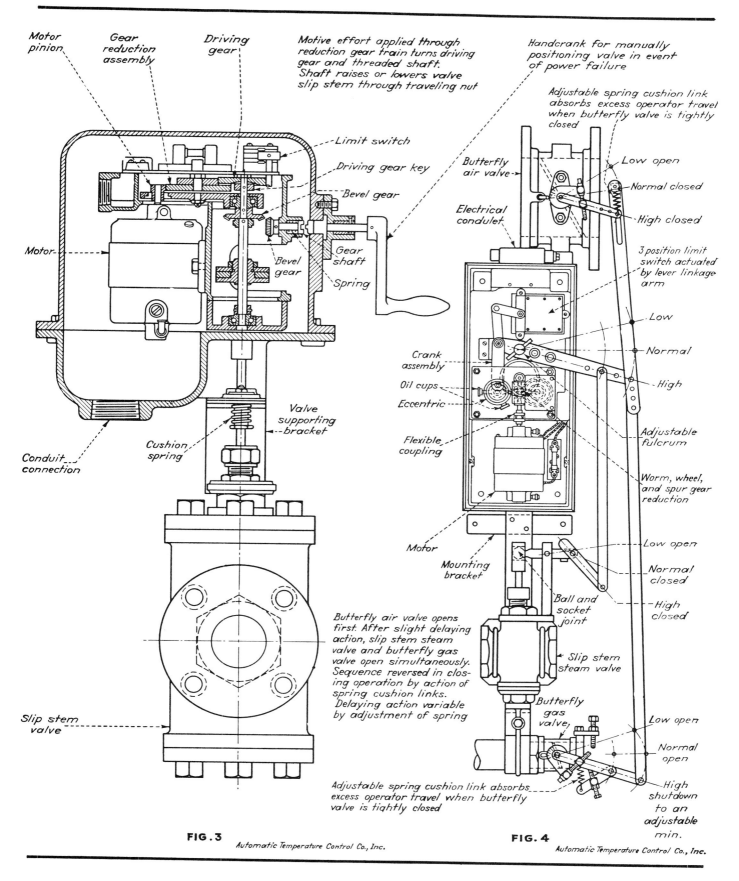

Motor pinion

Gear reduction assembly

Driving gear

Motive effort applied through reduction gear train turns driving gear and threaded shaft. Shaft raises or lowers valve slip stem through traveling nut

Handcrank for manually positioning valve in event of power failure

Adjustable spring cushion link absorbs excess operator travel when butterfly valve is tightly closed

Limit switch

Driving gear key

Bevel gear

Butterfly air valve

Low open

Normal closed

High closed

Motor

Bevel gear

Gear shaft

Spring

Electrical condulet

3 position limit switch actuated by lever linkage arm

Low

Normal

High

Crank assembly

Oil cups

Eccentric

Flexible coupling

Adjustable fulcrum

Valve supporting bracket

Cushion spring

Worm, wheel, and spur gear reduction

Conduit connection

Low open

Normal closed

High closed

Motor

Mounting bracket

Ball and socket joint

Slip stem steam valve

Butterfly air valve opens first. After slight delaying action, slip stem steam valve and butterfly gas valve open simultaneously. Sequence reversed in closing operation by action of spring cushion links. Delaying action variable by adjustment of spring

Butterfly gas valve

Low open

Normal open

High shutdown to an adjustable min.

Slip stem valve

Adjustable spring cushion link absorbs excess operator travel when butterfly valve is tightly closed

FIG. 3

Automatic Temperature Control Co., Inc.

FIG. 4

Automatic Temperature Control Co., Inc.

# Ways to make a

Low seat forces can keep a tight seal—
even for metal-to-metal seatings.

*DOMINIC J LAPERA, design engineer, Marotta Valve Corp, Boonton, NJ*

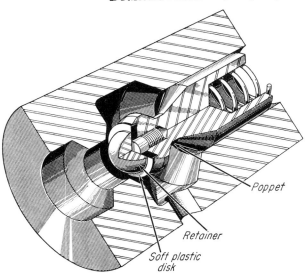

Poppet

Retainer

Soft plastic disk

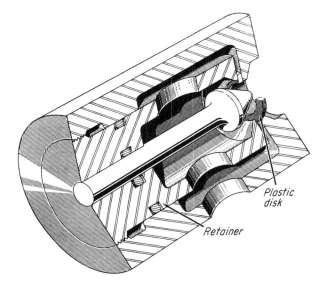

Plastic disk

Retainer

**CAPTIVE DISK** keeps bubble-tight seal when spring pushes it against conical seat in valve body. This, the most common design, is often found in checkvalves. It gives reliable service.

**CONICAL STEM** bears against sharp corner of soft plastic disk. Concentric retainer, which screws into the valve body, holds disk in place which is located by recess in body.

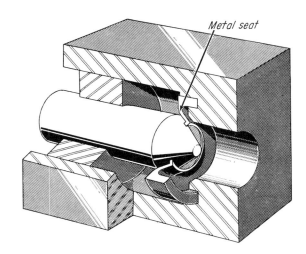

Metal seat

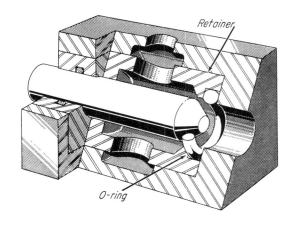

Retainer

O-ring

**FLEXIBLE METAL SEAT** can stand higher temperatures than plastic, but because flexing takes up some irregularities, it doesn't require the high seat loads normal with metal-to-metal valves.

**O-RING SEAT** will open at same pressure as consistently as much more expensive valves. However, cracking pressure must be quite high when compared to pressure at the normally rated flow.

# poppet valve

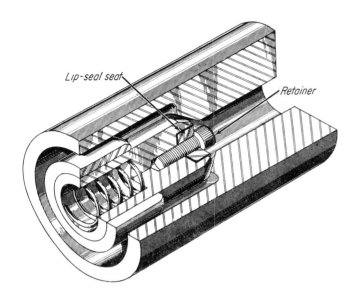

Lip-seal seat

Retainer

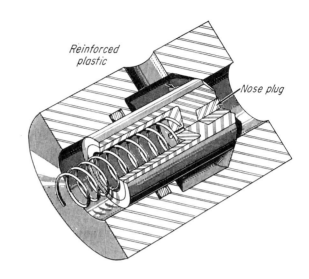

Reinforced plastic

Nose plug

 **LIP-SEAL SEAT** requires smallest force to be bubble-tight. Large forces flatten lip, so design works best when differential across seat is low. Example is a relief valve where fluid pressure opposes spring force.

**PLASTIC POPPET** cannot stand shock loading. Accurate machining for a good seal is easy because poppet guide and seat are in the same piece. Best angle between cone and seat is 20 to 30°.

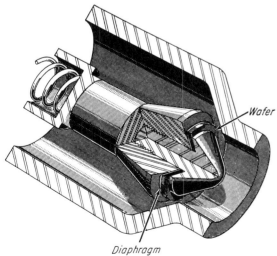

Wafer

Diaphragm

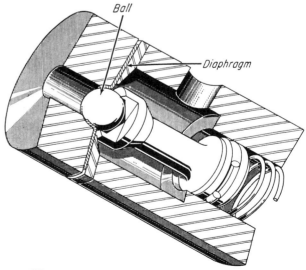

Ball

Diaphragm

 **METAL DIAPHRAGM** backs up seat wafer and presses it to contour of the cone. This compensates for irregularities common on large valves. Wafer must be thin enough not to wrinkle when deformed.

 **BALL** forces plastic diaphragm against spherical seat. Vent will keep pressure from building up behind the ball which is not a force-fit in socket. Spring strength determines cracking pressure.

237

# TYPES OF VALVES USED IN

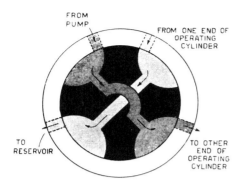

Valves are the nerve center of hydraulic circuits. In machine tools, they provide reversal of motion, dwell and throttling action, sequence control, and relief of oil pressure. Some of the common forms of these valves are illustrated. Data and illustrations supplied from Socony-Vacuum Oil Company publication "Hydraulic Systems."

*Fig. 1—Schematic diagram of rotary reversing valve. Oilways in an oscillating cylindrical plug register with ports which connect both the main oil line from the pump and the discharge line to the reservoir with either end of the operating cylinder. When oil is directed from the pump to one end of the operating cylinder, oil in the other end of the cylinder is discharged through the reversing valve to the reservoir. One position of the reversing valve shown.*

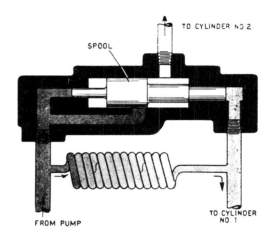

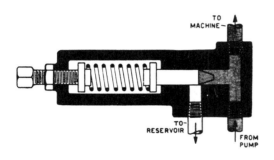

*Fig. 3 — Spring-loaded relief valve. This valve is placed in the pump discharge line to permit oil to escape from the line to the reservoir when the amount of oil delivered by a constant-discharge pump is more than is needed. High pressure overcomes the compression of the spring, lifts the valve from its seat, and by-passes the oil until the pressure drops below the compression adjustment of the spring.*

*Fig. 2—Sequence control valve. Some machines are designed so that one series of motions must be completed before another series can start. This type valve prevents the flow of oil to No. 2 operating cylinder until the motion in No. 1 cylinder has been completed. Both ends of the freely floating spool are under oil pressure. The end exposed to pump pressure is smaller than the end exposed to pressure from No. 1 cylinder. From the pump, oil flows through a coil of tubing which slightly restricts the oil flow.*

*Pressure in No. 1 cylinder and on No. 1 end of the valve spool is less than the pump pressure, and this difference on the ends of the valve shifts the spool towards the low pressure side. Flow of oil to No. 2 cylinder is prevented. When motion in No. 1 cylinder is completed, oil no longer flows through the coil. Pressure on both sides of the valve is equalized. Full pump pressure now acts on the large end of the spool, and the spool shifts to admit oil to No. 2 cylinder.*

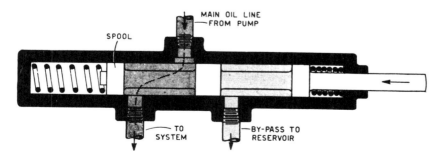

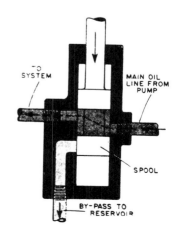

*Fig. 4—Stop valves usually placed in the main oil line from the pump are operated manually or by cams. They are designed to stop the machine at a predetermined point. When the spool is shifted to a stop position, the flow of oil is interrupted and machine motion halted. While the machine is idling, the oil is by-passed at low pressure to the reservoir thereby reducing power costs. The machine is restarted either manually by the operator, or by cams which move the valve to a new position.*

# HYDRAULIC TRANSMISSIONS

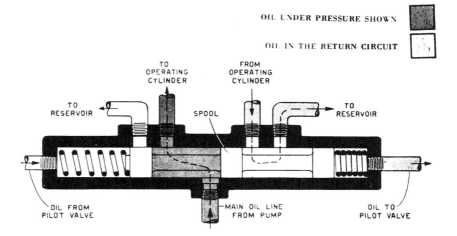

OIL UNDER PRESSURE SHOWN

OIL IN THE RETURN CIRCUIT

*Fig. 5—Reversing valve. This valve directs oil flow in and out of either end of an operating cylinder. A separate pilot valve, Fig. 6, controls the oil pressure. The reversing-valve spool maintains a central position and floats between two springs. Pilot valve action moves the spool. When the spool is at one end of the valve, oil under pressure flows from the pump through the valve into one end of the operating cylinder, and at the same time, oil in the other end of the operating cylinder is discharged into the reservoir.*

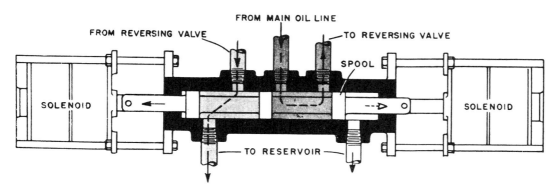

*Fig. 6—Pilot valve. (above and left) Spools of these valves are thrown by cams or dogs, or may be moved magnetically by solenoids. Oil pressure from the pump is directed alternately to both ends by means of a reversing valve, Fig. 5.*

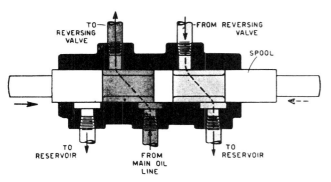

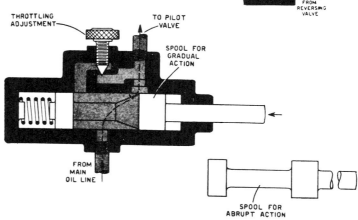

*Figs. 7 and 8—Dwell and throttling valves. These spring-loaded valves are actuated by cams or oil pressure. Cam action moves the spool and shuts off this free oil delivery, permitting only a restricted oil flow through throttling adjustment. In the pilot valve line, this valve delays action of the reversing valve and permits a period of dwell at the end of the stroke of the operating piston. The change from free to restricted flow may be abrupt or gradual, depending upon the spool employed. In pressure actuated valves, Fig. 8, the valve is normally held closed by the spring. Delivery of oil is restricted by a throttling adjustment as long as the valve is closed. When flow is reversed, oil pressure lifts the valve and permits free delivery of the oil.*

# VALVE FOLLOWER MECHANISMS

**A**NY power-operated positioning mechanism, wherein the power controlled element is caused to move to a position corresponding to that to which the manually-operated control lever or wheel has been shifted, must incorporate a valve follower mechanism. The purpose of the valve follower mechanism is to automatically return the control valve of the power or servo unit to its neutral position when the controlled element reaches the position corresponding to that to which the control lever has been shifted.

Mechanical follower mechanisms are of one of the following basic types: (1) Screw and nut, (2) wedges, (3) floating levers, (4) epicyclic gearing, (5) flexible cord and pulleys. Electrical and electronic circuits and devices are also possibilities that might be considered for certain applications.

**Fig. 1**—Schematic of screw-and-nut follower mechanism. Rotation of control wheel by the operator causes axial movement of the nut in one direction, thereby actuating the valve controlling the servo motor. Servo motor moves the rudder, motion of which causes rotation of pinion in such a direction as to cause opposite axial travel of the nut, thereby returning the valve to neutral position. This is an old mechanism used for steering ships. The servo motor can be a steam engine, hydraulic or pneumatic cylinder or engine or an electric motor. For the last type, the valve is replaced by an electric control switch.

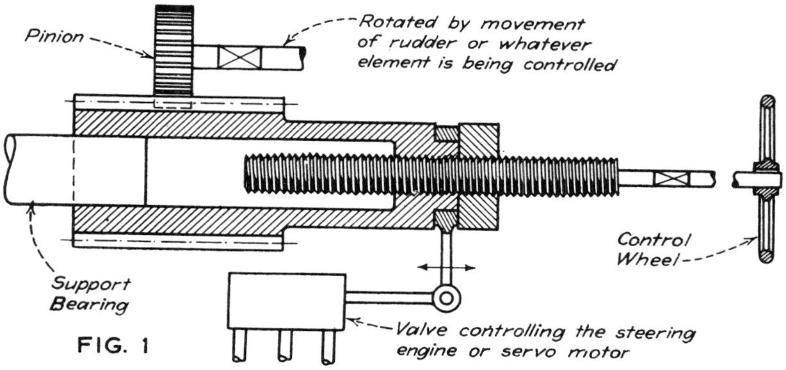

**Fig. 2**—A screw thread can be thought of as a modified inclined plane. Moving the control handle displaces the valve from its neutral position, causing servo motor to move the element being controlled. This last movement causes the follow rod to move in the same direction in which the control rod was moved, thereby returning valve to its neutral position.

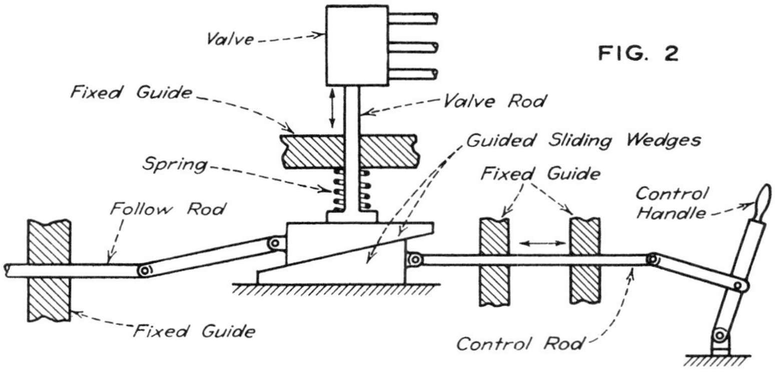

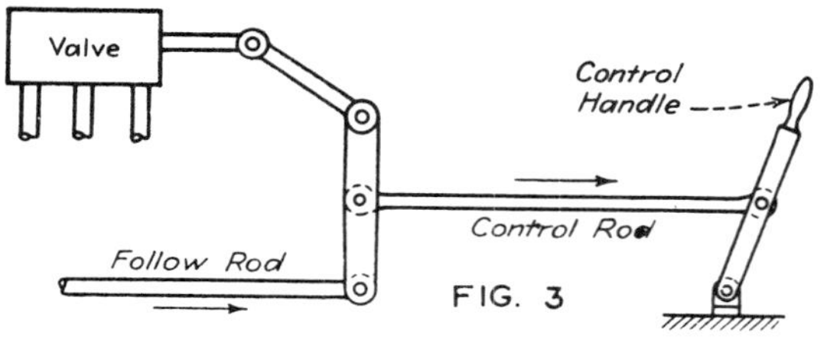

**Fig. 3**—The floating lever is the most commonly used type of follower mechanism. Movement of control handle opens valve, causing servo motor to operate the desired element, movement of which causes follow rod to move in same direction as movement of control rod. This brings valve back to neutral position.

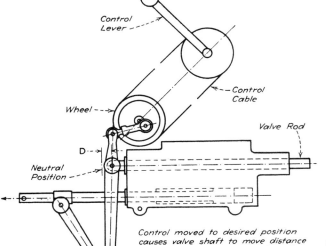

Control moved to desired position causes valve shaft to move distance "D" and open proper ports to actuating cylinder, causing power piston to travel to the left until valve rod has been moved back to neutral

**Fig. 4**—Application of the floating lever principle to the design of a follower mechanism developed by Curtiss-Wright Aircraft Corporation. The valve and servo power cylinder are a unit.

# FOR SERVO CONTROLS

**Fig. 5**—Modified form of floating lever principle applied to another Curtiss-Wright design. One advantage is the compact design made possible.

*Movement of control rod at "P" opens upper valves causing piston to move to right. Point "B" revolves about "C". Point "F" revolves about "E". Arm "D" remains as set by control. Motion continues till valve rocker arm has returned to neutral*

F

P

Valve for piston motion to right

D

E

B

C

Cylinder pivoted here

Valve for piston motion to left

## FIG. 5

Connected to controlled element and thus to servo unit

Hydraulic-valve rod

Control rod

## FIG. 6

**Fig. 6**—Epicyclic gearing can be considered a modified form of floating lever. This merely shows schematically the arrangement of the gears. The rod labeled "Hydraulic-valve rod" can actuate an electric rheostat or switch, pneumatic control valve, or any other device for the control of a power unit.

Cable connection to flap or rudder. Cable movement rotates sheave

Shaft of planetary gears

3   2

Control cable

Control cable

5   4   1

## FIG. 7

**Fig. 7**—Epicyclic follower mechanism is built into this "position control valve" developed by Adel Precision Products Company. Movement of control cable rotates gear *1*. **Shaft of planetary gears** remains stationary, hence angular rotation of gear *1* is transmitted to gear *4* keyed to valve shaft, thus operating the valve and causing the servo to move the flap, rudder or whatever the part may be. Movement of flap rotates the sheave and with it, the shafts of the planetary gears. Gear *1* remains stationary and planetaries roll on it. This causes rotation of valve shaft back to its neutral position.

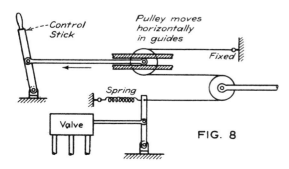

Control Stick

Pulley moves horizontally in guides

Fixed

Spring

Valve

## FIG. 8

**Fig. 8**—Flexible metal tape running over pulleys can be used for follower mechanisms. This type mechanism is specially suited where a greater number of movements are involved as it is merely necessary to increase the number of pulleys.

*Chapter 7*

# MECHANICAL MOVEMENTS AND LINKAGES

# 10 Ways to amplify

How levers, membranes, cams, and gears are arranged to measure, weigh, gage, adjust, and govern.

*FEDERICO STRASSER, Mankowitz & Strasser, Santiago, Chile*

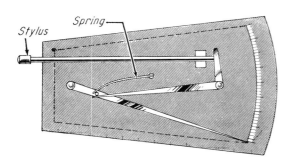

**1** **HIGH AMPLIFICATION** for simple measuring instruments is provided by double lever action. Accuracy can be as high as 0.0001 in.

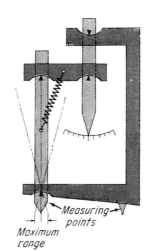

**2** **PIVOTED LEVERS** allow extremely sensitive action in comparator-type measuring device shown here. The range, however, is small.

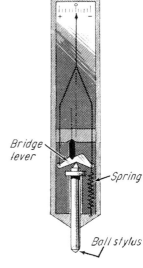

**3** **ULTRA-HIGH AMPLIFICATION**, with only one lever, is provided in the Hirth-Minimeter shown here. Again, the range is small.

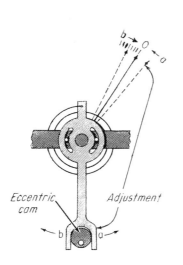

**7** **FOR CLOSE ADJUSTMENT**, electrical measuring instruments employ eccentric cams. Here movement is reduced, not amplified.

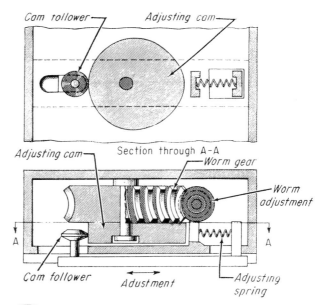

**8** **MICROSCOPIC ADJUSTMENT** is achieved here by employing a large eccentric-cam coupled to a worm-gear drive. Smooth, fine adjustment result.

# mechanical movements

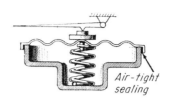

Air-tight sealing

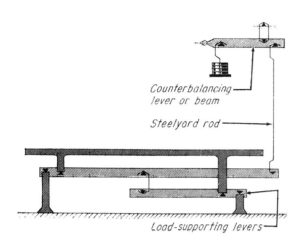

Counterbalancing lever or beam

Steelyard rod

Load-supporting levers

**5** **CAPSULE UNIT** for gas-pressure indicators should be provided with a compression spring to preload the membrane for more positive action.

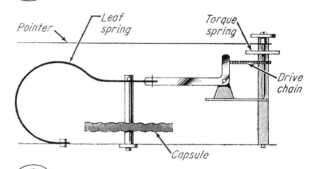

Pointer

Leaf spring

Torque spring

Drive chain

Capsule

**4** **LEVER - ACTUATED** weigh-scale needs no springs to maintain balance. The lever system, mounted on knife edges, is extremely sensitive.

**6** **AMPLIFIED MEMBRANE MOVEMENT** can be gained by the arrangement shown here. A small chain-driven gear links the lever system.

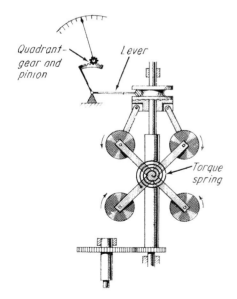

Quadrant-gear and pinion

Lever

Torque spring

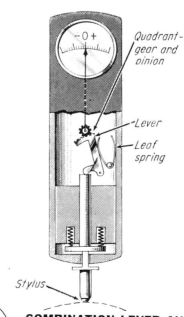

Quadrant-gear and pinion

Lever

Leaf spring

Stylus

**9** **QUADRANT-GEAR AND PINION** coupled to an L-lever provide ample movement of indicator needle for small changes in governor speed.

**10** **COMBINATION LEVER AND GEARED** quadrant are used here to give the comparator maximum sensitivity combined with ruggedness.

# 10 more ways to amplify

Levers, wires, hair, and metal bands are arranged to give high velocity ratios for adjusting and measuring.

*FEDERICO STRASSER, Mankowitz & Strasser, Santiago, Chile*

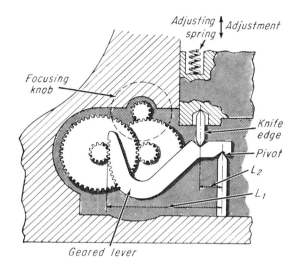

**1** **LEVER AND GEAR** train amplify the microscope control-knob movement. Knife edges provide frictionless pivots for lever.

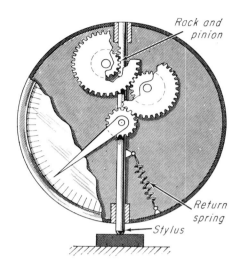

**2** **DIAL INDICATOR** starts with rack and pinion amplified by gear train. The return-spring takes out backlash.

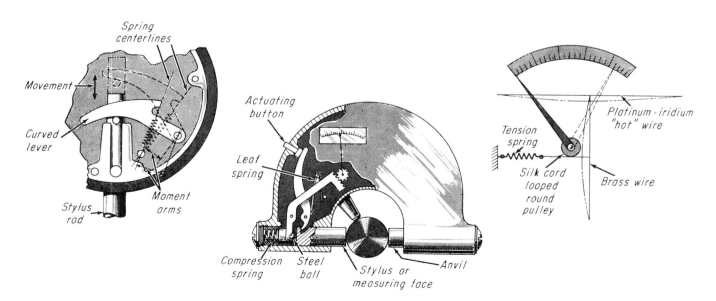

**3** **CURVED LEVER** is so shaped and pivoted that the force exerted on the stylus rod, and thus stylus pressure, remains constant.

**4** **ZEISS COMPARATOR** is provided with a special lever to move the stylus clear of the work. A steel ball greatly reduces friction.

**5** **"HOT-WIRE" AMMETER** relies on the thermal expansion of a current-carrying wire. A relatively large needle movement occurs.

246

# mechanical action

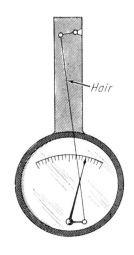

Hair

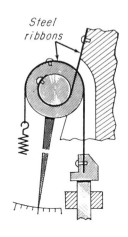

Steel ribbons

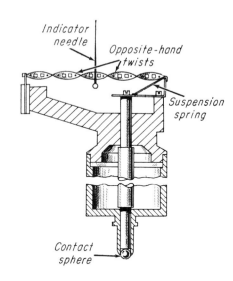

Indicator needle

Opposite-hand twists

Suspension spring

Contact sphere

**HYGROMETER** is actuated by a hair. When humidity causes expansion of the hair, its movement is amplified by a lever.

**STEEL RIBBONS** transmit movement without the slightest backlash. The movement is amplified by differences in diameter.

**METAL BAND** is twisted and supported at each end. Small movement of contact sphere produces large needle movement.

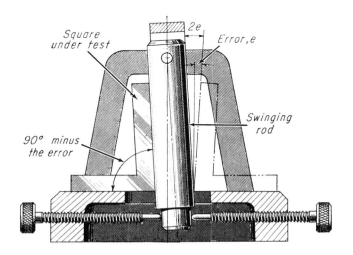

Square under test

2e

Error, e

Swinging rod

90° minus the error

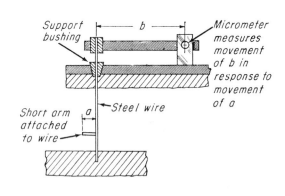

Support bushing

b

Micrometer measures movement of b in response to movement of a

Short arm attached to wire

a

Steel wire

**ACCURACY** of 90° squares can be checked with a device shown here. The rod makes the error much more apparent.

**TORSIONAL** deflection of the short arm is transmitted with low friction to the longer arm for micrometer measurement.

# 12 ways to put balls

Bearings, detents, valves, axial movements, clamps, and other devices can all have a ball as their key element.

*LOUIS DODGE, Consultant, New Richmond, Ohio*

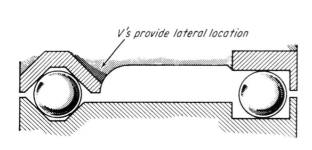

*V's provide lateral location*

**1** BALL-BEARING MACHINE WAY HAS LOW FRICTION.

*Dimple*

**2** DETENT POWER DEPENDS ON SPRING STRENGTH AND DIMPLE DEPTH.

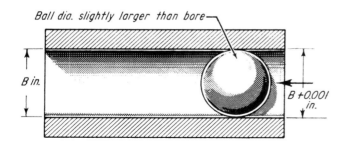

*Ball dia. slightly larger than bore*

B in.

B +0.001 in.

**5** BALL ACCURATELY FINISHES BUSHING BORE.

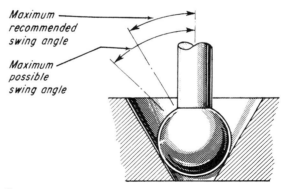

*Maximum recommended swing angle*

*Maximum possible swing angle*

**6** BALL SHAFT-END LETS SHAFT SWING.

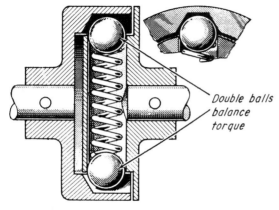

*Double balls balance torque*

**9** CLUTCH HAS LIMITED TORQUE TRANSMISSION.

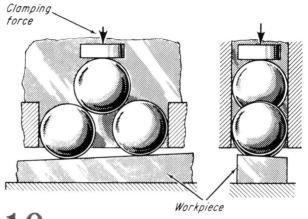

*Clamping force*

*Workpiece*

**10** CLAMP UNEVEN WORKPIECES.

# to work

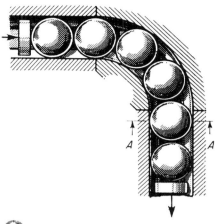

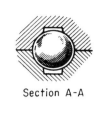

Section A-A

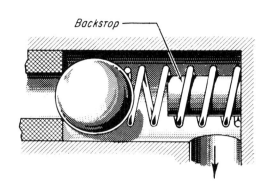

Backstop

**3** TRANSMIT AXIAL FORCE AROUND CURVES.

**4** CHECK VALVE BACKSTOP IS ADVISABLE.

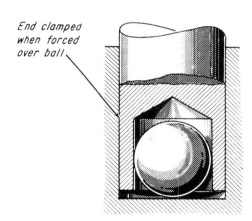

End clamped
when forced
over ball

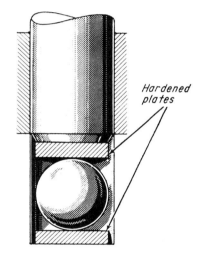

Hardened
plates

**7** BALL-LOCK FASTENS STUD IN BLIND HOLE .

**8** THRUST-BEARING TAKES LIGHT LOADS.

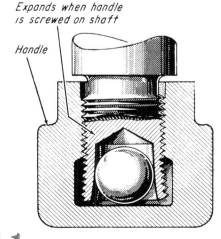

Expands when handle
is screwed on shaft

Handle

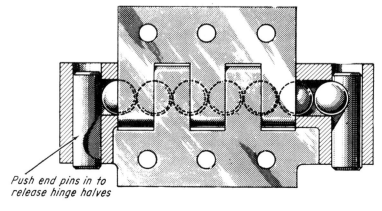

Push end pins in to
release hinge halves

**11** BALL LOCK SECURES HANDLE TO SHAFT.

**12** HINGE PIN IS SEPARABLE.

# For cable drives

When gears are too expensive, try a cable drive—low cost, durability and reliability are features.

*FRANK WILLIAM WOOD JR, president, Advanced Designs Inc , Vienna, Va.*

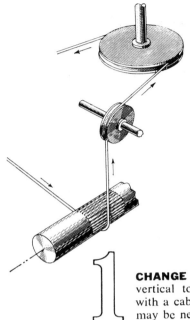

**1** **CHANGE OF DRIVE PLANE** from vertical to horizontal is no problem with a cable drive. One or more idlers may be needed—and watch friction.

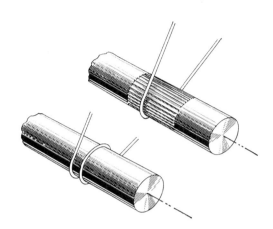

**2** **FINE STRAIGHT-KURL** or double-wrapped smooth shaft provides adequate non-slip friction for most drives. Slip occurs before drive is damaged.

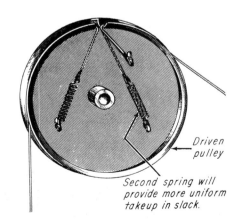

*Driven pulley*

*Second spring will provide more uniform takeup in slack.*

**5** **"INSIDE"** location for spring is right on the driven pulley itself. While one spring will often suffice, a second one provides uniformity.

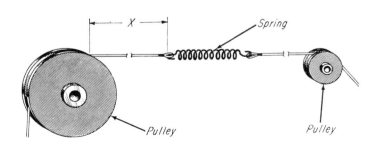

*X*

*Spring*

*Pulley*

*Pulley*

**6** **SPRINGS** can be located along any part of the cable, so long as distance $X$ is sufficient to prevent the spring from engaging pulley.

# —these design hints

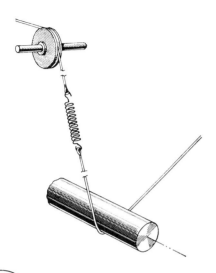

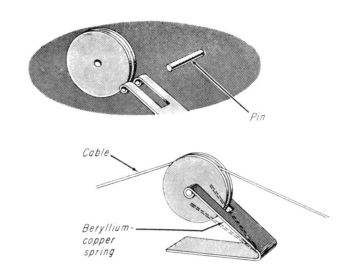

Pin

Cable

Beryllium-copper spring

**BACKLASH** in a drive system can be eliminated by using an extension spring preloaded so it won't stretch under normal drive forces.

**"OUTSIDE"** location for takeup spring often allows more freedom of design. Beryllium-copper springs need no protective plating.

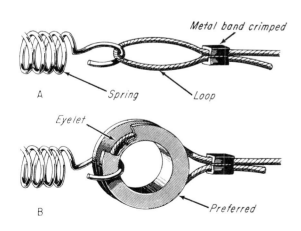

Metal band crimped

A

Spring    Loop

Eyelet

B

Preferred

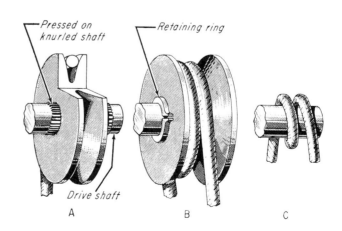

Pressed on knurled shaft    Retaining ring

Drive shaft

A    B    C

**SPRING ATTACHMENT** to the drive cable should be as secure as possible. Cable loop (A) is good; eyelet (B) causes less cable wear.

**PULLEYS** of nylon (A) give needed grip, yet slip at unsafe loads. Phenolic pulley (B) is free fit on shaft. Fixed polished shaft (C) adds friction.

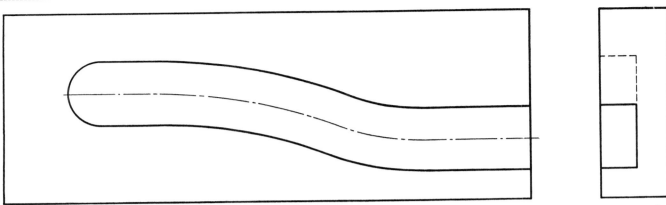

**FLAT PLATE CAM**—Essentially a displacement cam. With it, movement can be made from one point to another along any desired profile. Often used in place of taper attachments on lathes for form turning. Some have been built in sections up to 15 ft. long for turning the outside profile on gun barrels. Such cams can be made either on milling machines or profiling machines.

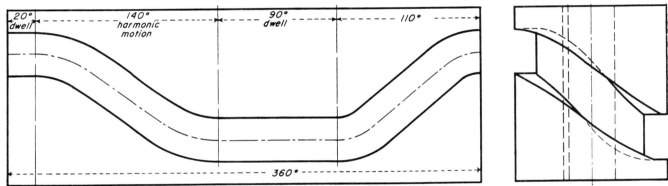

**BARREL CAM**—Sometimes called a cylindrical cam. The follower moves in a direction parallel to the cam axis and lever movement is reciprocating. As with other types of cam, the base curve can be varied to give any desired movement. Internal as well as external barrel cams are practical. A limitation: internal cams less than 11 in. in diam. are difficult to make on cam millers.

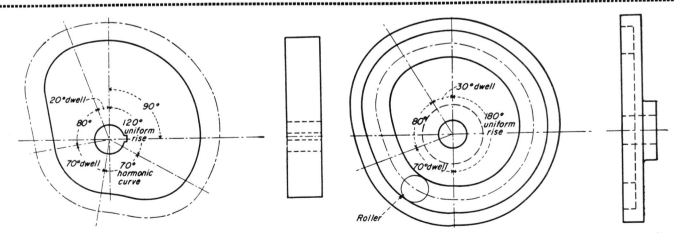

**NON-UNIFORM FACE CAM**—Sometimes called a disk cam. Follower can be either a roller, hexagon or pointed bar. Profile can be derived from a straight line, modified straight line, harmonic, parabolic or non-uniform base curve. Generally, the shock imposed by a cam designed on a straight line base curve is undesirable. Follower usually is weight loaded, although spring, hydraulic or pneumatic loading is satisfactory.

**BOX CAM**—Gives positive movement in two directions. A profile can be based on any desired base curve, as with face cams, but a cam miller is needed to cut it; whereas with face cams, a band saw and disk grinder could conceivably be used. No spring, pneumatic or hydraulic loading is needed for the followers. This type cam requires more material than for a face cam, but is no more expensive to mill.

# Basic Types of Cams

EDWARD RAHN
Chief Engineer, Rowbottom Machine Co. Inc.

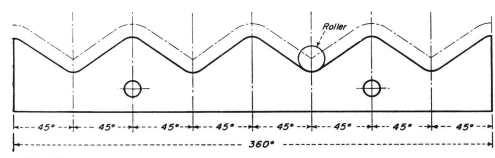
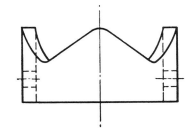

SIDE CAM—Essentially a barrel cam having only one side. Can be designed for any type of motion, depending on requirements and speed of operation. Spring or weight loaded followers of either the pointed or roller type can be used. Either vertical or horizontal mounting is permissible. Cutting of the profile is usually done on a shaper or a cam miller equipped with a small diameter cutter, although large cams 24 in. in diameter are made with 7-in. cutters.

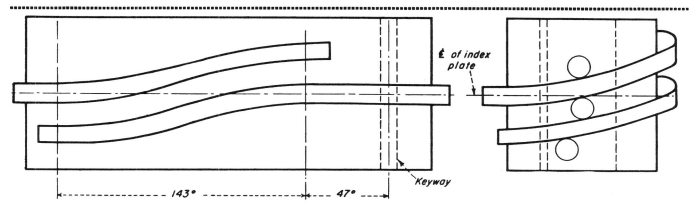

INDEX CAM—Within limits, such cams can be designed for any desired acceleration, deceleration and dwell period. A relatively short period for acceleration can be alloted on high speed cams such as those used on zipper-making equipment on which indexing occurs 1,200 to 1,500 times per minute. Cams of this sort can also be designed with four or more index stations.

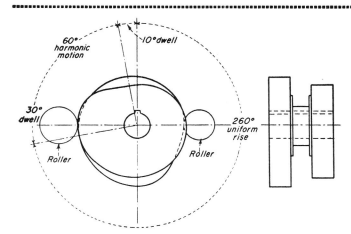

DOUBLE FACE CAM—Similar to single face cam except that it provides positive straight line movement in two directions. The supporting fork for the rollers can be mounted separately or between the faces. If the fork fulcrum is extended beyond the pivot point, the cam can be used for oscillatory movement. With this cam, the return stroke on a machine can be run faster than the feed stroke. Cost is more than that for a box cam

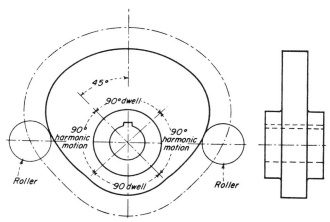

SINGLE-FACE CAM WITH TWO FOLLOWERS—Similar in action to a box or double face cam except flexibility is less than that for the latter type. Cam action for feed and return motions must be the same to prevent looseness of cam action. Used in place of box cams or double face cams to conserve space, and instead of single face cams to provide more positive movement for the roller followers.

# Four-Bar Linkages and Typical

All mechanisms can be broken down into equivalent four-bar linkages. They can be

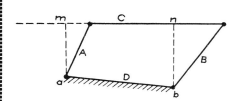

**FOUR-BAR LINKAGE**—Two cranks, a connecting rod and a line between the fixed centers of the cranks make up the basic four-bar linkage. Cranks can rotated if *A* is smaller than *B* or *C* or *D*. Link motion can be predicted.

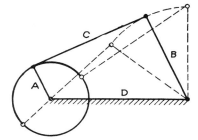

**CRANK AND ROCKER**— Following relations must hold for operation: $A+B+C>D$; $A+D+B>C$; $A+C-B<D$, and $C-A+B>D$.

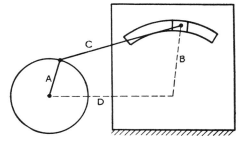

**FOUR-BAR LINK WITH SLIDING MEMBER**—One crank replaced by circular slot with effective crank distance of *B*.

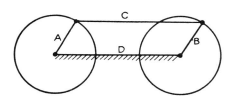

**PARALLEL CRANK FOUR-BAR**—Both cranks of the parallel crank four-bar linkage always turn at the same angular speed but they have two positions where the crank cannot be effective. They are used on locomotive drivers.

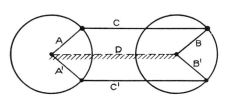

**DOUBLE PARALLEL CRANK**—This mechanism avoids dead center position by having two sets of cranks at 90 deg advancement. Connecting rods are always parallel. Sometimes used on driving wheels of locomotives.

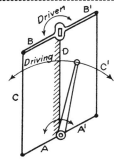

**PARALLEL CRANKS**—Steam control linkage assures equal valve openings.

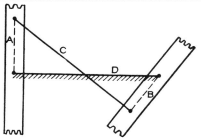

**NON-PARALLEL EQUAL CRANK**—The centrodes are formed as gears for passing dead center and can replace ellipticals.

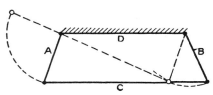

**SLOW MOTION LINK**—As crank *A* is rotated upward it imparts motion to crank *B*. When *A* reaches dead center position, the angular velocity of crank *B* decreases to zero. This mechanism is used on the Corliss valve.

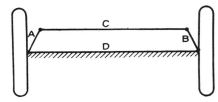

**TRAPAZOIDAL LINKAGE**—This linkage is not used for complete rotation but can be used for special control. Inside moves through larger angle than outside with normals intersecting on extension of rear axle in cars.

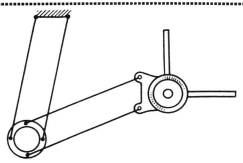

**DOUBLE PARALLEL CRANK MECHANISM**—This mechanism forms the basis for the universal drafting machine.

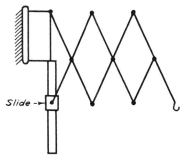

**ISOSCELES DRAG LINKS**—"Lazy-Tong" device made of several isosceles links; used for movable lamp support.

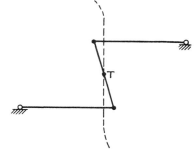

**WATT'S STRAIGHT-LINE MECHANISM**—Point **T** describes line perpendicular to parallel position of cranks.

# Industrial Applications

thought of as the basic mechanism and are useful in many mechanical operations.

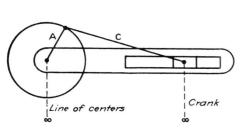

**STRAIGHT SLIDING LINK**—This is the form in which a slide is usually used to replace a link. The line of centers and the crank *B* are both of infinite length.

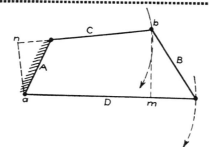

**DRAG LINK**—This linkage used as the drive for slotter machines. For complete rotation: $B>A+D-C$ and $B<D+C-A$.

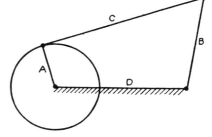

**ROTATING CRANK MECHANISM**—This linkage is frequently used to change a rotary motion to swinging movement.

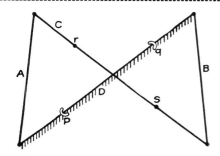

**NON-PARALLEL EQUAL CRANK**—If crank *A* has uniform angular speed, *B* will vary.

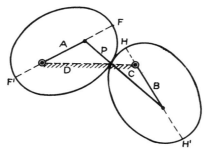

**ELLIPTICAL GEARS**—They produce same motion as non-parallel equal cranks.

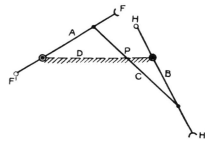

**NON-PARALLEL EQUAL CRANK**—Same as first but with crossover points on link ends.

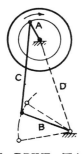

**TREADLE DRIVE**—This four-bar linkage is used in driving grind-wheels and sewing machines.

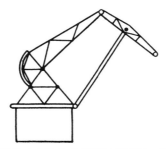

**DOUBLE LEVER MECHANISM**—Slewing crane can move load in horizontal direction by using D-shaped portion of top curve.

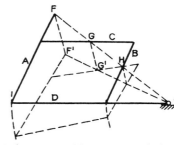

**PANTOGRAPH**—The pantograph is a parallelogram in which lines through *F*, *G* and *H* must always intersect at a common point.

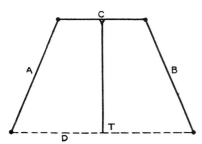

**ROBERT'S STRAIGHT-LINE MECHANISM**—The lengths of cranks *A* and *B* should not be less than 0.6 *D*; *C* is one half *D*.

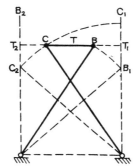

**TCHEBICHEFF'S**—Links made in proportion: $AB=CD=20$, $AD=16$, $BC=8$.

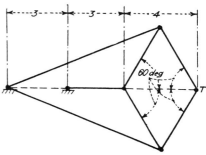

**PEUCELLIER'S CELL** — When proportioned as shown, the tracing point *T* forms a straight line perpendicular to the axis.

255

# Permanent Magnet Mechanisms

DEVELOPMENTS IN MAGNETIC MATERIALS having and capable of retaining high magnetic flux density have multiplied the possible applications of permanent magnets because of the corresponding increase in holding forces that are developed without an electric power supply. Some of the uses of permanent magnets in mechanical devices were illustrated in March PRODUCT ENGINEERING. These included a vertical shaft suspension, thermostatic switch coupling, thread tensioning device, reel brake, door latch, sheet glass holding clamp, and others. Other applications include work holders and chucks, timer controls, meter drive, control instrument coupling, tachometers, weld tester, horizontal shaft suspension, pressure release device for presses, filters, advertising mechanisms, snap action electric switches, finders for hidden parts, and movable drafting machine pivot. Some of these are illustrated herewith. Most of these devices were developed for well-known manufacturers and have been put into use in forms similar to those illustrated.

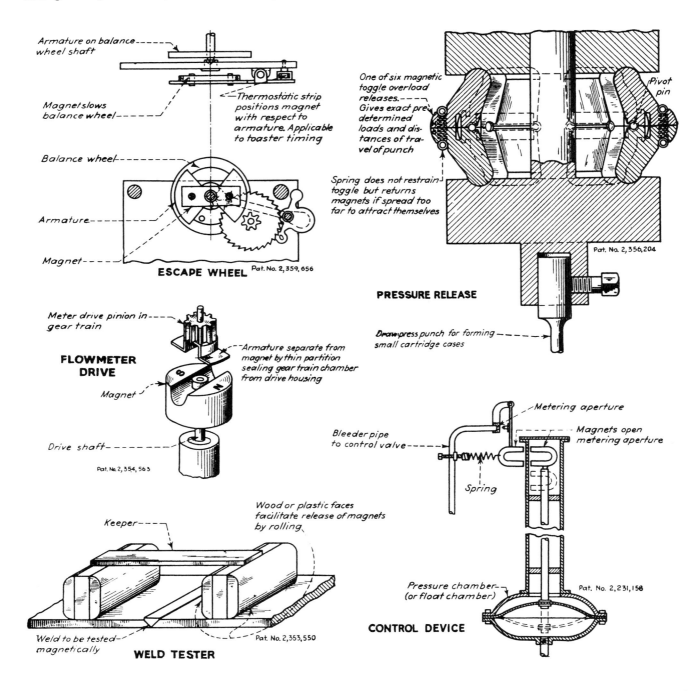

Armature on balance wheel shaft

Magnet slows balance wheel

Thermostatic strip positions magnet with respect to armature. Applicable to toaster timing

Balance wheel

Armature

Magnet

**ESCAPE WHEEL** Pat. No. 2,359,656

One of six magnetic toggle overload releases. Gives exact predetermined loads and distances of travel of punch

Pivot pin

Spring does not restrain toggle but returns magnets if spread too far to attract themselves

Pat. No. 2,356,204

**PRESSURE RELEASE**

Draw press punch for forming small cartridge cases

Meter drive pinion in gear train

**FLOWMETER DRIVE**

Armature separate from magnet by thin partition sealing gear train chamber from drive housing

Magnet

Drive shaft

Pat. No. 2,354,563

Bleeder pipe to control valve

Metering aperture

Magnets open metering aperture

Spring

Wood or plastic faces facilitate release of magnets by rolling

Keeper

Pressure chamber (or float chamber)

Pat. No. 2,231,158

**CONTROL DEVICE**

Weld to be tested magnetically

Pat. No. 2,353,550

**WELD TESTER**

# *And Their Applications*

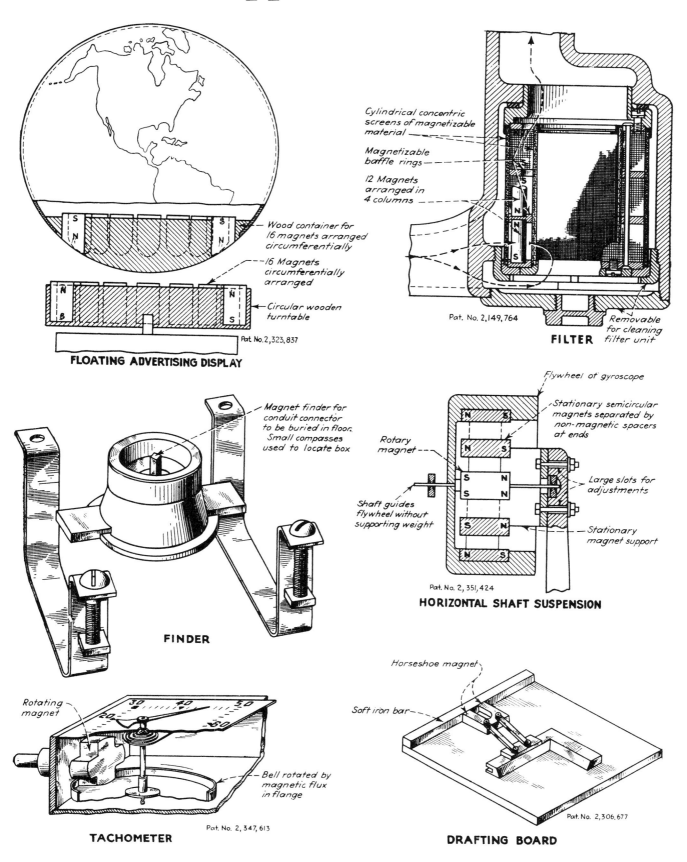

Wood container for
16 magnets arranged
circumferentially

16 Magnets
circumferentially
arranged

Circular wooden
turntable

Pat. No. 2,323,837

**FLOATING ADVERTISING DISPLAY**

Cylindrical concentric
screens of magnetizable
material

Magnetizable
baffle rings

12 Magnets
arranged in
4 columns

Pat. No. 2,149,764

Removable
for cleaning
filter unit

**FILTER**

Magnet finder for
conduit connector
to be buried in floor.
Small compasses
used to locate box

**FINDER**

Flywheel of gyroscope

Stationary semicircular
magnets separated by
non-magnetic spacers
at ends

Rotary
magnet

Large slots for
adjustments

Shaft guides
flywheel without
supporting weight

Stationary
magnet support

Pat. No. 2,351,424

**HORIZONTAL SHAFT SUSPENSION**

Rotating
magnet

Bell rotated by
magnetic flux
in flange

Pat. No. 2,347,613

**TACHOMETER**

Horseshoe magnet

Soft iron bar

Pat. No. 2,306,677

**DRAFTING BOARD**

# Basic Push-pull

## These arrangements are invariably the root of all linkage devices

FRANK WILLIAM WOOD JR
President, Advanced Design Inc, Vienna, Va

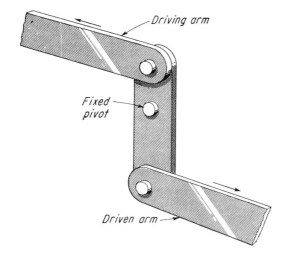

Driving arm

Fixed pivot

Driven arm

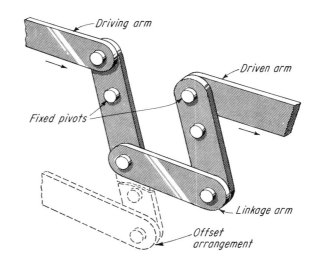

Driving arm

Driven arm

Fixed pivots

Linkage arm

Offset arrangement

 **FIXED PIVOTS** on arm lengths are located to control ratio of input and output movements of this push-pull-actuated linkage. Mechanism can be either flat bars or round rods of adequate thickness to prevent bowing under compression.

**PUSH-PULL LINKAGE** for same direction of motion can be obtained by adding linkage arm to previous design. In both cases, if arms are bars it might be best to make them forked rather than merely flatted at their linkage ends.

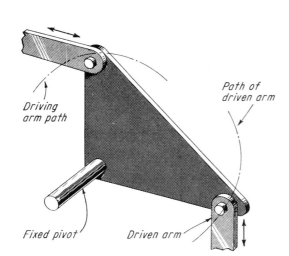

Path of driven arm

Driving arm path

Fixed pivot

Driven arm

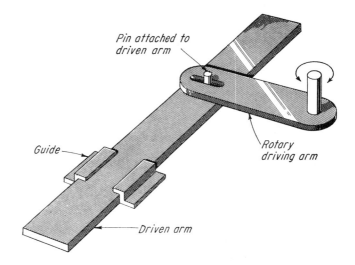

Pin attached to driven arm

Guide

Rotary driving arm

Driven arm

 **VERTICAL OUTPUT MOVEMENT** from horizontal input is gained with this push-pull linkage. Although the triangular-shaped plate could be substituted by an L-shaped arm, the plate gives greater freedom of driving- and driven-arm location.

**FOR LIMITED STRAIGHT-LINE** 2-direction motion use this rotary-actuated linkage. Friction between the pin and sides of slot limit this design to small loads. A bearing on the pin will reduce friction and slot wear to negligible proportions.

# Linkages

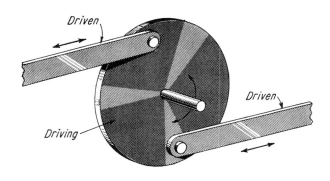

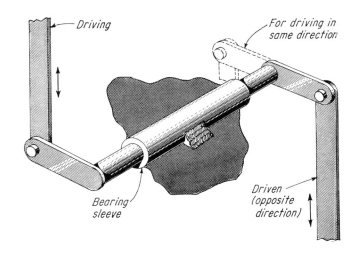

**ROTARY-ACTUATED LINKAGE** gives opposite direction of motion and can be obtained by using 3-bar linkage with pivot point of middle link located at midpoint of arm length. Disk should be adequately strengthened for heavy loads.

**SAME-DIRECTION MOTION** is given by this rotary-actuated linkage when end arms are located on the same sides; for opposite-direction motion, locate the arms on opposite sides. Use when a crossover is required between input and output.

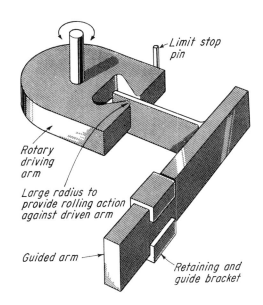

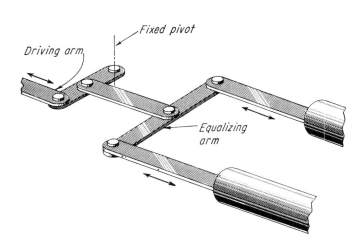

**THIS ROTARY-ACTUATED** linkage for straight-line 2-direction motion has rotary driving arm with a modified dovetail opening that fits freely around a flat sheet or bar arm. Driven arm reciprocates in slot as rotary driving arm is turned.

**EQUALIZING LINKAGE** here has an equalizing arm that balances the input force to two output arms. This arrangement is most suitable for air or hydraulic systems where equal force is to be exerted on the pistons of separate cylinders.

# NO TEETH ON THESE RATCHETS

*With springs, rollers and other devices they keep motion going one way.*

**L KASPER**
*design consultant*
*Philadelphia*

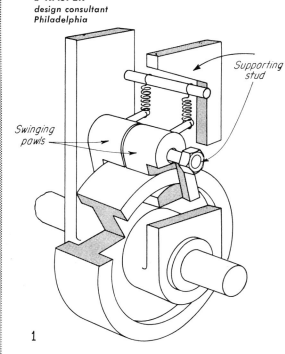

Supporting stud

Swinging pawls

1

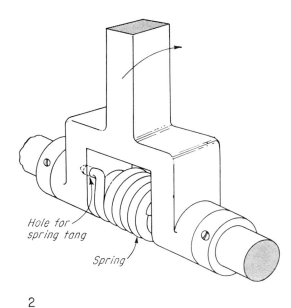

Hole for spring tang

Spring

2

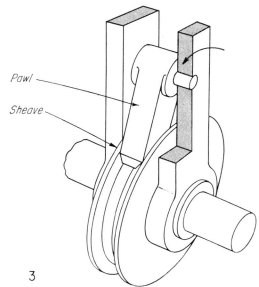

Pawl

Sheave

3

**1** SWINGING PAWLS lock on rim when lever swings forward, and release on return stroke. Oversize holes for supporting stud make sure both top and bottom surfaces of pawls make contact.

**2** HELICAL SPRING grips shaft because its inner diameter is smaller than the outer diameter of shaft. During forward stroke, spring winds tighter; during return stroke, it expands.

**3** V-BELT SHEAVE is pushed around when pawl wedges in groove. For a snug fit, bottom of pawl is tapered like a V-belt.

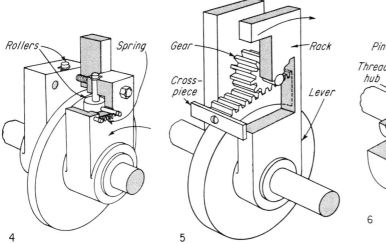

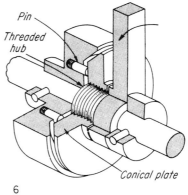

4    5    6

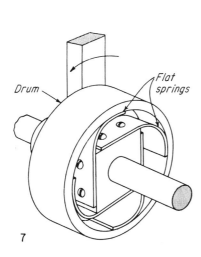

7

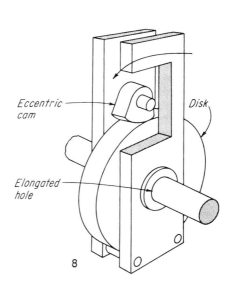

8

**4**  **ECCENTRIC ROLLERS** squeeze disk on forward stroke. On return stroke, rollers rotate backwards and release their grip. Springs keep rollers in contact with disk.

**5**  **RACK** is wedge-shape so that it jams between the rolling gear and the disk, pushing the shaft forward. When the driving lever makes its return stroke, it carries along the unattached rack by the crosspiece.

**6**  **CONICAL PLATE** moves as a nut back and forth along the threaded center hub of the lever. Light friction of spring-loaded pins keeps the plate from rotating with the hub.

**7**  **FLAT SPRINGS** expand against inside of drum when lever moves one way, but drag loosely when lever turns drum in opposite direction.

**8**  **ECCENTRIC CAM** jams against disk during motion half of cycle. Elongated holes in the levers allow cam to wedge itself more tightly in place.

# How to prevent reverse

Wedges, ratchet-and-pawl arrangements, internal pins, friction pads, and sliding key action can protect mechanisms from torque feedback.

*L. KASPER, Philadelphia*

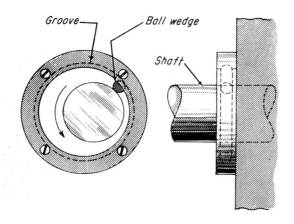

Groove — Ball wedge

Shaft

  **INTERNALLY GROOVED** ring is located eccentrically with the rotating shaft. Ball wedges if shaft reverses direction of rotation.

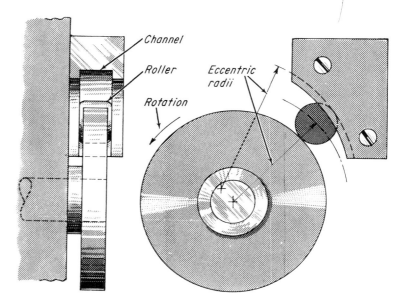

Channel

Roller

Rotation

Eccentric radii

2  **ROLLER WEDGES** when direction of rotation is reversed as in previous device. For vertical shafts, hold roller in place with a spring.

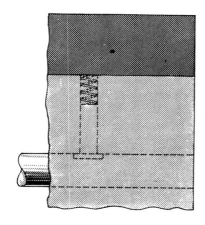

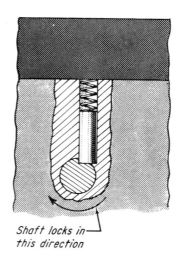

Shaft locks in this direction

5  **SPRING-LOADED PIN** device is applicable when no part of the shaft is exposed. Blacklash here can be equal to almost one revolution.

# rotation

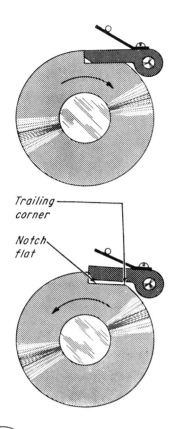

*Trailing corner*

*Notch flat*

**SINGLE-TOOTH RATCHET** has special pawl, shaped to avoid annoying sound. The notch corner engages pawl before it can hit the flat.

**SWINGING PAWL** will operate silently in any position. As one pawl tooth leaves the ratchet, the other tooth engages at about half depth.

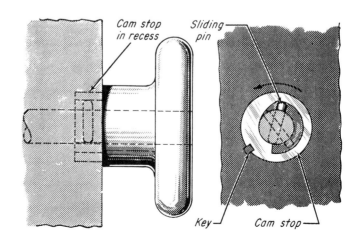

*Cam stop in recess*     *Sliding pin*

*Key*     *Cam stop*

**SLIDING PIN** is moved into position (during normal rotation) to prevent reverse rotation. Key the cam stop into housing.

*continued*

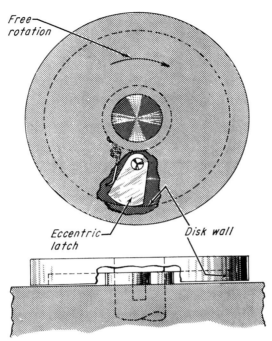

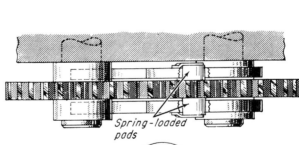

Shaft lug

Free rotation

Eccentric latch

Disk wall

**7** ECCENTRIC LATCH allows shaft to rotate in one direction; attempted reversal immediately causes latch to wedge against disk wall.

**8**

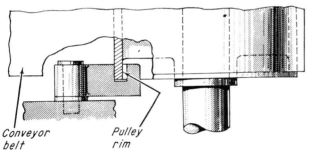

Conveyor belt

Pulley rim

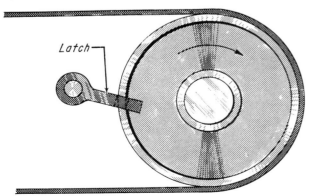

Latch

**10** LATCH ON RIM of pulley is free only when rotation is in direction shown. This arrangement is ideal for conveyor-belt pulleys.

Spring-loaded pads

**11** SPRING-LOADED FRICTION PADS contact the right gear. Idler meshes and locks gear set when rotation is reversed.

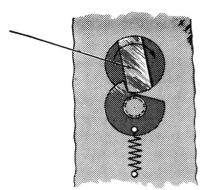

Forward

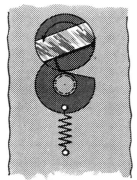

Reverse

**LUG ON SHAFT** pushes the notched disk free during normal rotation. Disk periphery stops lug to prevent reverse rotation.

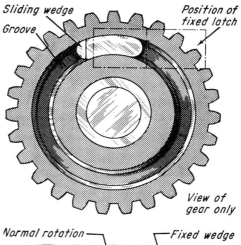

Sliding wedge

Groove

Position of fixed latch

View of gear only

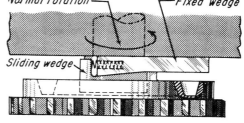

Normal rotation

Fixed wedge

Sliding wedge

**FIXED WEDGE AND SLIDING WEDGE** tend to disengage when the gear is turning clockwise. The wedges jam in reverse direction.

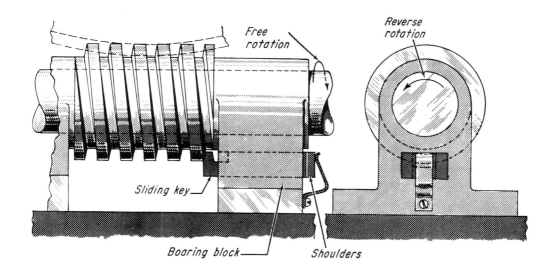

Free rotation

Reverse rotation

Sliding key

Boaring block

Shoulders

**SLIDING KEY** has tooth which engages the worm threads. In reverse rotation key is pulled in until its shoulders contact block.

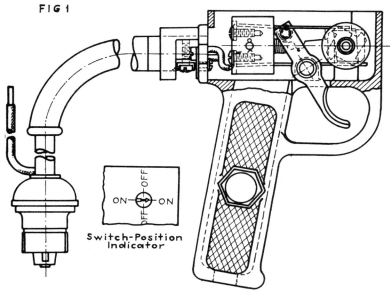

FIG 1

# Electric Switches

B. B. RAMEY
*Chief Engineer*
*Black & Decker Manufacturing Company*

●

Switch-Position Indicator

**Fig. 1**—Trigger operated ratchet-type single pole switch, a design no longer in general use. An arrow stamped on the end of the shaft shows through a hole in the cover plate to indicate the position of the switch. Spring blades pressing on the faces of the square contact block give a snap action and hold the block in position.

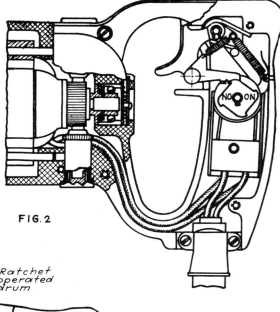

FIG. 2

**Fig. 2**—Ratchet-type switch with double pole for 3-phase. Can also be used for single phase. The word "on" is stamped on diametrically opposite points on the ratchet wheel. With switch in "on" position, the word shows through a hole in the cover plate. A spring level snaps into the star wheel, giving quick snap action. As in Figs. 1 and 3, to open the switch a definite movement of the trigger is required.

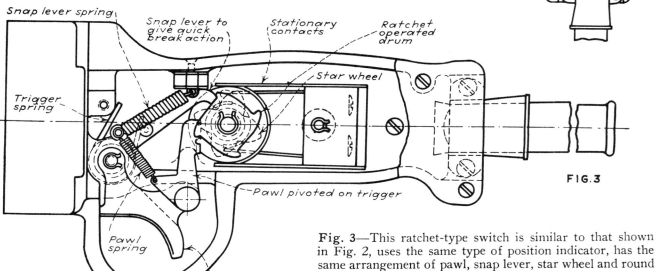

Snap lever spring

Snap lever to give quick break action

Stationary contacts

Ratchet operated drum

Star wheel

Trigger spring

Pawl pivoted on trigger

Pawl spring

Trigger

FIG. 3

**Fig. 3**—This ratchet-type switch is similar to that shown in Fig. 2, uses the same type of position indicator, has the same arrangement of pawl, snap lever, star wheel and round contact block. Only the type of handle is different.

# and Switch Mountings—I

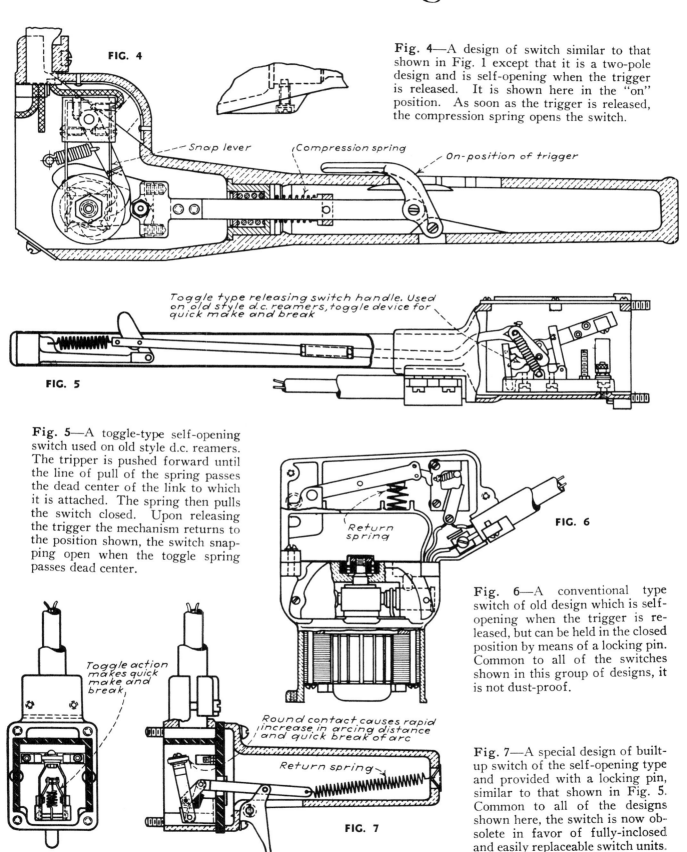

**FIG. 4**

**Fig. 4**—A design of switch similar to that shown in Fig. 1 except that it is a two-pole design and is self-opening when the trigger is released. It is shown here in the "on" position. As soon as the trigger is released, the compression spring opens the switch.

Snap lever | Compression spring | On-position of trigger

Toggle type releasing switch handle. Used on old style d.c. reamers, toggle device for quick make and break

**FIG. 5**

**Fig. 5**—A toggle-type self-opening switch used on old style d.c. reamers. The tripper is pushed forward until the line of pull of the spring passes the dead center of the link to which it is attached. The spring then pulls the switch closed. Upon releasing the trigger the mechanism returns to the position shown, the switch snapping open when the toggle spring passes dead center.

Return spring

**FIG. 6**

**Fig. 6**—A conventional type switch of old design which is self-opening when the trigger is released, but can be held in the closed position by means of a locking pin. Common to all of the switches shown in this group of designs, it is not dust-proof.

Toggle action makes quick make and break

Round contact causes rapid increase in arcing distance and quick break of arc

Return spring

**FIG. 7**

**Fig. 7**—A special design of built-up switch of the self-opening type and provided with a locking pin, similar to that shown in Fig. 5. Common to all of the designs shown here, the switch is now obsolete in favor of fully-inclosed and easily replaceable switch units.

# Switch Handles

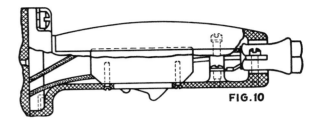

FIG.8

FIG.9

B. B. RAMEY
*Chief Engineer*
*Black & Decker Manufacturing Company*

FIG.10

Fig. 10—A rocker type switch such as used on polishers and portable sanders. It is not self releasing and is now being replaced by plunger-operated dust-tight switches such as shown in Fig. 14.

Fig. 11—Another style of mounting a commercial type switch in a side handle. The switch is replaceable as a unit and is self-opening, as soon as the trigger is released; the return spring being shown dotted.

Fig. 8—A modern type commercial switch mounted in a side handle. Such switches are readily replaced as a unit, are inexpensive and sealed against the entrance of dirt. The switch opens as soon as the trigger is released unless the locking pin is set, in which case a slight pull on the trigger releases the locking pin and opens the switch.

Fig. 9—Another example of a modern commercial switch mounted as a unit in a grip type end handle.

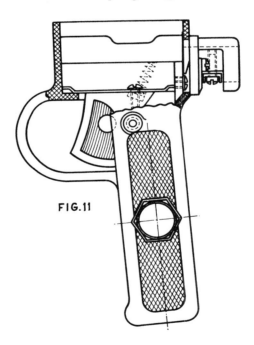

FIG.11

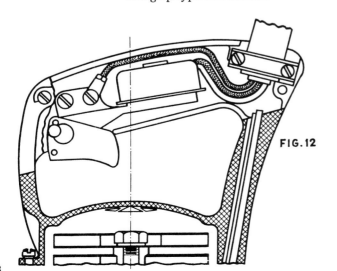

FIG.12

Fig. 12—In this switch mounting the trigger actuates the switch by means of a lift rod attached to the back of the trigger. A tension spring attached to the upper end of the lift rod and anchored to the lower end of the switch plate pulls the switch open as soon as the trigger is released. If the locking pin is depressed when the trigger is pulled back it passes through the hole in the trigger which then cannot return to the open position. As soon as the trigger is pressed the locking pin is released, snaps back and releases the trigger.

# and Switch Mountings—II

Fig. 13—A slider operated switch. The slider moves back and forth as indicated in the drawing. This switch is not provided with any release arrangement. It is used only on light model tools where no damage would be done if the tool were laid down with the power still on.

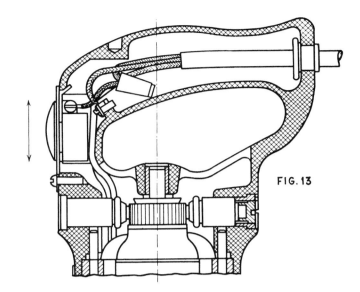

FIG. 13

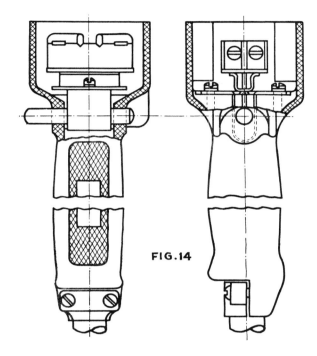

FIG. 14

Fig. 14—Latest type switch handle for polishers, sanders, and portable grinders. The switch is in a dust-tight chamber and is operated by a plunger instead of a trigger, which eliminates the necessity of an opening such as is required when triggers or rockers are used. The plunger makes a close fit. Switch is not self-releasing, it being necessary to push the plunger for both on and off positions.

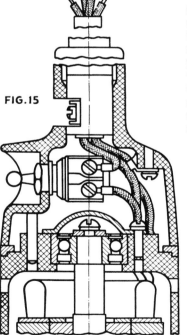

FIG.15

Fig. 15—Latest design of switch arrangement for small die grinders and sanders. The toggle-operated switch unit is mounted in a dust-tight compartment and a dust-seal is provided where the toggle comes through the case. This type of switch does not have a release arrangement that opens it automatically.

Fig. 16—This switch is of the same type as shown in Fig. 11. It is mounted in a longer handle, being actuated by a remote trigger arrangement. It is provided with an additional return spring for quick action and also has a locking pin for holding the switch in the closed position when the trigger is released. A slight pull on the trigger releases the locking pin and opens the switch.

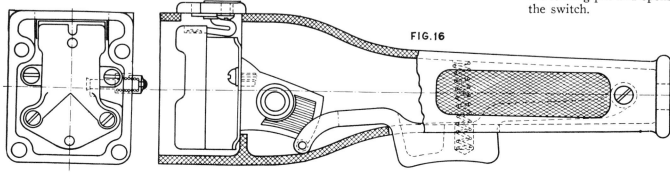

FIG.16

# Chapter 8

# MECHANICAL POWER
# TRANSMISSION

# 4 ways to eliminate

Wedges take up freedom in threads and gears, hold shaft snug against bearing.

*L. KASPER, Philadelphia*

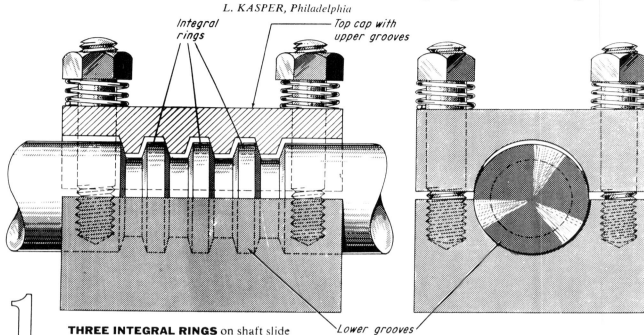

**THREE INTEGRAL RINGS** on shaft slide in grooves to prevent axial movement of shaft. Grooves in cap are offset axially.

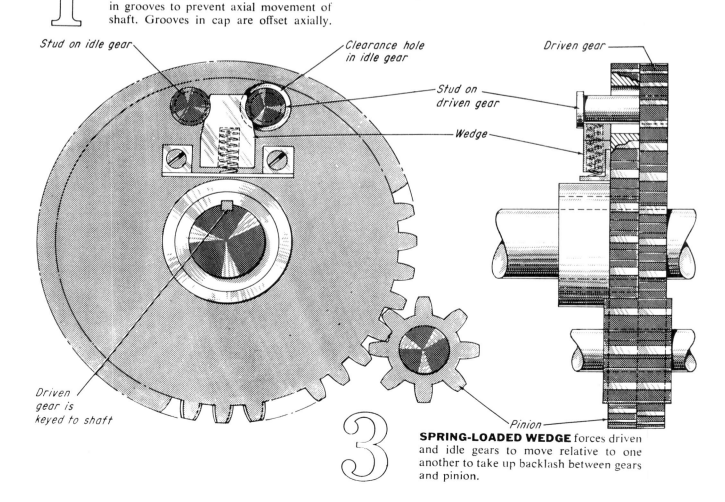

**SPRING-LOADED WEDGE** forces driven and idle gears to move relative to one another to take up backlash between gears and pinion.

# backlash

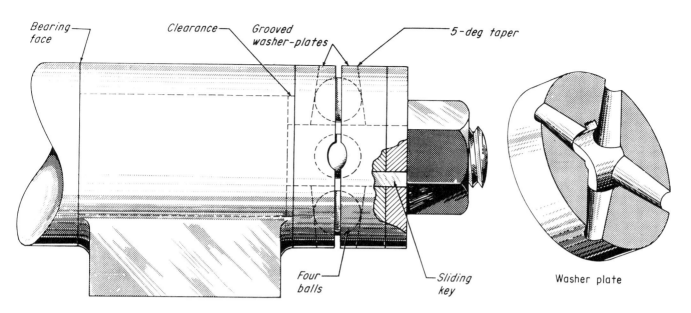

Bearing face · Clearance · Grooved washer-plates · 5-deg taper · Four balls · Sliding key

Washer plate

**CENTRIFUGAL FORCE** causes balls to exert force on grooved washer-plates when shaft rotates, pulling it against bearing face.

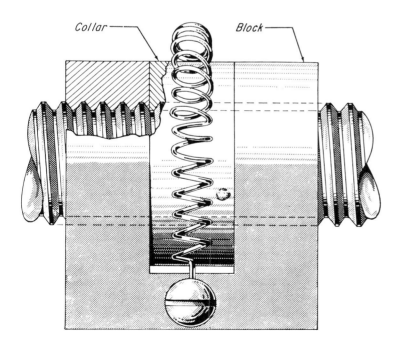

Collar · Block

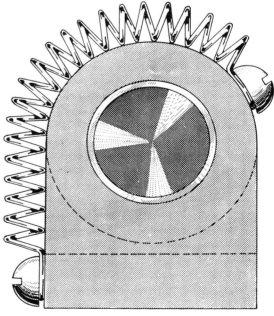

**COLLAR AND BLOCK** have continuous V-thread. When wear takes place in lead screw, the collar always maintains pressure on threads.

# 4 more ways to

Springs combine with wedging
action to ensure that threads, gears,
and toggles respond smoothly.

*L. KASPER, Philadelphia*

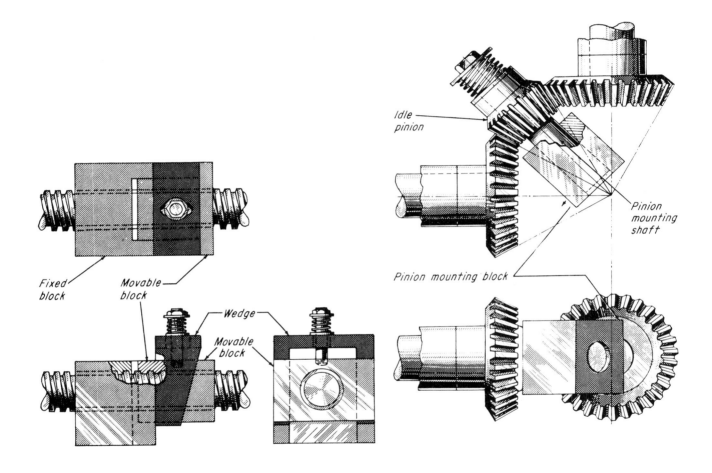

Idle pinion

Pinion mounting shaft

Pinion mounting block

Fixed block

Movable block

Wedge

Movable block

**2** SPRING-LOADED PINION is mounted on a
shaft located so that the spring forces
pinion teeth into gear teeth to take up
lost motion or backlash.

**1** MOVABLE BLOCK is forced away from
fixed block by spring-loaded wedge.
Pressure is applied to both sides of lead
screw, thus ensuring snug fit.

# prevent backlash

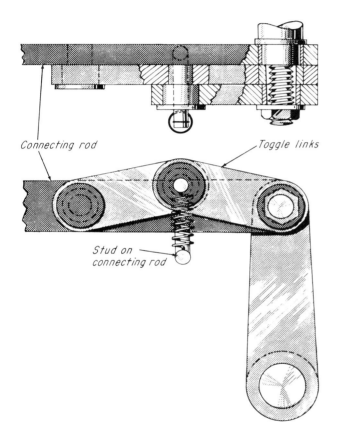

Connecting rod

Toggle links

Stud on
connecting rod

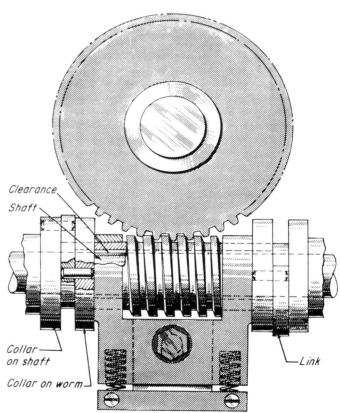

Clearance

Shaft

Collar
on shaft

Collar on worm

Link

**TOGGLE LINKS** are spring-loaded and approach alignment to take up lost motion as wear in the joint takes place. Smooth response is thus gained.

**HOLLOW WORM** has clearance for shaft, which drives worm through pinned collars and links. As wear occurs, springs move worm into teeth.

# Anti-Friction Bearing

HENRY J. MARTIN

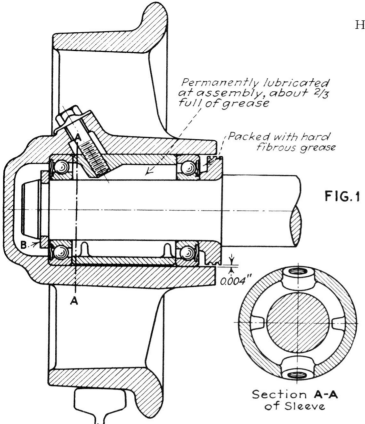

Permanently lubricated at assembly, about 2/3 full of grease

Packed with hard fibrous grease

FIG.1

0.004"

Section A-A of Sleeve

**Fig. 1**—Mine car wheel rotates about stationary axle. Bearings and sleeve are held on shaft by snap ring *B*. Wheel hub forms bearing housing and is held on by diagonally placed locked screws which also regulate axial play.

*Courtesy Marlin-Rockwell Corporation*

**Fig. 2**—Conveyor head and tail pulley is supported in self aligning pillow blocks. Bearings are pressed on split sleeve, ends taper threaded. Nuts clamp bearings and bind sleeve to shaft. Cup and washer grease seals prevent entrance of dirt. Slidable along angle iron way for belt take-up by screw.

*Courtesy Timken Roller Bearing Company*

**Fig. 3**—Planetary driving pulley, made of two castings, ball bearing mounted top and bottom in overhanging arm of machine. Three sets of planet gears are mounted in lower half. Lower central pinion, meshing with planets, is supported by one ball bearing. Felt seals protect bearings.

*Courtesy New Departure Manufacturing Company*

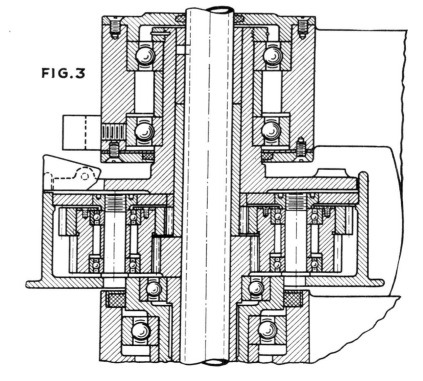

FIG.3

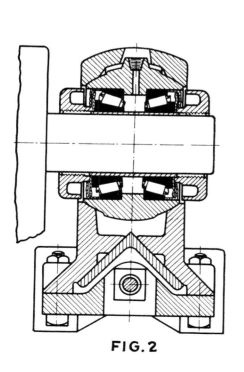

FIG.2

# Pulley Mountings

**Fig. 4**—Internal grinding spindle pulley is mounted in sleeves with two Ex-Cell-O double row bearings, and protected by felt seals and retained by double lock nuts. Running at 10,000 r.p.m., bearings are lubricated by sight feed oilers.

*Courtesy Ex-Cell-O Aircraft & Tool Corporation*

**Fig. 5**—Multiple vee-belt idler pulley rotates about stationary shaft. Below centerline is shown design for oil lubrication, above for grease. Pulley has 0.005-0.010 in. end play for alignment of running belt. Clamped with one nut.

*Courtesy Marlin-Rockwell Corporation*

**Fig. 6**—Mine car wheel rotates about one built-in seal and one plain ball bearing. Combination grease and felt seal in cap retains the lubricant and keeps out foreign material.

*Courtesy Marlin-Rockwell Corporation*

**Fig. 7**—Large idler pulley runs on built-in seal bearings pressed on non-rotating shaft. Bearings have thin collar assembled in outer race with small clearance over inner ring, thereby sealing-in lubricant. Pocket between bearings filled with grease when assembled. Pulley assembly is supported on rods *A-A*.

*Courtesy Marlin-Rockwell Corporation*

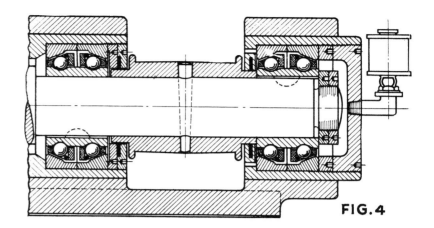

FIG.4

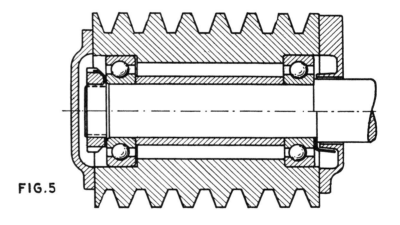

FIG.5

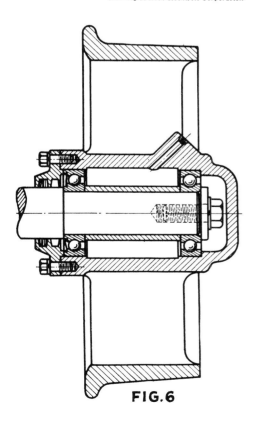

FIG.6

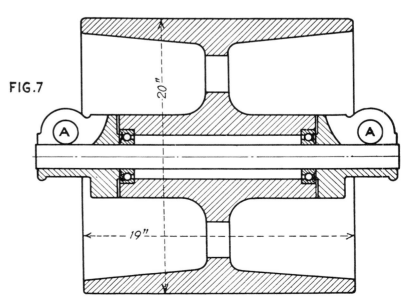

FIG.7

# Assembling Radial-Thrust Bearings

Twenty-four possibilities to consider exploring

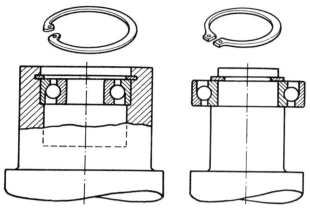

Fig.1 – Retainer ring holds the bearing in place on the shaft.

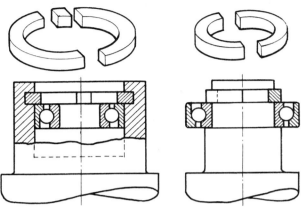

Fig.2 – Split flange can be assembled after bearing is mounted

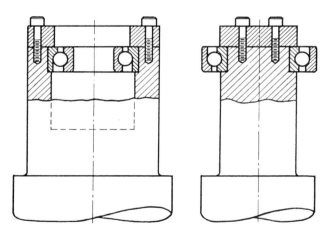

Fig.3 – Flange is fastened with screws to the shaft.

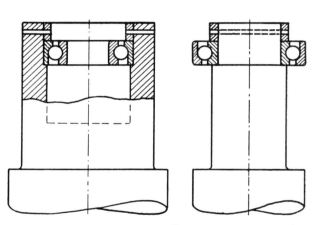

Fig.4 – Flange is keyed on the shaft to support the bearing.

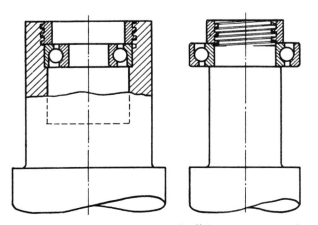

Fig.5 – Flange is screwed on the shaft to support the bearing.

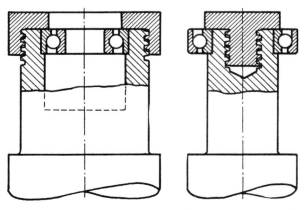

Fig.6 – Flange is screwed on the shaft to support the bearing.

# on Shafts with Blind Ends

when confronted with rigid requirements.

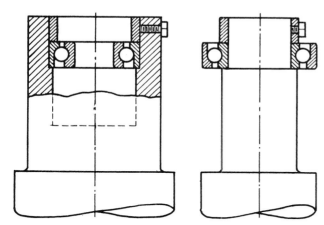

Fig.7-Flange is fastened to the shaft by set screw.

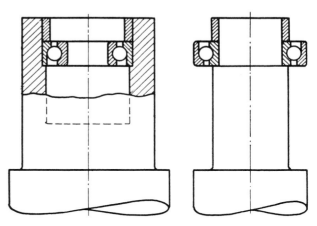

Fig.8 - Flange is fastened to the shaft by shrink fit.

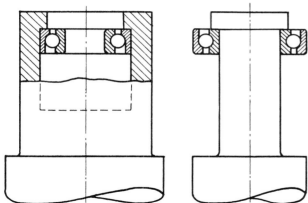
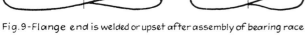

Fig.9-Flange end is welded or upset after assembly of bearing race

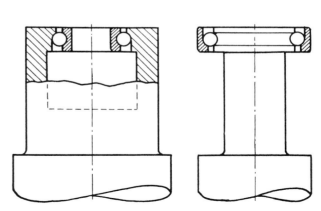

Fig.10-Bearing race is constructed integral with shaft.

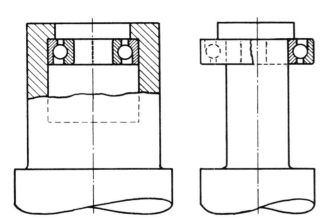

Fig.11-Bearing race is split Flange is integral with shaft

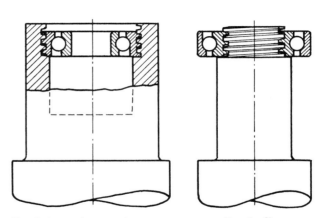

Fig.12-Threaded bearing race screws on the shaft.

279

# Methods of Sealing

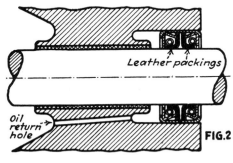

## Seals as applied to plain or sleeve-type bearings for retaining the lubricant or for excluding foreign materials or a combination of both

**Fig. 1**—For retaining lubricant, the seal is assembled with the flanged leather projecting toward the bearing. The leather packing is clamped near the outer edge of the flange by the inner of two telescoping metal cups, thereby assuring a tight joint at the face. A garter type spring compresses the leather about the shaft. Should misalignment occur the seal is maintained by virtue of the flexibility of the leather and garter spring. To drain off the surplus oil passing the end of the bearing, a small hole is drilled in the casting connecting the reservoir.

**Fig. 2**—Installation of double seal unit for retaining lubricant in bearing recess and for guarding against entrance of foreign material. Seal is of same general construction as shown in Fig. 1 except that two flanged leathers are mounted opposed to each other.

**Fig. 3**—Used for the same general purposes as arrangement shown in Fig. 2. Seal has but one garter spring for the oil retention leather flange. The leather washer for dust exclusion shown at right has a beveled lip which contacts the shaft.

**Fig. 4**—Sometimes felt is used on the dust exclusion side of the seal in place of leather shown in Figs. 2 and 3. Both sealing materials are retained by spinning the outer casing over the leather clamping cup.

**Fig. 5**—Where there is considerable difference in the diameters, the face of the shoulder thus formed can be utilized as the sealing surface. A soft ring of cork or leather is beveled at the outer surface as shown. A flat spiral spring, coiled to a greater diameter than the hole in the sealing material expands the packing outwards against the beveled ring and wedges it against the face of the shaft shoulder.

**Fig. 6**—Working on the same wedging principle as that shown in Fig. 5, except that the packing is beveled on the inner surface and is retained by a sheet metal flange. The cork or leather sealing material is compressed against the two bearing surfaces by a garter spring as shown. Seals shown in Figs. 5 and 6 are limited to approximately 1/32 in. end play.

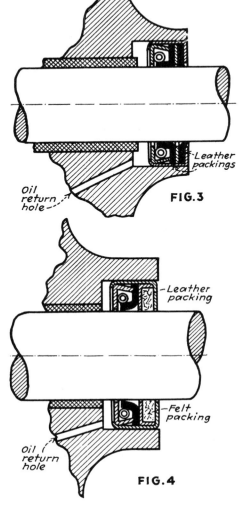

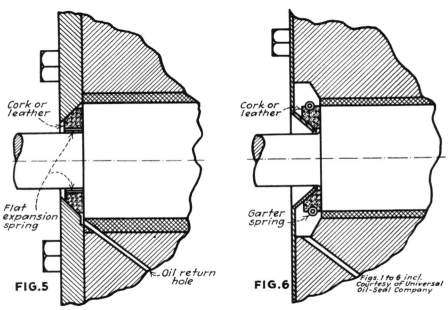

*Figs. 1 to 6 incl.
Courtesy of Universal
Oil-Seal Company*

# Sleeve Bearings

R. G. N. EVANS
*The Bunting Brass & Bronze Company*

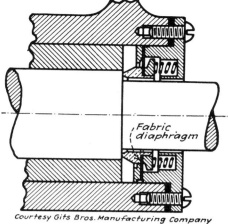

Courtesy Gits Bros. Manufacturing Company

**FIG. 7**

**Fig. 7**—Another type of seal wherein a bronze ring bears against the shoulder of the shaft. The sealing materials is in the form of a diaphragm of heat resisting fabric which retains oil in the bearing and excludes dirt. In the flanged member that is screwed to the housing is a series of compression springs which hold the ring against the shaft shoulder. These springs not only take up wear but provide for end play of the shaft. To avoid torsional strain on the diaphragm guide pins are used between the outer flange and spring bearing washer.

**Fig. 8**—When grease is used as a lubricant, it is sometimes desirable to assemble a single seal to keep dirt from reaching the bearing rather than retain the grease in the bearing. The illustration shows an installation wherein a right hand spiral groove is cut in the bearing bore to lead the lubricant outwards. Surplus grease is forced past the seal thereby keeping the bearing clean.

**Fig. 9**—Leather flange seal with garter spring mounted in a flanged end plate. Spring tension is such as to give small area of contact between leather and shaft, thereby minimizing friction. Bronze thrust washer between bearing and bearing housing.

**Fig. 10**—The labyrinth seal shown does not rely on non-metallic materials but on the small clearances within the assembly. A steel washer contacting a bronze thrust washer, is clamped against the shaft shoulder after the formed dust seal cup is pressed into the counterbored hole.

**Fig. 11**—When oil seals are to be installed after a mechanism has been assembled or to preclude the necessity of disassembling heavy shafts and bearings when making seal renewals, split seals can be used in such installations. The spreader spring and packing ring are split while the retaining cup is made in two halves. The packing is scarf-cut to form an oil-tight joint when assembled.

**Fig. 12**—Another mounting of small worm drive shaft for domestic washing machine and domestic stoker. The composition sealing material is held against the shaft by a V-formed spreader spring having serrated edges which nests into the sealing ring. The angle of the V in the spring is greater than the groove in the seal so that the fingers of the spring exert a light pressure on the sealing lip. An oil return hole is drilled outside the bearing to relieve built-up pressure against the seal.

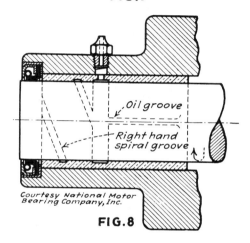

Courtesy National Motor Bearing Company, Inc.

**FIG. 8**

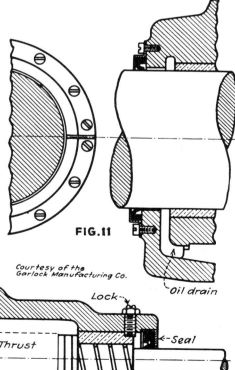

Courtesy of the Garlock Manufacturing Co.

**FIG. 11**

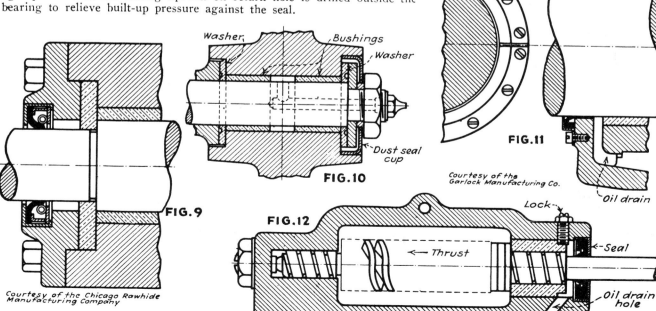

Courtesy of the Chicago Rawhide Manufacturing Company

**FIG. 9**

**FIG. 10**

**FIG. 12**

# Improved Closures for

## Felt seals, metal sealing rings, labyrinths, grooves

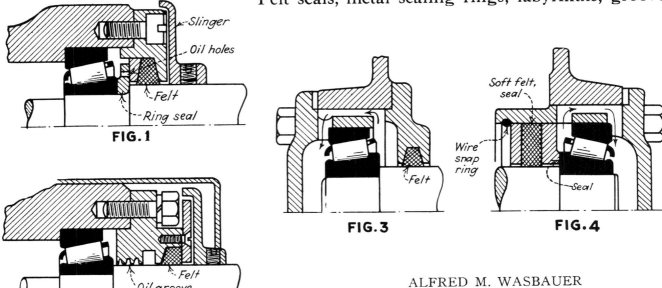

FIG. 1

FIG. 2

FIG. 3

FIG. 4

ALFRED M. WASBAUER

**Fig. 1**—Combination metal ring seal, felt and slinger closure, an economical and efficient type. Oil holes must be drilled through the sealing rings to insure oil saturation of the felt.

**Fig. 2**—Combination oil groove, felt groove and slinger closure for excluding water. This design is cheaper but less effective than that shown in Fig. 1.

**Fig. 3**—Conventional felt groove closure, which can be reasonably oil-tight only as long as the felt makes good contact on the shaft.

**Fig. 4**—Permanent metal seal held in place by a wire snap ring and bearing against inner ring of the roller bearing. Owing to the large section of the felt ring, a soft felt should be used.

**Fig. 5**—Double metal seal closure for drenched or submerged operation. The two seal rings and the felt ring within the end cap must be held stationary and must be drilled to permit saturation of the felt.

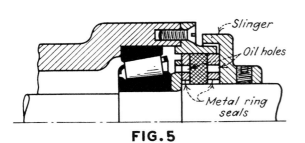

FIG. 5

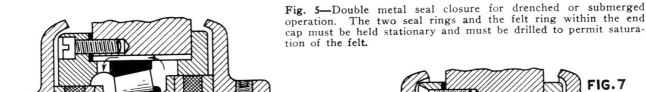

FIG. 6

FIG. 7

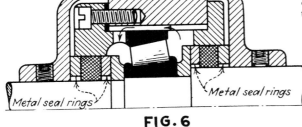

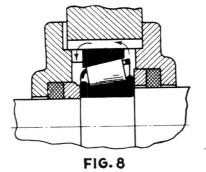

FIG. 8

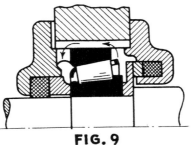

FIG. 9

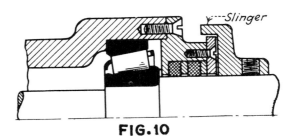

FIG. 10

# Anti-Friction Bearings

## and slingers as used for sealing bearing housings

**FIG. 11**

**FIG. 12**

**FIG. 13**

**FIG. 14**

**FIG. 15**

**FIG. 16**

**FIG. 17**

**Fig. 6**—The metal seal rings must be drilled as in Fig. 1 to permit lubrication of the outer seal.

**Fig. 7**—Labyrinth slingers in combination with annular oil groove. This closure requires accurate machining of the slingers. Its ability to exclude water when the shaft is at rest is doubtful.

**Figs. 8 and 9**—Two designs of closures using felt and metal sealing rings.

**Fig. 10**—Combination double felt groove and slinger closure, a type used in some paper making machinery as an effective method of excluding water from the bearings.

**Figs. 11 to 18**—Various types of closures using leather, felt, oil grooves.

**Figs. 19 to 26**—The closures shown here are of the same general design as those shown in Figs. 11 to 18, but are also equipped with metal sealing rings for the more positive retention of lubricant and exclusion of dirt.

**FIG. 18**

**FIG. 19**

**FIG. 20**

**FIG. 21**

**FIG. 22**

**FIG. 23**

**FIG. 24**

**FIG. 25**

**FIG. 26**

# Methods of Actuating Brakes—

Satisfactory braking depends, in addition to other factors, on speedy and reliable actuating mechanisms. These may be of a variety of types, some of which, utilizing electricity, magnetism and vacuum as a source of power, are described and illustrated below

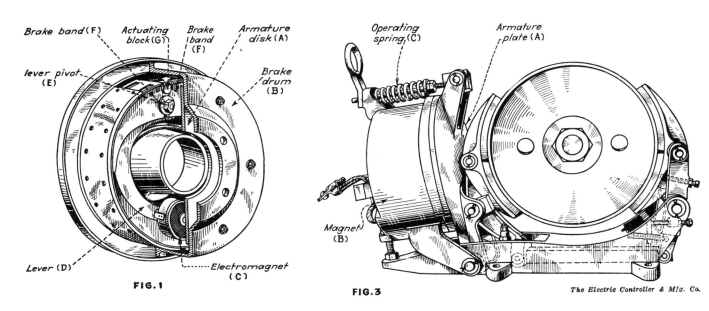

FIG. 1

FIG. 3
The Electric Controller & Mfg. Co.

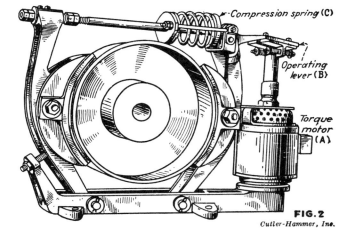

FIG. 2
Cutler-Hammer, Inc.

Fig. 1—The armature disk (A) is secured to and rotates with the brake drum (B). The electro-magnet (C) is supported on the end of lever (D), and is always in light contact with the armature disk. Lever pivot (E) is at a point between the ends of the brake band (F). The electrical input is varied through a controller. As the current flows through the electromagnet, the energized magnet is attracted to the armature disk, which is rotating with the brake drum. The frictional force developed by the magnet pressing against the armature disk draws the lever in the direction in which the brake drum is rotating. This movement of the lever changes the position of the actuating block (G), thereby spreading the brake band so that it presses against the drum. A small flow of current from the controller gives a light braking action. Heavier flows of current permit stronger braking.

Fig. 2—The vertically mounted torque motor (A) operates a simple anti-friction ball jack. When the power is applied to the motor of the brake, the motor shaft turns and lifts the operating lever (B) to release the brake. When the brake is fully released, the torque motor is stalled across the line. When power is interrupted, the torque motor is de-energized and the heavy compression spring (C) applies the brake.

Fig. 3—The armature plate (A) is held away from the magnet (B) by the operating spring (C) which provides the necessary pressure between the brake shoes and the wheel. When the magnet is energized, the armature plate is pulled up to the magnet against the spring pressure, which releases the brake. The magnet remains stationary.

Fig. 4—The plunger action of the solenoid (A) releases the brake. The brake is applied, upon power failure or interruption through a pilot device, by a strong spring action (B).

Fig. 5—The vacuum power cylinder (A) is under control by the hydraulic pressure from the master cylinder (C). Force from the vacuum power cylinder piston is applied through the piston rod to the piston of the hydraulic cylinder. This force is transmitted directly to the wheel cylinders through the hydraulic lines. The vacuum power cylinder piston-rod bears against a valve in the hydraulic cylinder piston. This valve is open when the vacuum power cylinder is in released position, allowing fluid to flow through a passage in the hydraulic piston. The valve remains open until hydraulic line pressure builds up to the point of opening the control valve (B), in response to which the power cylinder piston moves into applied position.

Fig. 6—When the brake pedal is depressed, hydraulic liquid is forced from (A) through the hollow control piston (B) to the brake line (C), which moves the brake shoes into contact with

# Electric, Magnetic and Vacuum

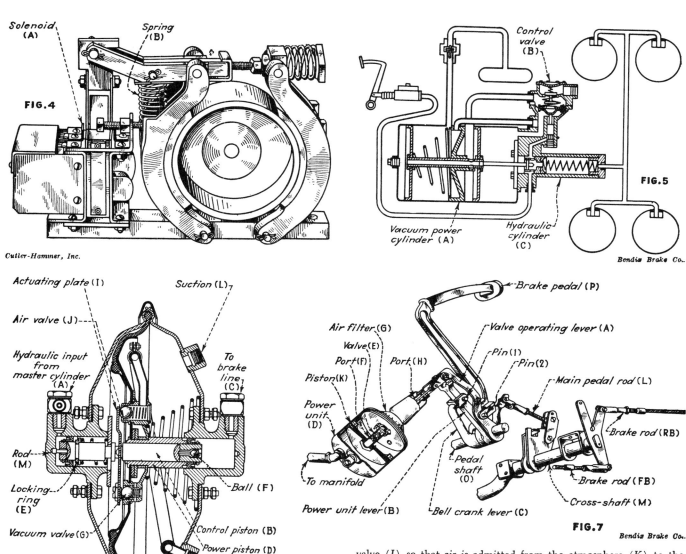

Solenoid (A)

Spring (B)

**FIG.4**

*Cutler-Hammer, Inc.*

Control valve (B)

**FIG.5**

Vacuum power cylinder (A)

Hydraulic cylinder (C)

*Bendix Brake Co.*

Actuating plate (I)

Suction (L)

Air valve (J)

Hydraulic input from master cylinder (A)

To brake line (C)

Rod (M)

Locking ring (E)

Ball (F)

Vacuum valve (G)

Control piston (B)

Power piston (D)

**FIG.6**

Diaphragm (H)

Atmosphere (K)

*Empire Electric Brake Co.*

Brake pedal (P)

Air filter (G)

Valve operating lever (A)

Valve (E)

Pin (I)

Port (F)

Pin (2)

Port (H)

Main pedal rod (L)

Piston (K)

Power unit (D)

Brake rod (RB)

Pedal shaft (O)

Brake rod (FB)

To manifold

Cross-shaft (M)

Power unit lever (B)

Bell crank lever (C)

**FIG.7**

*Bendix Brake Co.*

valve (J) so that air is admitted from the atmosphere (K) to the pressure side of the diaphragm while the vacuum on the other side is maintained through the continuous suction (L) from the intake manifold. The admission of air into the booster is modulated to apply the brakes with a force proportional to the pedal pressure. As the brake pedal is further depressed, air continues to flow into the pressure side of the diaphragm, reaching atmospheric pressure when full force has been expended on the pedal. The vacuum-hydraulic power is then fully applied. The rod (M) in control piston (B) meets ball (F) when the brake pedal is fully released.

Fig. 7—As the brake pedal (P) is depressed, the initial travel operates the internal valve (E) within the power unit (D) through the valve operating lever (A). Atmosphere is admitted through port (F), first passing through air filter (G) and past (H) to the rear chamber of the cylinder. Atmospheric pressure forces the piston (K) forward, actuating power unit lever (B) which in turn relays the power through bell crank lever (C) to the main pedal rod (L) connected with the cross-shaft (M). Due to the fact that the power unit lever (B) has a clearance around the pedal shaft (O) and is pivoted at pin (1) a certain proportion of the power derived from the cylinder is balanced against the brake pedal (P) through pin (2). Cables (RB) and (FB) transmit the power from cross-shaft (M) to the shoes and drums.

the brake drum. As the pedal is depressed further, the control piston (B) running through the center of power piston (D) is forced to move toward the secondary end by the increasing pressure of the liquid against the primary end of the piston. The primary end of the piston has a larger surface than the secondary end because of the locking ring (E) back of the piston cup. As the piston moves, the ball (F) is free to seal, permitting the flow of fluid from points (A) to (C), but checking the flow in the opposite direction. Simultaneously, the vacuum valve (G) connecting the two sides of the rubber diaphragm (H) is forced to close by the movement of the valve actuating plate (I) so that vacuum can no longer pass from one side of the diaphragm to the other. When the brake pedal is depressed slightly further and the hydraulic pressure is increased accordingly, the resulting movement of the control piston (B) causes the actuating plate (I) to open air

# METHODS OF ACTUATING BRAKES—

In addition to the methods presented in the January issue, other methods are in constant use. Some of these, utilizing air, magnetism, and hydraulics as a source of power, are described and illustrated below.

**FIG. 1** — Compressed air enters the diaphragm at (A) and actuates rod and pin (B), connected to linkage (C) which applies the shoes to the wheel.

**FIG. 2** — Armature plate (A) is held away from magnet (B) by operating spring (C) which provides the necessary pressure between the brake shoes and the wheel. When the magnet is energized, the armature plate is pulled up to the magnet against the spring pressure, which releases the brake. Air diaphragm (D), to which a compressed air line is attached, aids in pulling the armature plate up to the magnet against the spring pressure when the brake is released.

**FIG. 3** — Sketch I represents the application valve in the released position. Exhaust check valve (A) is open. Inlet check valve (B) is seated. The inlet chamber is under pressure through port (C) which is connected to the air reservoir. The application side of the system is open to atmosphere through port (D). When the brake pedal is depressed, pressure is applied by the valve actuating linkage to metering spring plunger (E), plunger movement causes metering spring (F), piston (G) and diaphragm (H)

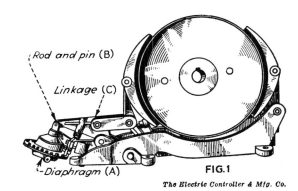

**FIG. 1**

*The Electric Controller & Mfg. Co.*

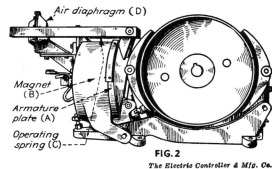

**FIG. 2**

*The Electric Controller & Mfg. Co.*

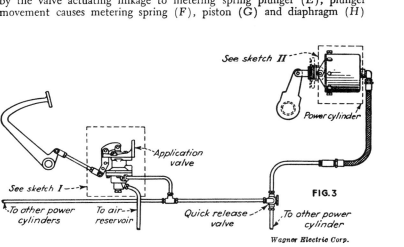

**FIG. 3**

*Wagner Electric Corp.*

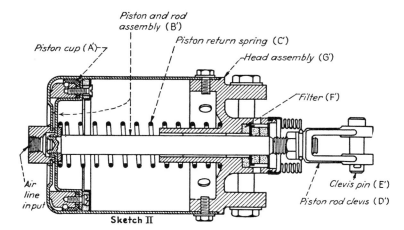

**Sketch II**

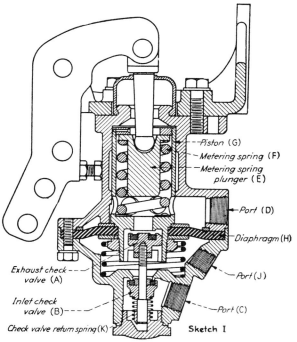

**Sketch I**

# PNEUMATIC, MAGNETIC AND HYDRAULIC

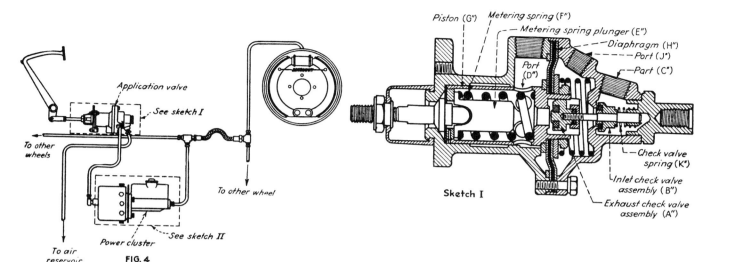

Piston (G") — Metering spring (F")
— Metering spring plunger (E")
— — Diaphragm (H")
— Port (J")
Port (D") — Part (C")
— Check valve spring (K")
Inlet check valve assembly (B")
Exhaust check valve assembly (A")

**Sketch I**

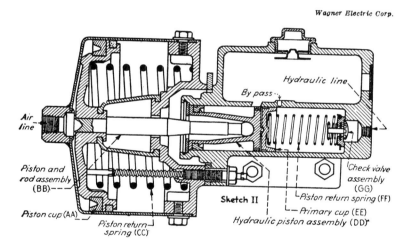

Wagner Electric Corp.

Hydraulic line
By pass
Air line
Piston and rod assembly (BB)
Piston cup (AA)
Piston return spring (CC)
**Sketch II**
Check valve assembly (GG)
Piston return spring (FF)
Primary cup (EE)
Hydraulic piston assembly (DD)

**FIG. 4** — Sketch I illustrates application valve assembly in the released position. Exhaust check valve assembly (A") is open. Inlet check-valve assembly (B") is seated. The inlet chamber is under pressure through port (C") which is connected to the air reservoir. The application side of system is open to atmosphere through port (D"). When brake pedal is depressed, pressure is applied by valve actuating linkage to metering spring plunger (E"), plunger movement causes metering spring (F") piston (G"), and diaphragm (H") to move downward closing exhaust check valve assembly (A") and forcing inlet check valve assembly (B") from its seat. This admits air pressure to the application side of the system through port (J"). As the brake pedal is further depressed, reaction or balance takes place in the application valve assembly. The air pressure on the application side of the system forces diaphragm (H") upward, compressing metering spring (F") and allowing check valve spring (K") to move inlet check valve assembly (B") upward to its seat. In this position the application valve assembly holds the applied air pressure constant until the brake pedal is further depressed or released. The power cluster (Sketch II) provides a predetermined top operating hydraulic line pressure. The power unit is illustrated in the released position. When air pressure is admitted through the air inlet port, piston cup (AA) seals against the cylinder wall. Piston and rod assembly (BB) moves inward, compressing piston return spring (CC) and contacts hydraulic piston assembly (DD). As the air pressure is increased, hydraulic assembly (DD) and primary cup (EE), which seals the hydraulic cylinder, moves inward closing the by-pass port and compressing piston return spring (FF). This begins the hydraulic pressure stroke, and fluid under pressure flows through check valve assembly (GG), into the hydraulic line. When the applied air pressure is released, piston return springs (CC and FF) force piston and rod assembly (BB) and piston assembly (DD) to their released position. The air pressure is exhausted through the exhaust port of the air brake valves. Hydraulic fluid, under pressure, returning through the lines raises check valve assembly (GG) from its seat, allowing the fluid to flow through the by-pass port into the fluid reservoir. Atmospheric pressure is admitted and expelled through the air cylinder breather port.

to move downward closing exhaust check valve assembly (A) and forcing inlet check valve assembly (B) from its seat. This admits air pressure to the application side of the system through port (J). As the brake pedal is further depressed, reaction or balance takes place in the application valve assembly. The air pressure on the application side of the system forces diaphragm (H) upward, compressing metering spring (F) and allowing check valve return spring (K) to move inlet check valve assembly (B) upward to its seat. In this position the application valve assembly holds the applied air pressure constant until the brake pedal is further depressed or released. The air power cylinder assembly (Sketch II) converts the energy contained in compressed air into mechanical force which, through linkage, expands the brake shoes. Sketch II illustrates the power cylinder assembly in the released position. When the air pressure is admitted through the inlet port, piston cup (A') seals against the cylinder wall. Piston and rod assembly (B') moves forward, compressing piston return spring (C') and actuating the brake linkage which is attached to piston rod clevis (D') by clevis pin (E'). When the applied air pressure is released, piston return spring (C') forces piston and rod assembly (B') to its released position. Atmospheric pressure is admitted and expelled through breather port in assembly (G'), passing through filter (F').

# TYPICAL METHODS OF COUPLING

Methods of coupling rotating shafts vary from simple bolted flange constructions to complex spring and synthetic rubber mechanisms. Some types incorporating chain belts, splines, bands, and rollers are described and illustrated below.

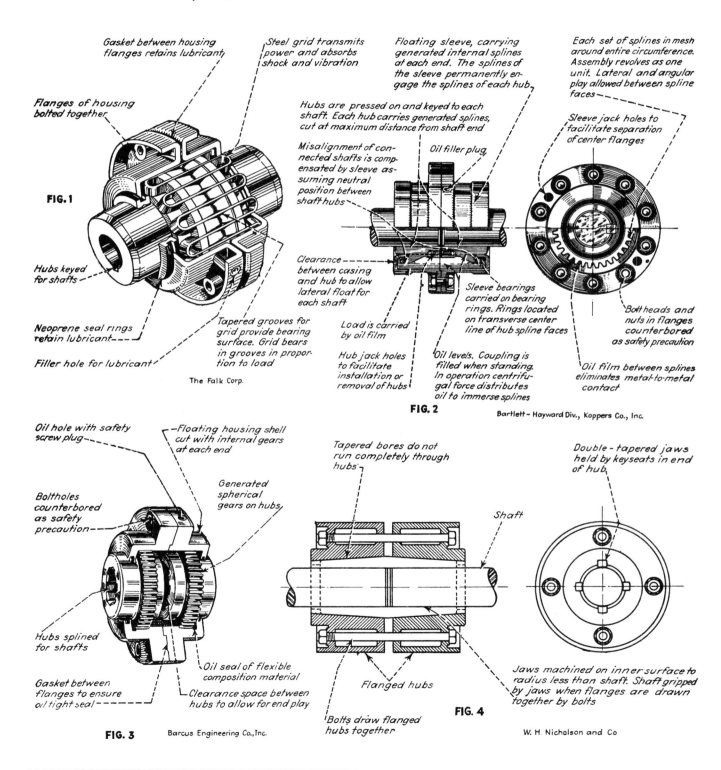

**FIG. 1**

Gasket between housing flanges retains lubricant

Flanges of housing bolted together

Hubs keyed for shafts

Neoprene seal rings retain lubricant

Filler hole for lubricant

The Falk Corp.

Steel grid transmits power and absorbs shock and vibration

Tapered grooves for grid provide bearing surface. Grid bears in grooves in proportion to load

Floating sleeve, carrying generated internal splines at each end. The splines of the sleeve permanently engage the splines of each hub

Hubs are pressed on and keyed to each shaft. Each hub carries generated splines, cut at maximum distance from shaft end

Misalignment of connected shafts is compensated by sleeve assuming neutral position between shaft hubs

Oil filler plug

Clearance between casing and hub to allow lateral float for each shaft

Load is carried by oil film

Hub jack holes to facilitate installation or removal of hubs

Sleeve bearings carried on bearing rings. Rings located on transverse center line of hub spline faces

Oil levels. Coupling is filled when standing. In operation centrifugal force distributes oil to immerse splines

Each set of splines in mesh around entire circumference. Assembly revolves as one unit. Lateral and angular play allowed between spline faces

Sleeve jack holes to facilitate separation of center flanges

Bolt heads and nuts in flanges counterbored as safety precaution

Oil film between splines eliminates metal-to-metal contact

**FIG. 2**

Bartlett-Hayward Div., Koppers Co., Inc.

Oil hole with safety screw plug

Boltholes counterbored as safety precaution

Hubs splined for shafts

Gasket between flanges to ensure oil tight seal

Floating housing shell cut with internal gears at each end

Generated spherical gears on hubs

Oil seal of flexible composition material

Clearance space between hubs to allow for end play

**FIG. 3**    Barcus Engineering Co., Inc.

Tapered bores do not run completely through hubs

Shaft

Flanged hubs

Bolts draw flanged hubs together

Double-tapered jaws held by keyseats in end of hub

Jaws machined on inner surface to radius less than shaft. Shaft gripped by jaws when flanges are drawn together by bolts

**FIG. 4**    W. H. Nicholson and Co

# ROTATING SHAFTS—I

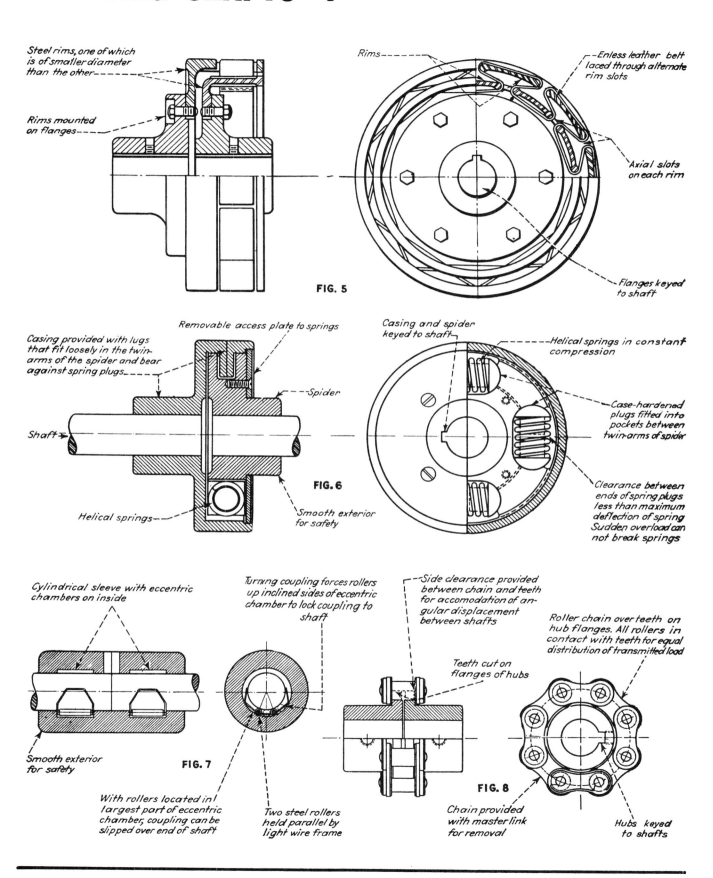

Steel rims, one of which is of smaller diameter than the other----

Rims mounted on flanges----

Rims----

-Enless leather belt laced through alternate rim slots

Axial slots on each rim

Flanges keyed to shaft

**FIG. 5**

Casing provided with lugs that fit loosely in the twin-arms of the spider and bear against spring plugs----

Removable access plate to springs

Casing and spider keyed to shaft-

Spider

-Helical springs in constant compression

Shaft

Helical springs----

Smooth exterior for safety

**FIG. 6**

Case-hardened plugs fitted into pockets between twin-arms of spider

Clearance between ends of spring plugs less than maximum deflection of spring Sudden overload can not break springs

Cylindrical sleeve with eccentric chambers on inside

Turning coupling forces rollers up inclined sides of eccentric chamber to lock coupling to shaft

Side clearance provided between chain and teeth for accomodation of angular displacement between shafts

Teeth cut on flanges of hubs

Roller chain over teeth on hub flanges. All rollers in contact with teeth for equal distribution of transmitted load

Smooth exterior for safety

**FIG. 7**

With rollers located in largest part of eccentric chamber, coupling can be slipped over end of shaft

Two steel rollers held parallel by light wire frame

**FIG. 8**

Chain provided with master link for removal

Hubs keyed to shafts

# TYPICAL METHODS OF COUPLING

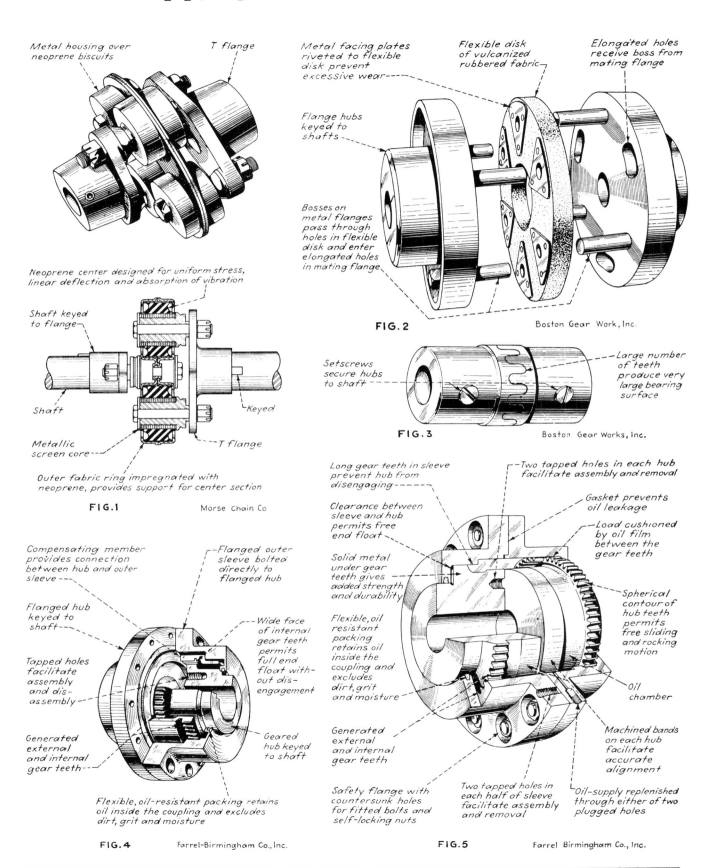

Metal housing over neoprene biscuits

T flange

Neoprene center designed for uniform stress, linear deflection and absorption of vibration

Shaft keyed to flange

Shaft

Metallic screen core

T flange

Keyed

Outer fabric ring impregnated with neoprene, provides support for center section

**FIG.1**          Morse Chain Co

Metal facing plates riveted to flexible disk prevent excessive wear

Flange hubs keyed to shafts

Bosses on metal flanges pass through holes in flexible disk and enter elongated holes in mating flange

Flexible disk of vulcanized rubbered fabric

Elongated holes receive boss from mating flange

**FIG.2**          Boston Gear Work, Inc.

Setscrews secure hubs to shaft

Large number of teeth produce very large bearing surface

**FIG.3**          Boston Gear Works, Inc.

Compensating member provides connection between hub and outer sleeve

Flanged hub keyed to shaft

Tapped holes facilitate assembly and disassembly

Generated external and internal gear teeth

Flanged outer sleeve bolted directly to flanged hub

Wide face of internal gear teeth permits full end float without disengagement

Geared hub keyed to shaft

Flexible, oil-resistant packing retains oil inside the coupling and excludes dirt, grit and moisture

**FIG.4**          Farrel-Birmingham Co., Inc.

Long gear teeth in sleeve prevent hub from disengaging

Clearance between sleeve and hub permits free end float

Solid metal under gear teeth gives added strength and durability

Flexible, oil resistant packing retains oil inside the coupling and excludes dirt, grit and moisture

Generated external and internal gear teeth

Safety flange with countersunk holes for fitted bolts and self-locking nuts

Two tapped holes in each half of sleeve facilitate assembly and removal

Two tapped holes in each hub facilitate assembly and removal

Gasket prevents oil leakage

Load cushioned by oil film between the gear teeth

Spherical contour of hub teeth permits free sliding and rocking motion

Oil chamber

Machined bands on each hub facilitate accurate alignment

Oil-supply replenished through either of two plugged holes

**FIG.5**          Farrel Birmingham Co., Inc.

# ROTATING SHAFTS—II

Shaft couplings that utilize internal and external gears, balls, pins, and non-metallic parts to transmit torque are shown herewith.

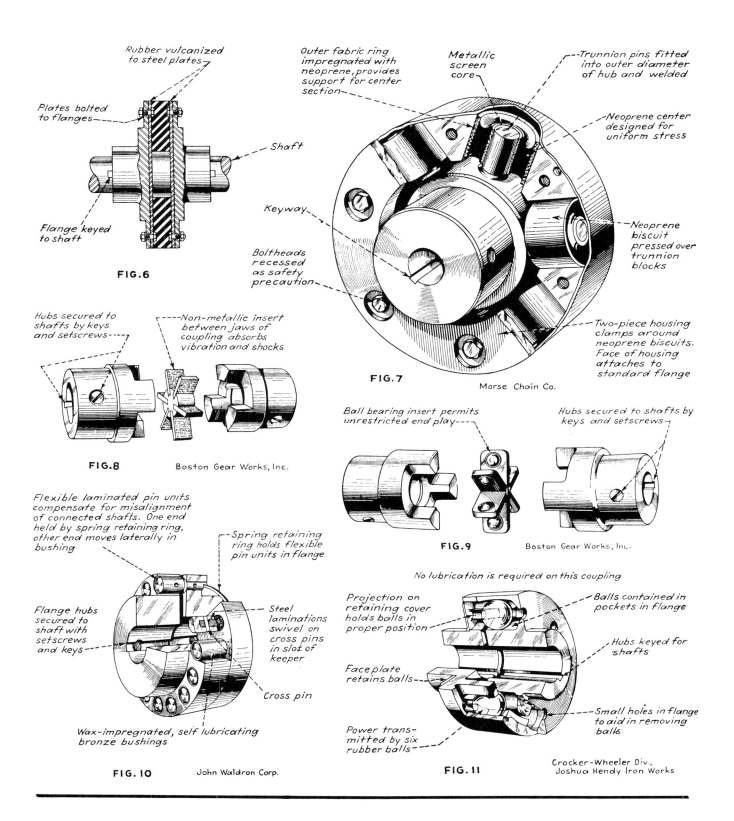

Rubber vulcanized to steel plates

Plates bolted to flanges

Shaft

Flange keyed to shaft

**FIG. 6**

Outer fabric ring impregnated with neoprene, provides support for center section

Metallic screen core

Trunnion pins fitted into outer diameter of hub and welded

Neoprene center designed for uniform stress

Keyway

Boltheads recessed as safety precaution

Neoprene biscuit pressed over trunnion blocks

Two-piece housing clamps around neoprene biscuits. Face of housing attaches to standard flange

**FIG. 7**    Morse Chain Co.

Hubs secured to shafts by keys and setscrews

Non-metallic insert between jaws of coupling absorbs vibration and shocks

**FIG. 8**    Boston Gear Works, Inc.

Ball bearing insert permits unrestricted end play

Hubs secured to shafts by keys and setscrews

**FIG. 9**    Boston Gear Works, Inc.

Flexible laminated pin units compensate for misalignment of connected shafts. One end held by spring retaining ring, other end moves laterally in bushing

Spring retaining ring holds flexible pin units in flange

Flange hubs secured to shaft with setscrews and keys

Steel laminations swivel on cross pins in slot of keeper

Cross pin

Wax-impregnated, self lubricating bronze bushings

**FIG. 10**    John Waldron Corp.

No lubrication is required on this coupling

Projection on retaining cover holds balls in proper position

Face plate retains balls

Power transmitted by six rubber balls

Balls contained in pockets in flange

Hubs keyed for shafts

Small holes in flange to aid in removing balls

**FIG. 11**    Crocker-Wheeler Div., Joshua Hendy Iron Works

# Typical Methods of Providing

Below are shown various lubricating systems that can serve as guides

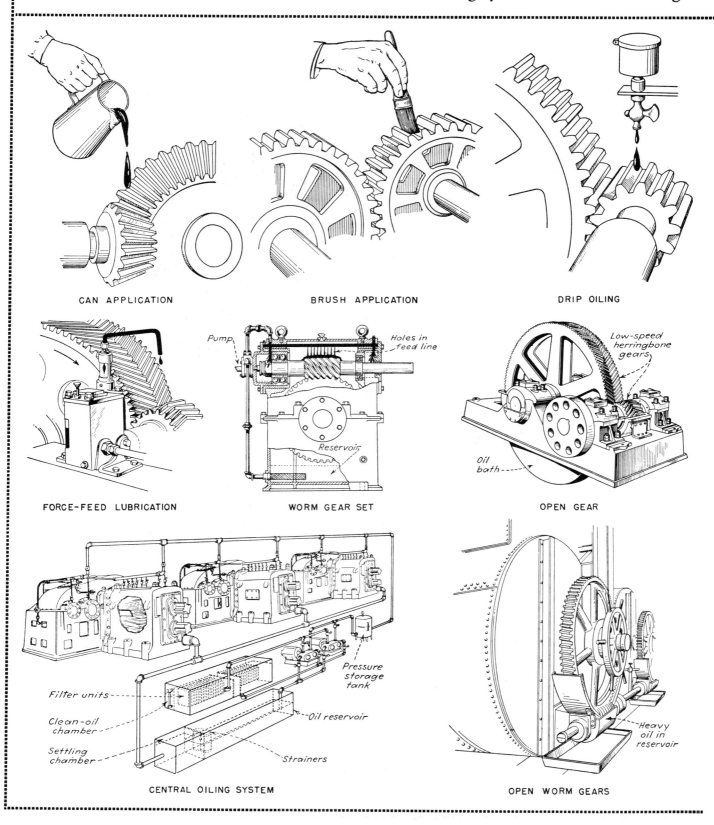

CAN APPLICATION

BRUSH APPLICATION

DRIP OILING

FORCE-FEED LUBRICATION

WORM GEAR SET

Pump

Holes in feed line

Reservoir

OPEN GEAR

Low-speed herringbone gears

Oil bath

CENTRAL OILING SYSTEM

Filter units

Clean-oil chamber

Settling chamber

Pressure storage tank

Oil reservoir

Strainers

OPEN WORM GEARS

Heavy oil in reservoir

# Lubrication for Gear Systems

When designing for successful, efficient gear systems.

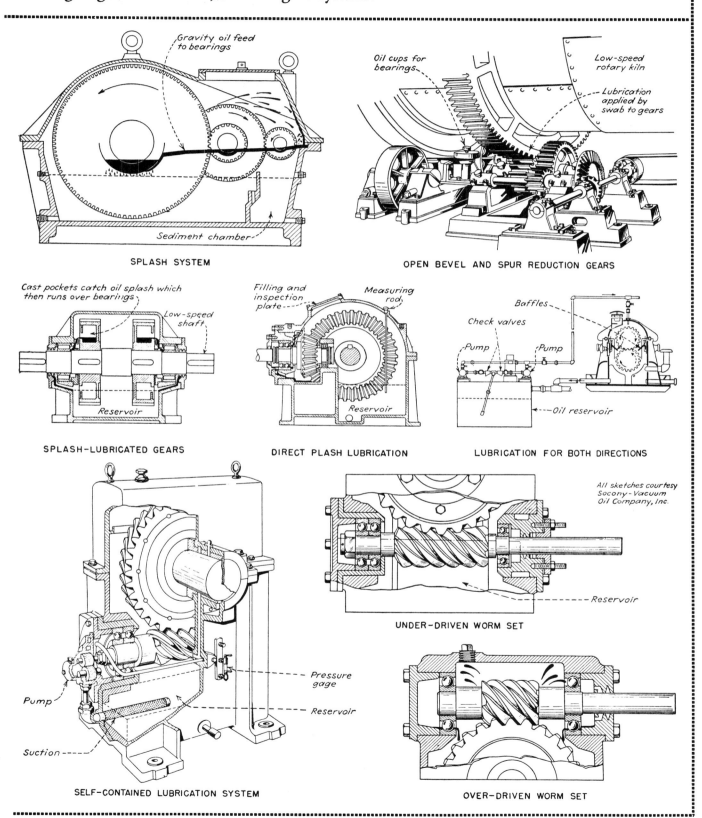

**SPLASH SYSTEM**

**OPEN BEVEL AND SPUR REDUCTION GEARS**

**SPLASH-LUBRICATED GEARS**

**DIRECT PLASH LUBRICATION**

**LUBRICATION FOR BOTH DIRECTIONS**

**SELF-CONTAINED LUBRICATION SYSTEM**

**UNDER-DRIVEN WORM SET**

**OVER-DRIVEN WORM SET**

All sketches courtesy Socony-Vacuum Oil Company, Inc.

# 1-WAY OUTPUT FROM SPEED REDUCERS

When input reverses, these 5 slow-down mechanisms continue supplying a non-reversing rotation.

**LOUIS SLEGEL**
*Head, Dept of Mechanical Engineering*
*Oregon State College*
*Corvallis, Ore*

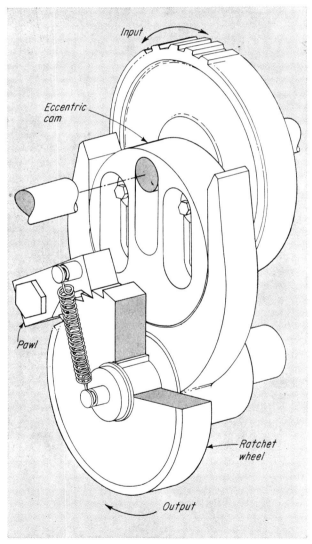

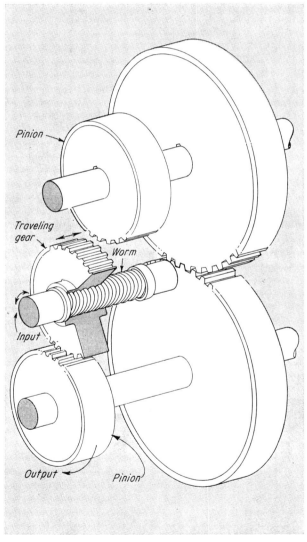

**1** ECCENTRIC CAM adjusts over a range of high-reduction ratios, but unbalance limits it to low speeds. When direction of input changes, there is no lag in output rotation. Output shaft moves in steps because of ratchet drive through pawl which is attached to U-follower.

**2** TRAVELING GEAR moves along worm and transfers drive to other pinion when input rotation changes direction. To ease engagement, gear teeth are tapered at ends. Output rotation is smooth, but there is a lag after direction changes as gear shifts. Gear cannot be wider than axial offset between pinions, or there will be interference.

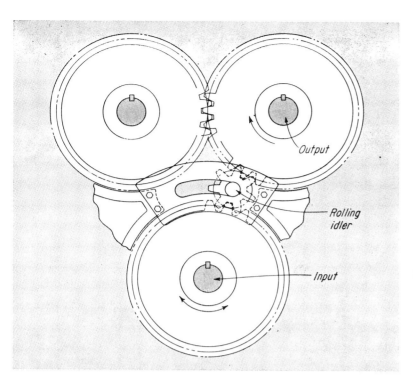

**3** **ROLLING IDLER** also gives smooth output and slight lag after input direction changes. Small drag on idler is necessary, so that it will transfer into engagement with other gear and not sit spinning in between.

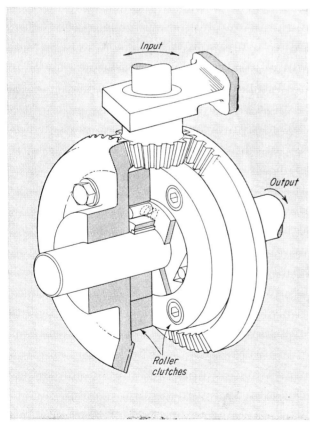

**4** **TWO BEVEL GEARS** drive through roller clutches. One clutch catches in one direction; the other catches in the opposite direction. There is negligible interruption of smooth output rotation when input direction changes.

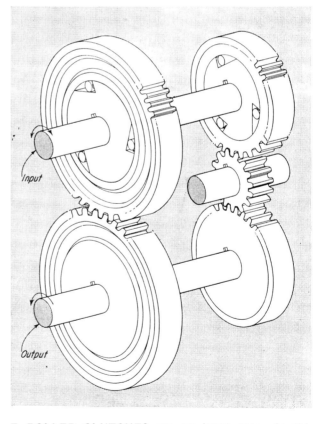

**5** **ROLLER CLUTCHES** are on input gears in this drive, again giving smooth output speed and little output lag as input direction changes.

295

# TORQUE-LIMITERS PROTECT
# LIGHT-DUTY DRIVES

In such drives the light parts break easily when overloaded.
These eight devices disconnect them from dangerous torque
surges.

**L KASPER,**
*design consultant*
*Philadelphia*

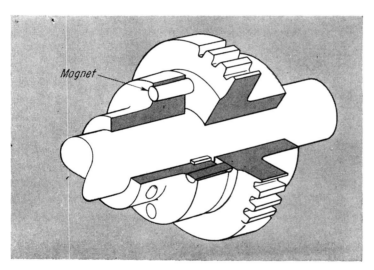

**1**
**MAGNETS** transmit torque according to their number and size.
In-place control is limited to lowering torque capacity by remov-
ing magnets.

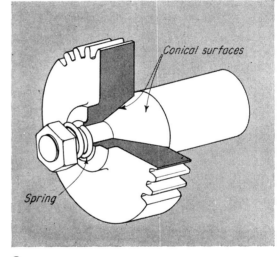

**2**
**CONE CLUTCH** is formed by mating taper on
shaft to beveled hole through gear. Tightening
down on nut increases torque capacity.

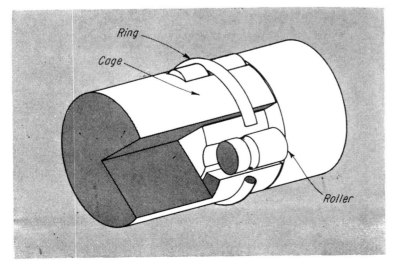

**3**
**RING** fights natural tendency of rollers to jump
out of grooves cut in reduced end of one shaft.
Slotted end of hollow shaft is like a cage.

# TORQUE LIMITERS continued

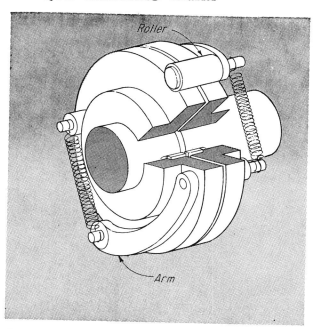

**4**
**ARMS** hold rollers in slots which are cut across disks mounted on ends of butting shafts. Springs keep rollers in slots; over-torque forces them out.

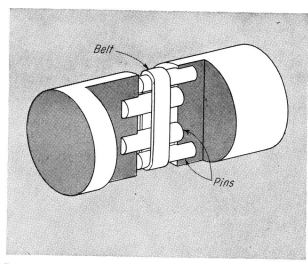

**5**
**FLEXIBLE BELT** wrapped around four pins transmits only lightest loads. Outer pins are smaller than inner pins to ensure contact.

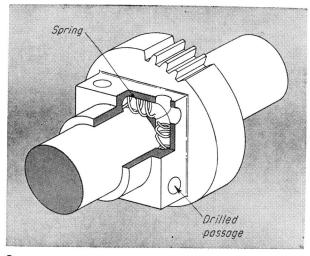

**6**
**SPRINGS** inside drilled block grip the shaft because they distort during mounting of gear.

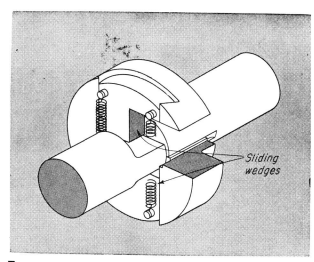

**7**
**SLIDING WEDGES** clamp down on flattened end of shaft; spread apart when torque gets too high. Strength of springs which hold wedges together sets torque limit.

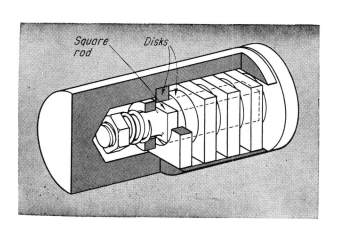

**8**
**FRICTION DISKS** are compressed by adjustable spring. Square disks lock into square hole in left shaft; round ones lock onto square rod on right shaft.

*Chapter 9*

# SPRING DEVICES

# How spring clamps

Here's a review of ways in which spring clamp devices can help you get a grip on things.

*FEDERICO STRASSER, Mankowitz and Strasser, Santiago, Chile*

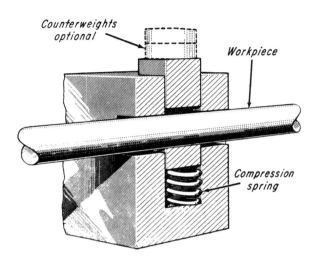

**1** **RODS OF DIFFERENT SECTION** can be easily held by this device. Strength of grip can be varied if necessary.

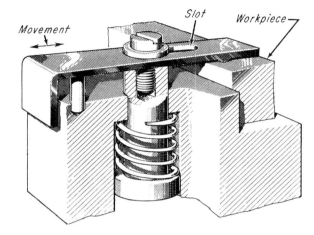

**2** **SECOND-CLASS LEVER** gives low clamping forces for parts that are easily marked or require gentle handling.

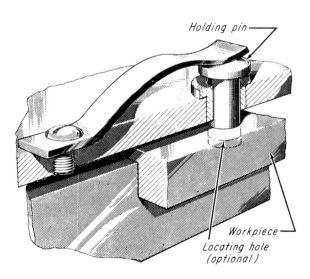

**5** **FLAT SPRING ACTS THROUGH PIN** that holds the workpiece in the fixture. This device also positively locates parts.

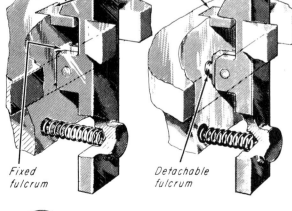

**6** **COVER LATCH** is an ideal application for spring and notched lever. Make the fulcrum detachable for ease of repair.

# hold workpieces

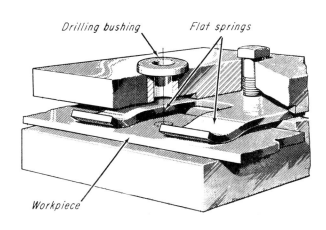

Drilling bushing — Flat springs

Workpiece

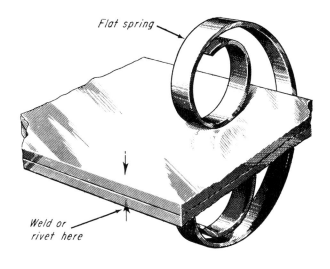

Flat spring

Weld or rivet here

**FLAT WORKPIECES** of constant thickness are held with a couple of flat springs attached to the jig table.

**SIMPLE CLAMPING FIXTURE** is ideal for holding two flat pieces of material together for either welding or riveting.

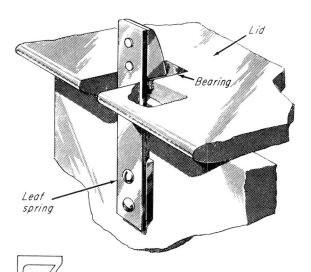

Lid

Bearing

Leaf spring

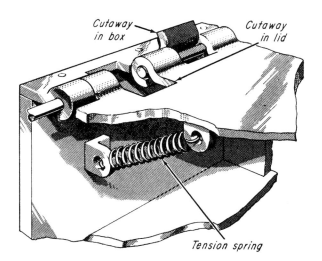

Cutaway in box — Cutaway in lid

Tension spring

**LEAF-SPRING** latch can be fashioned as shown, or the spring itself can be formed to provide its own latching notch.

**POSITIVE OPEN-OR-SHUT** lid relies upon a spring. Over-center spring action makes the lid a simple toggle.

301

# Flat springs in

These devices all rely on a flat spring for their efficient actions, which would otherwise need more complex configurations.

*L. KASPER, Philadelphia*

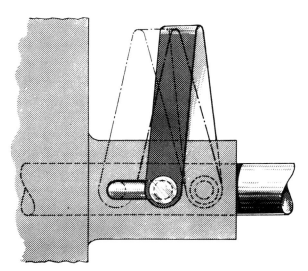 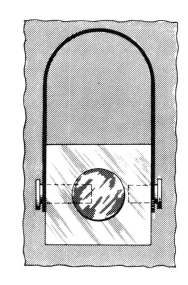

**1** **CONSTANT FORCE** is approached because of the length of this U-spring. Don't align studs or spring will fall.

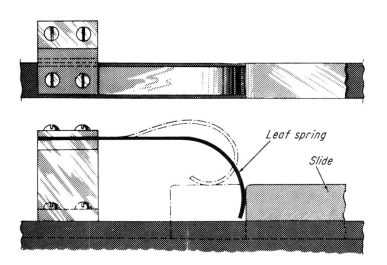

Leaf spring

Slide

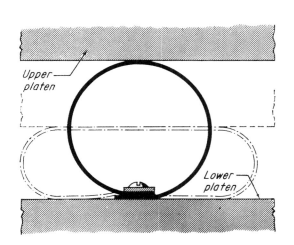

Upper platen

Lower platen

**4** **SPRING-LOADED SLIDE** will always return to its original position unless it is pushed until the spring kicks out.

**5** **INCREASING SUPPORT AREA** as the load increases on both upper and lower platens is provided by a circular spring.

# mechanisms

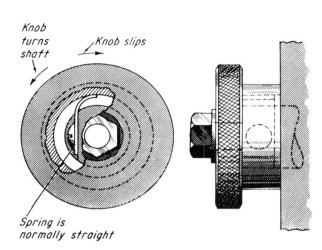

Knob
turns
shaft

Knob slips

Spring is
normally straight

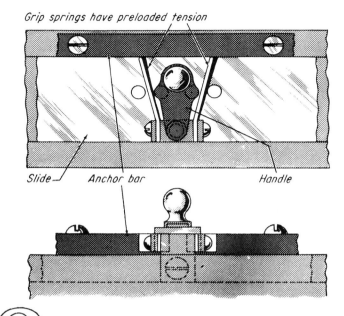

Grip springs have preloaded tension

Slide   Anchor bar   Handle

**FLAT-WIRE SPRAG** is straight until the knob is assembled; thus tension helps the sprag to grip for one-way clutching.

**EASY POSITIONING** of the slide is possible when the handle pins move a grip spring out of contact with the anchor bar.

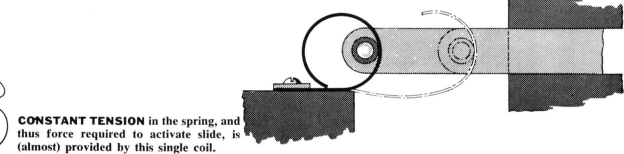

**CONSTANT TENSION** in the spring, and thus force required to activate slide, is (almost) provided by this single coil.

Frame

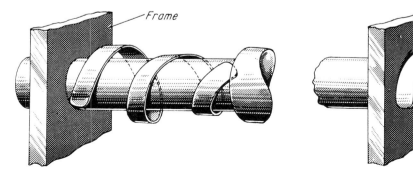

**VOLUTE SPRING** here lets the shaft be moved closer to the frame, thus allowing maximum axial movement.

# Flat springs find

Five additional examples of the way flat springs perform important jobs in mechanical devices.

*L. KASPER, Philadelphia*

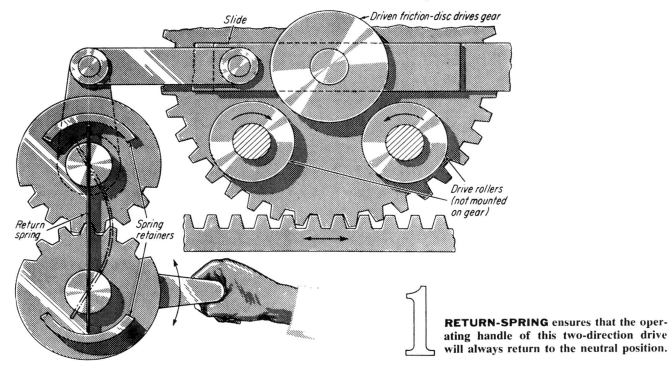

Slide

Driven friction-disc drives gear

Drive rollers (not mounted on gear)

Return spring

Spring retainers

**1** **RETURN-SPRING** ensures that the operating handle of this two-direction drive will always return to the neutral position.

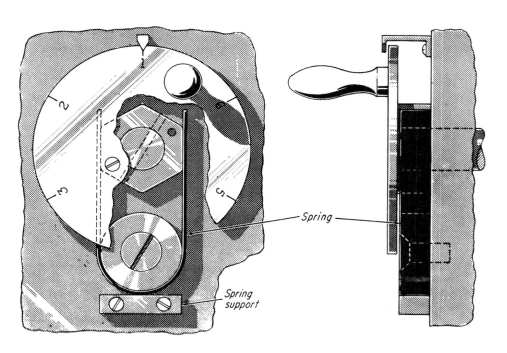

Spring

Spring support

**3** **INDEXING** is accomplished simply, efficiently, and at low cost by the flat-spring arrangement shown here.

# more work

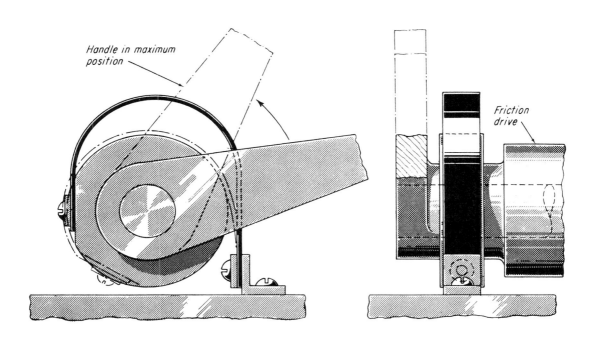

Handle in maximum position

Friction drive

**SPRING-MOUNTED DISK** changes center position as handle is rotated to move friction drive, also acts as built-in limit stop.

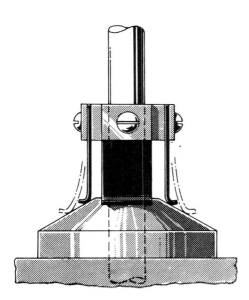

**CUSHIONING** device features rapid increase of spring tension because of the small pyramid angle. Rebound is minimum, too.

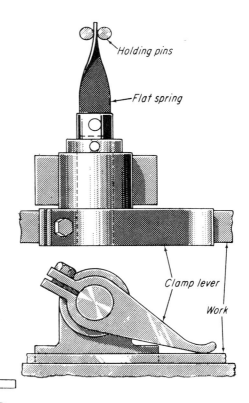

Holding pins

Flat spring

Clamp lever

Work

**HOLD-DOWN CLAMP** has flat spring assembled with initial twist to provide clamping force for thin material.

# SPRING MOTORS AND TYPICAL

MANY applications of spring motors in clocks, phonographs, motion picture cameras, rotating barber poles, game machines and other mechanisms offer practical ideas for adaptation to any mechanism in which operation for an appreciable length of time is desirable. While spring motors are usually limited to comparatively small power applications where other sources of power are unavailable or impracticable, they may also be useful for intermittent operation requiring

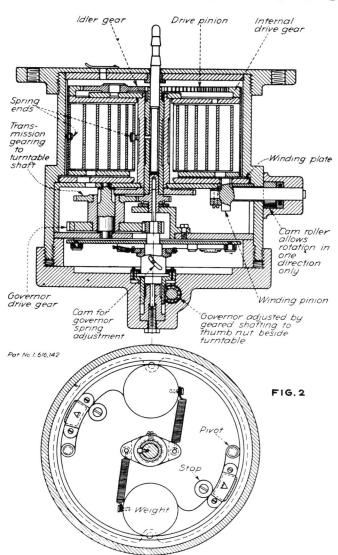

Idler gear  Drive pinion  Internal drive gear

Spring ends
Transmission gearing to turntable shaft

Winding plate

Cam roller allows rotation in one direction only

Governor drive gear

Cam for governor spring adjustment

Winding pinion

Governor adjusted by geared shafting to thumb nut beside turntable

Pat No 1,616,142

FIG. 2

Pivot

Stop

Weight

Governor

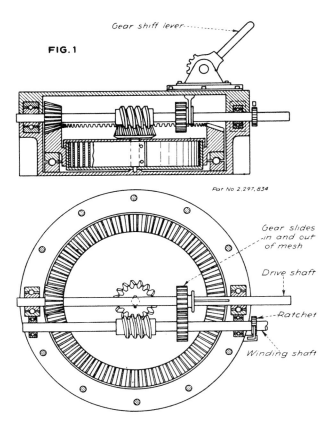

Gear shift lever

FIG. 1

Pat No 2,297,834

Gear slides in and out of mesh

Drive shaft

Ratchet

Winding shaft

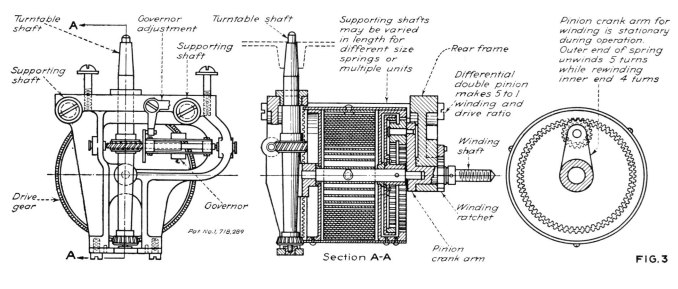

Turntable shaft

Governor adjustment

Supporting shaft

Supporting shaft

Drive gear

Governor

Pat. No. 1,718,289

Turntable shaft

Supporting shafts may be varied in length for different size springs or multiple units

Rear frame

Differential double pinion makes 5 to 1 winding and drive ratio

Winding shaft

Winding ratchet

Section A-A

Pinion crank arm

Pinion crank arm for winding is stationary during operation. Outer end of spring unwinds 5 turns while rewinding inner end 4 turns

FIG. 3

# ASSOCIATED MECHANISMS

comparatively high torque or high speed, using a low power electric motor or other means for building up energy.

The accompanying patented spring motor designs show various methods of transmission and control of spring motor power. Flat-coil springs, confined in drums, are most widely used because they are compact, produce torque directly, and permit long angular displacement. Gear trains and feed-back mechanisms hold down excess power so that it can be applied for a longer time, and governors are commonly used to regulate speed.

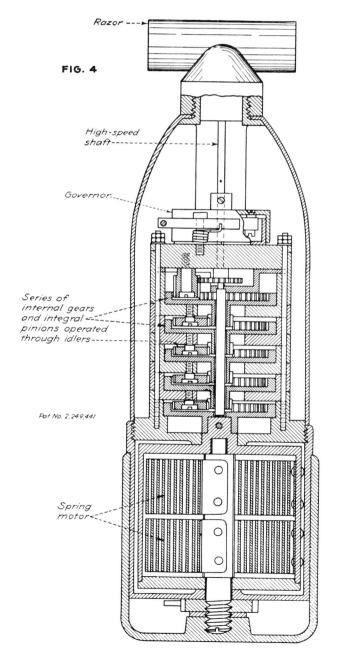

FIG. 4

Razor

High-speed shaft

Governor

Series of internal gears and integral pinions operated through idlers

Pat. No. 2,249,441

Spring motor

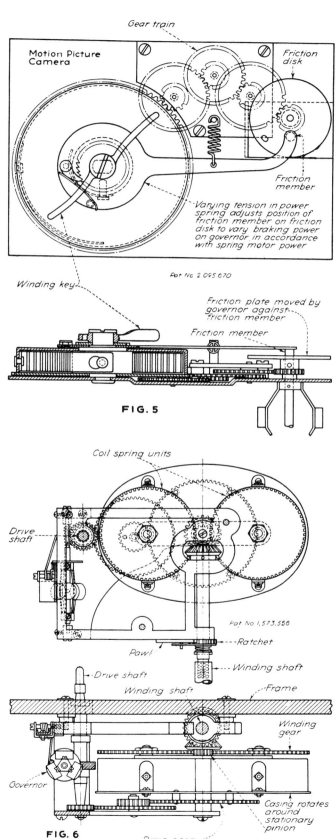

Gear train

Motion Picture Camera

Friction disk

Friction member

Varying tension in power spring adjusts position of friction member on friction disk to vary braking power on governor in accordance with spring motor power

Winding key

Pat No 2,095,670

Friction plate moved by governor against friction member

Friction member

FIG. 5

Coil spring units

Drive shaft

Pat. No. 1,573,556

Ratchet

Pawl

Winding shaft

Drive shaft

Winding shaft

Frame

Winding gear

Governor

Casing rotates around stationary pinion

FIG. 6

Drive gear

# 8 Electrical jobs

Put these handy assembly devices to work as terminals, connectors, actuators, etc.

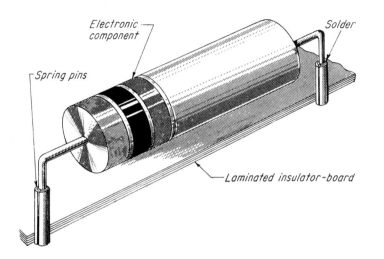

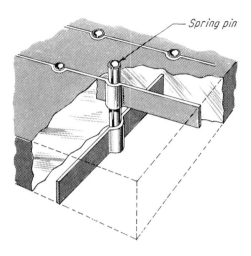

**1** **LOW-COST TERMINALS** are made by assembling two 1/16-in.-dia tin-dipped Rollpins into phenolic board. The board should be about 3/32 in. thick.

**2** **AS ELECTRICAL CONNECTORS** in "patchboard" circuits, spring pins have ample conductivity. Select various circuits by removing or inserting pins.

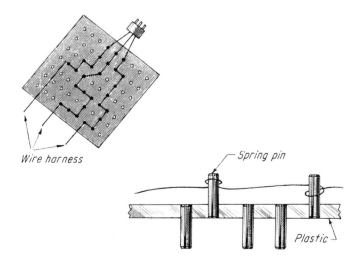

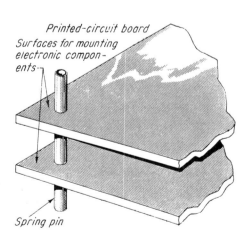

**5** **FORMING FIXTURE** for wire harnesses is quickly adjusted when different harness-shapes are needed. Plastic sheet has pin holes on ¼-in. centers.

**6** **STAND-OFFS** for printed-circuit boards can be spring pins. Select a pin long enough to ensure adequate spacing between the boards.

# for spring pins

*ANDREW J TURNER, Rollpin product manager, Elastic Stop Nut Corp, Union, NJ*

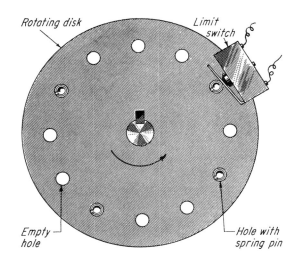

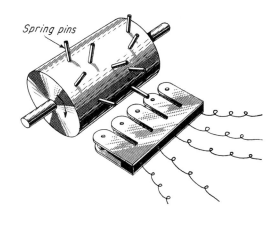

**SWITCH ACTUATORS** can be quickly relocated in rotating disk if spring pins are employed. Hard steel of pin gives excellent wear resistance.

**DRUM-MOUNTED ACTUATORS** function in similar way to spring-pin actuators in Fig. 3. Protruding length of pins may be critical, but is easily adjusted.

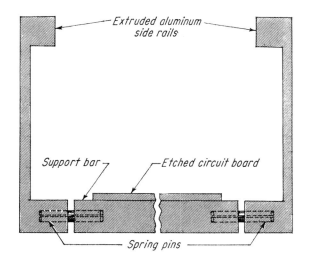

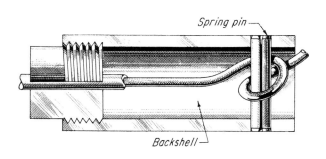

**SUPPORT BARS** in electronic units can be easily and quickly installed into the sliding chassis with spring pins. Close tolerances are not needed.

**STRAIN RELIEF** for wire in electrical connectors will not slip during assembly. Loop wire then fill shell with potting compound to seal wire in place.

# 8 Unusual jobs

Be sure you get top value from these versatile assembly devices. These examples show how.

ANDREW J TURNER, Rollpin product manager, Elastic Stop Nut Corp, Union, NJ

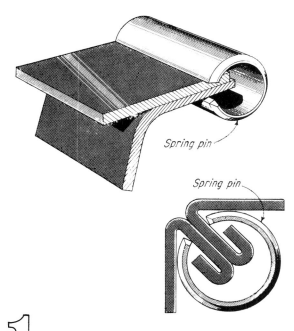

Spring pin

Spring pin

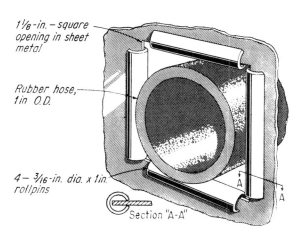

1⅛-in.-square opening in sheet metal

Rubber hose, 1in O.D.

4 – ³/₁₆-in. dia. x 1in. rollpins

Section "A-A"

**1** **SLOT IN PIN** does duty as anchoring device, holding two pieces together. Fastening can be either permanent or temporary. Parts can be metal or non-metal.

**2** **PROTECT HYDRAULIC** tubing or electrical wires touching sharp edges of casings by clipping pins over the edges of the hole. Its size is only slightly reduced.

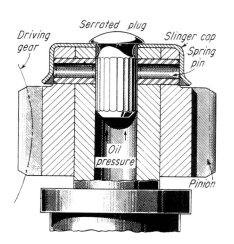

Driving gear

Serrated plug

Slinger cap

Spring pin

Oil pressure

Pinion

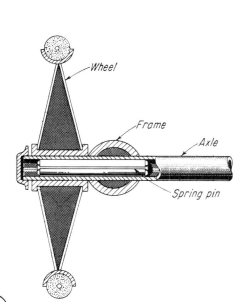

Wheel

Frame

Axle

Spring pin

**5** **LUBRICANT PASSAGE** is combined with retaining pin for gear. Also, slinger ring not only performs functionally but improves appearance too.

**6** **STIFFEN LIGHT-DUTY** structures such as tubular axles with spring pins; they are simple to install and add considerable strength to the assembly.

# for spring pins

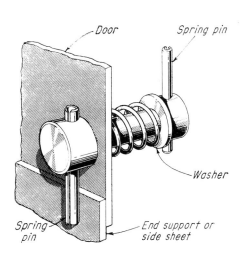

Door
Spring pin
Washer
Spring pin
End support or side sheet

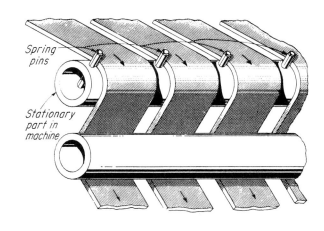

Spring pins
Stationary part in machine

**TWO PINS SERVE AS HANDLE** and latch. This low-cost assembly replaces an expensive forged handle and a fabricated-metal latch-piece.

**AS BELT GUIDES,** spring pins eliminate molded spacers, or costly machined grooves for spacer rings which would otherwise be needed.

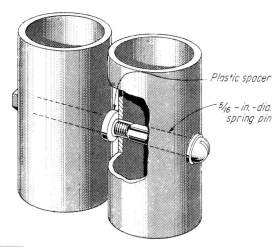

Plastic spacer
5/16 - in. - dia. spring pin

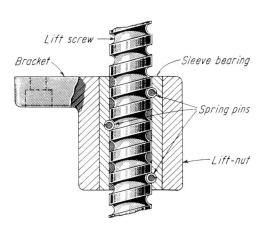

Lift screw
Bracket
Sleeve bearing
Spring pins
Lift-nut

**HARDENED STEEL SLEEVE** for pivot-screw gives durability to legs of folding table illustrated here, while keeping costs competitively low.

**LOW-COST THREAD** in lift-nut can be made by fitting spring pins at correct pitch-positions as shown. Rotate the pins to reduce wear.

# ONE SPRING RETURNS THE HAND LEVER

These seven designs need only a single spring—compression, extension, flat or torsion.

**L KASPER,** consultant
*Philadelphia*

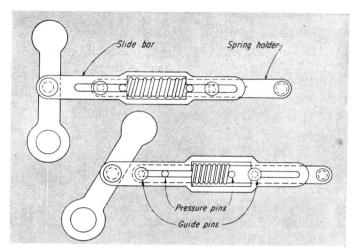

**1**
**SLIDE BAR** attached to lever compresses spring against pressure pins in either direction. Guide pins in spring holder hit end of slot to limit movement.

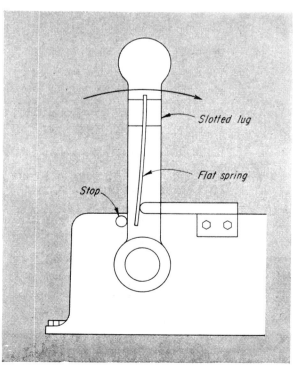

**2**
**FLAT SPRING** has initial tension which gives positive return for even a small lever-movement.

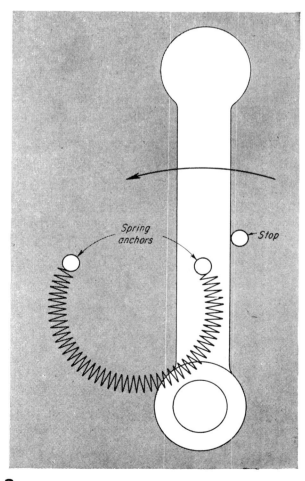

**3**
**CLOSE-WOUND HELICAL SPRING** gives almost constant return force. Anchor post for spring also acts as limit stop.

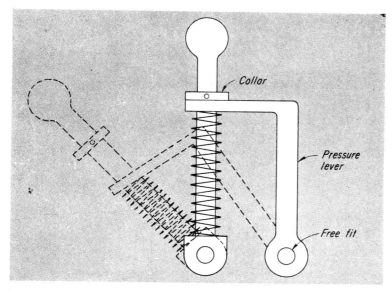

**4**
**PRESSURE LEVER** returns hand lever because it rotates on a different center. Collar sets starting position.

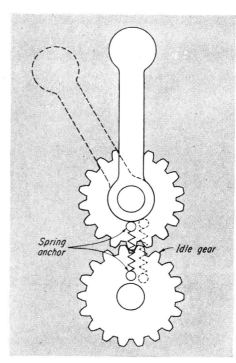

**5**
**GEARS** extend spring when lever moves up to 180° in either direction.

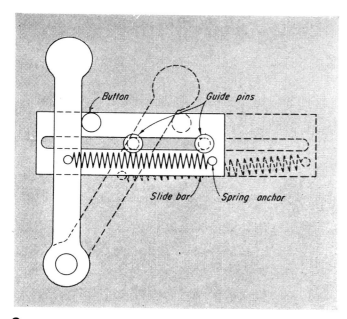

**6**
**SLIDE BAR** rides on guide pins as lever pushes it to right. Stretched spring pulls slide bar against lever to return lever to vertical position.

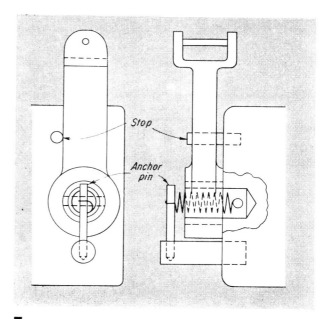

**7**
**OPEN-WOUND HELICAL SPRING** extends inside shaft of handle. Coils must be wound in direction of movement so that spring tightens instead of unwinds as lever turns.

# ONE SPRING
# RETURNS THE HAND LEVER

A flat, torsion or helical spring does the job alone.

**L KASPER,** *consultant*
*Philadelphia*

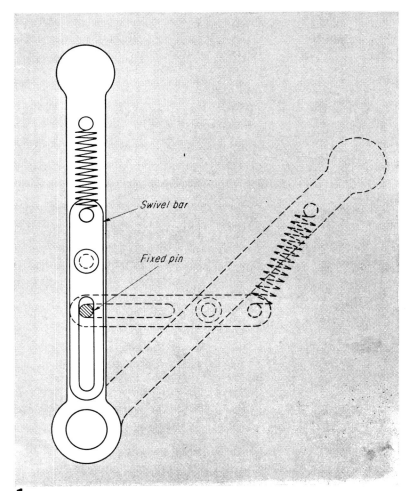

**1**
SWIVEL BAR, which slides on fixed pin, returns hand lever. Slot in swivel bar is limit stop for movement either way.

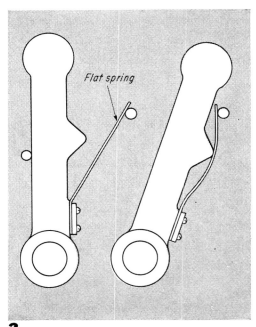

**2**
HIGHER SPRING RATE, when the projection hits the flat spring, warns operator he's approaching end of travel and assures quick disengagement.

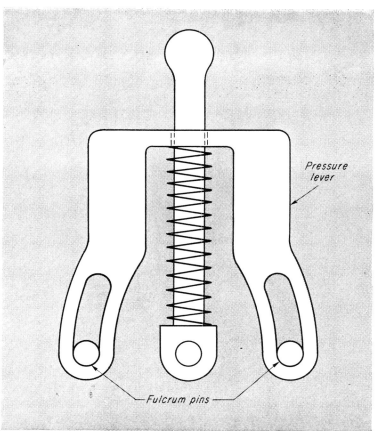

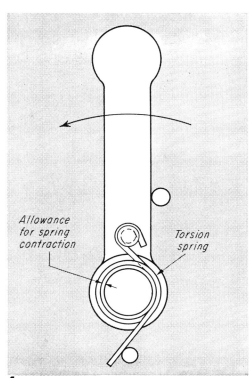

**4**
**TORSION SPRING** must have coil diameter larger than shaft diameter to allow for spring contraction during windup.

**3**
**DOUBLE PRESSURE-LEVER** returns handle to center from either direction by compressing spring. Lever pivots on one pin and comes to stop against the other pin.

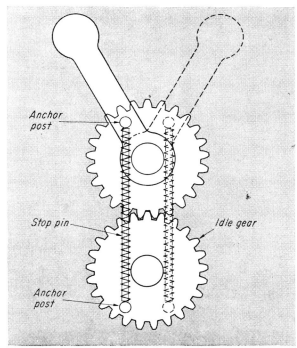

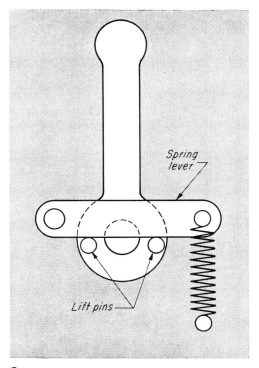

**5**
**LEVER** flops to stop because of spring pull. Stop-pins inside springs limit movement.

**6**
**SELF-CENTERING HAND LEVER** returns to vertical as soon as it's released. Any movement lifts spring lever and creates a righting force.

# 12 ways to put springs

Variable-rate arrangements, roller
positioning, space saving, and other
ingenious ways to get the most from springs.

*L. KASPER, Philadelphia*

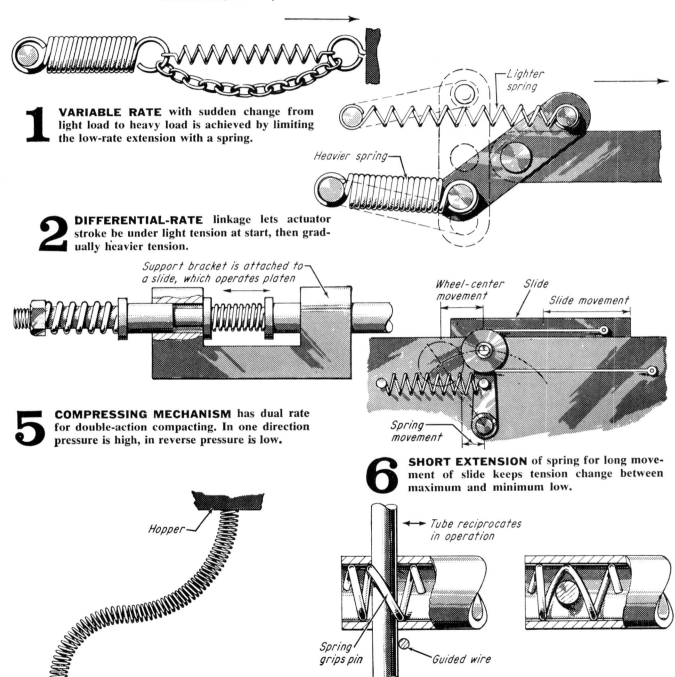

**1** **VARIABLE RATE** with sudden change from
light load to heavy load is achieved by limiting
the low-rate extension with a spring.

**2** **DIFFERENTIAL-RATE** linkage lets actuator
stroke be under light tension at start, then gradually heavier tension.

Lighter spring

Heavier spring

Support bracket is attached to
a slide, which operates platen

Wheel-center movement   Slide   Slide movement

Spring movement

**5** **COMPRESSING MECHANISM** has dual rate
for double-action compacting. In one direction
pressure is high, in reverse pressure is low.

**6** **SHORT EXTENSION** of spring for long movement of slide keeps tension change between
maximum and minimum low.

Hopper

Tube reciprocates
in operation

Spring grips pin

Guided wire

**9** **CLOSE-WOUND SPRING** is attached to a
hopper and will not buckle when used as a
movable feed-duct for nongranular material.

**10** **PIN GRIP** is spring that holds pin by friction
against end movement or rotation, but lets pin
be repositioned without tools.

# to work

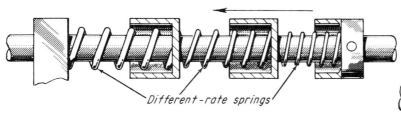

Different-rate springs

**3** **THREE-STEP RATE** change at predetermined positions. The lighter springs will always compress first regardless of their position.

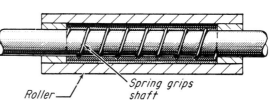

Roller—

Spring grips shaft

**4** **ROLLER POSITIONING** by tight-wound spring on shaft obviates necessity for collars. Roller will slide under excess end thrust.

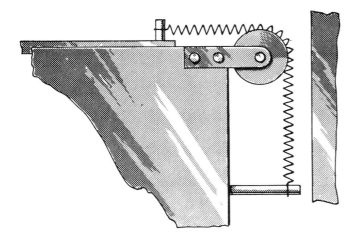

**7** **SPRING WHEEL** helps distribute deflection over more coils than if spring rested on corner. Less fatigue and longer life result.

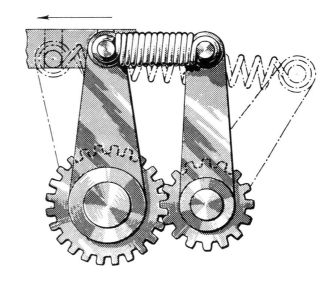

**8** **INCREASED TENSION** for same movement is gained by providing a movable spring mount and gearing it to the other movable lever.

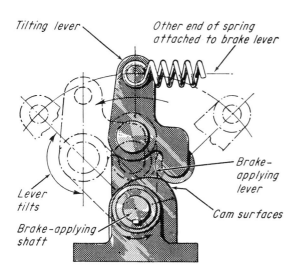

Tilting lever

Other end of spring attached to brake lever

Brake-applying lever

Cam surfaces

Lever tilts

Brake-applying shaft

**11** **TENSION VARIES** at different rate when brake-applying lever reaches the position shown. Rate is reduced when tilting lever tilts.

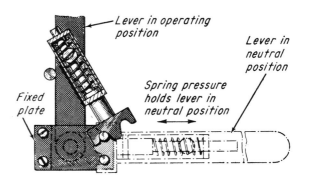

Lever in operating position

Lever in neutral position

Fixed plate

Spring pressure holds lever in neutral position

**12** **TOGGLE ACTION** here is used to make sure the gear-shift lever will not inadvertently be thrown past neutral.

# Chapter 10

# WELDING AND BRAZING

# EXAMPLES OF VARIOUS WELDING

Sketches showing various ways to conserve weld material and to strengthen welded joints. Schematic diagrams depicting many applications of welding techniques.

## JOINING DISSIMILAR METALS

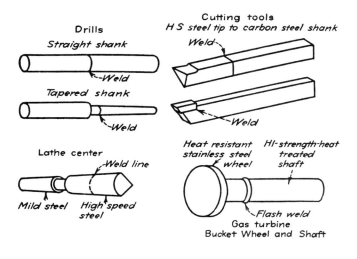

Drills
Straight shank
—Weld

Tapered shank
—Weld

Cutting tools
H S steel tip to carbon steel shank
Weld

Weld

Lathe center
—Weld line
Mild steel    High speed steel

Heat resistant stainless steel wheel    HI-strength-heat treated shaft
Flash weld
Gas turbine Bucket Wheel and Shaft

## PROJECTION WELDING

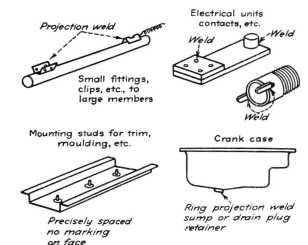

Projection weld
Small fittings, clips, etc., to large members

Electrical units contacts, etc.
Weld    Weld
Weld

Mounting studs for trim, moulding, etc.
Precisely spaced no marking on face

Crank case
Ring projection weld sump or drain plug retainer

## WELDING FOR STRENGTH AND APPEARANCE

Handles
Weld button for wire handle

Oil filter
Seam weld
Projection weld on sump ring

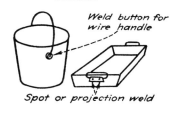

Spot or projection weld

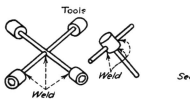

Tools
Weld

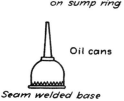

Oil cans
Seam welded base

## JOINING ODD SHAPES

Gratings, mats, etc.

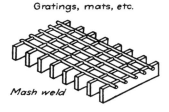

Mash weld

Spot weld

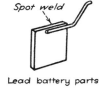

Lead battery parts

Seam welding bellows

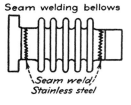

Seam weld Stainless steel

Metal tubing

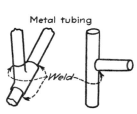

Weld

## TEMPORARY AND PERMANENT JOINING

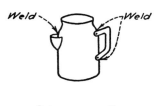

Weld    Weld

Pots, pans, pails etc.

Screens

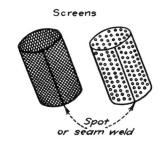

Spot or seam weld

Spot weld key to can top

Containers

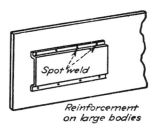

Spot weld

Reinforcement on large bodies

# DESIGNS AND TECHNIQUES

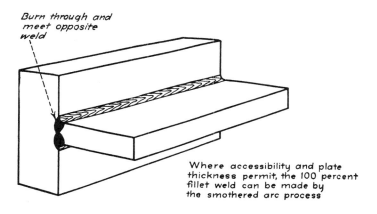

Where accessibility and plate thickness permit, the 100 percent fillet weld can be made by the smothered arc process

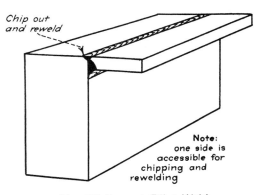

Note: one side is accessible for chipping and rewelding

**The 100 Percent Fillet Weld**

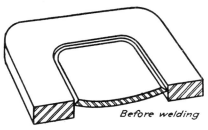

*Before welding*

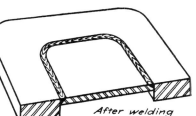

*After welding*

Closing accessibility openings
Note closure plate is dished before welding

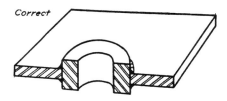

*Correct*

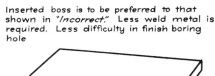

Inserted boss is to be preferred to that shown in *"Incorrect."* Less weld metal is required. Less difficulty in finish boring hole

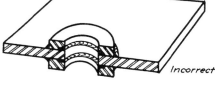

*Incorrect*

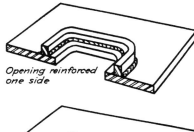

*Opening reinforced one side*

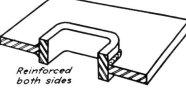

*Reinforced both sides*

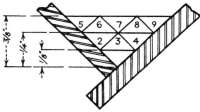

The deposited metal goes up as the square of the fillet size

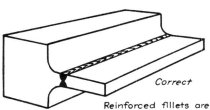

*Correct*

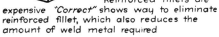

*Incorrect*

Reinforced fillets are expensive *"Correct"* shows way to eliminate reinforced fillet, which also reduces the amount of weld metal required

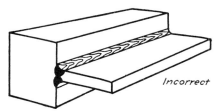

*Correct*

*Incorrect*

When possible, make weld in lightest plate

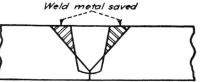

*Weld metal saved*

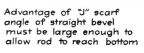

Advantage of "J" scarf angle of straight bevel must be large enough to allow rod to reach bottom

# Methods for Maintaining Positions and

A series of sketches indicating various ways to hold the positions and dimensions of parts during the brazing process. Examples are shown of welding and assembly techniques, permanent and temporary methods of support and three instances of poor practice. Sketches courtesy the General Electric Company.

### POSITIONS HELD BY SPOT AND TACK WELDING

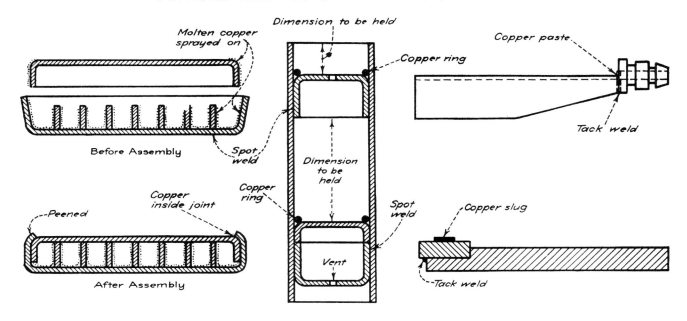

### TYPE OF ASSEMBLY KEEPS POSITION

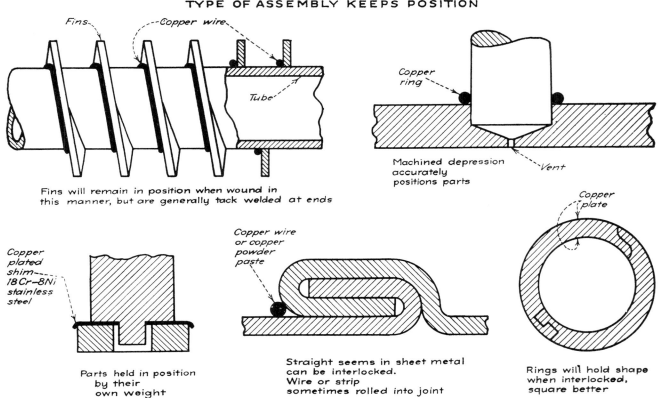

Fins will remain in position when wound in this manner, but are generally tack welded at ends

Machined depression accurately positions parts

Parts held in position by their own weight

Straight seems in sheet metal can be interlocked. Wire or strip sometimes rolled into joint

Rings will hold shape when interlocked, square better

# Dimensions of Parts During Brazing

## POSITIONS HELD BY WEDGES, PINS, AND SCREWS

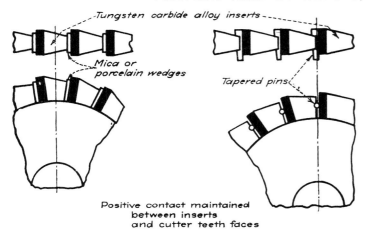

Positive contact maintained
between inserts
and cutter teeth faces

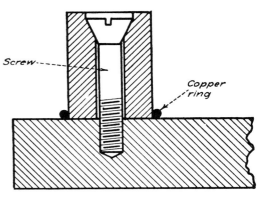

Exact position maintained

## PERMANT AND TEMPORARY METHODS OF HOLDING PARTS

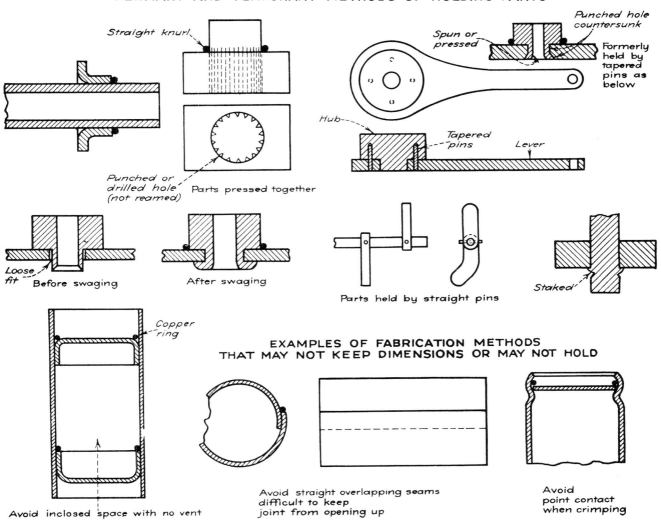

Parts pressed together

Parts held by straight pins

### EXAMPLES OF FABRICATION METHODS
### THAT MAY NOT KEEP DIMENSIONS OR MAY NOT HOLD

Avoid inclosed space with no vent

Avoid straight overlapping seams
difficult to keep
joint from opening up

Avoid
point contact
when crimping

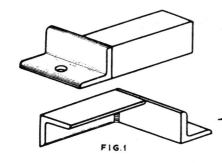

# Typical Joints of Arc-Welded Structurals—I

R. A. GAST
*The Lincoln Electric Company*

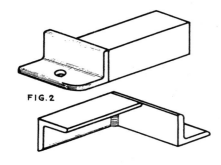

Examples of welded joints showing various methods of joining at right angles, standard structural angles, channels, H-sections, I-beams and combinations of these shapes.

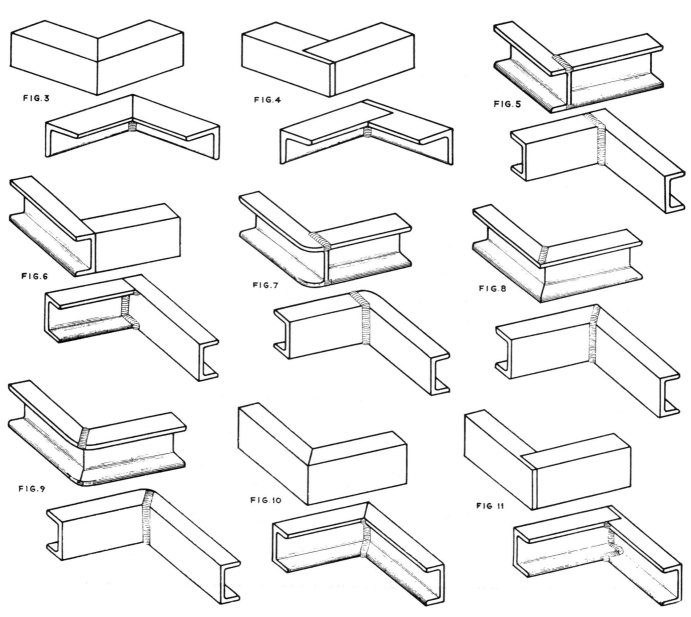

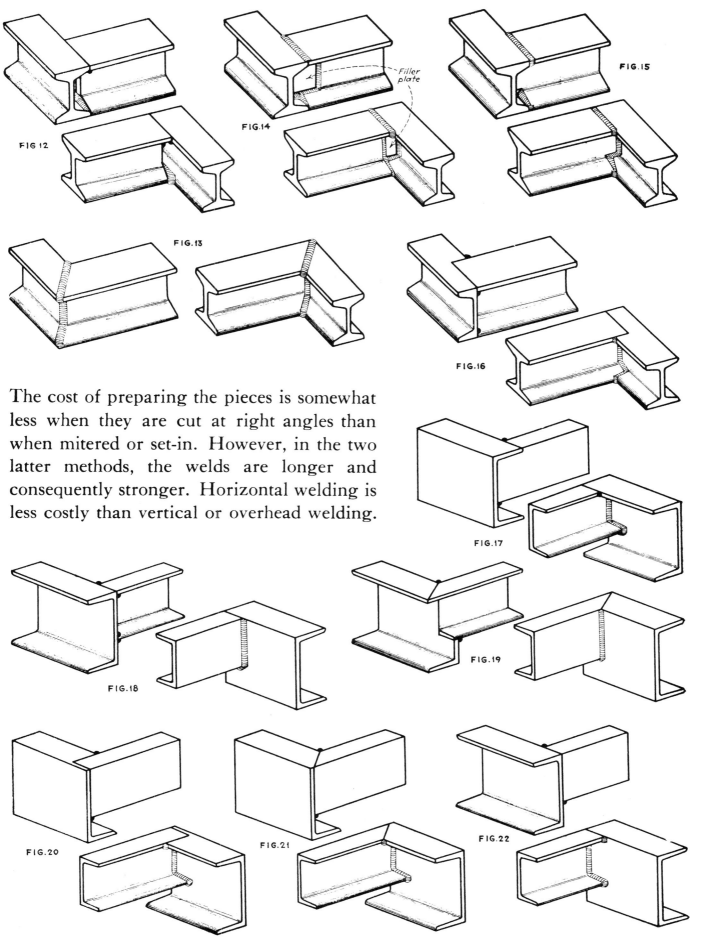

FIG 12

FIG.14

Filler plate

FIG.15

FIG.13

FIG.16

The cost of preparing the pieces is somewhat less when they are cut at right angles than when mitered or set-in. However, in the two latter methods, the welds are longer and consequently stronger. Horizontal welding is less costly than vertical or overhead welding.

FIG.17

FIG.18

FIG.19

FIG.20

FIG.21

FIG.22

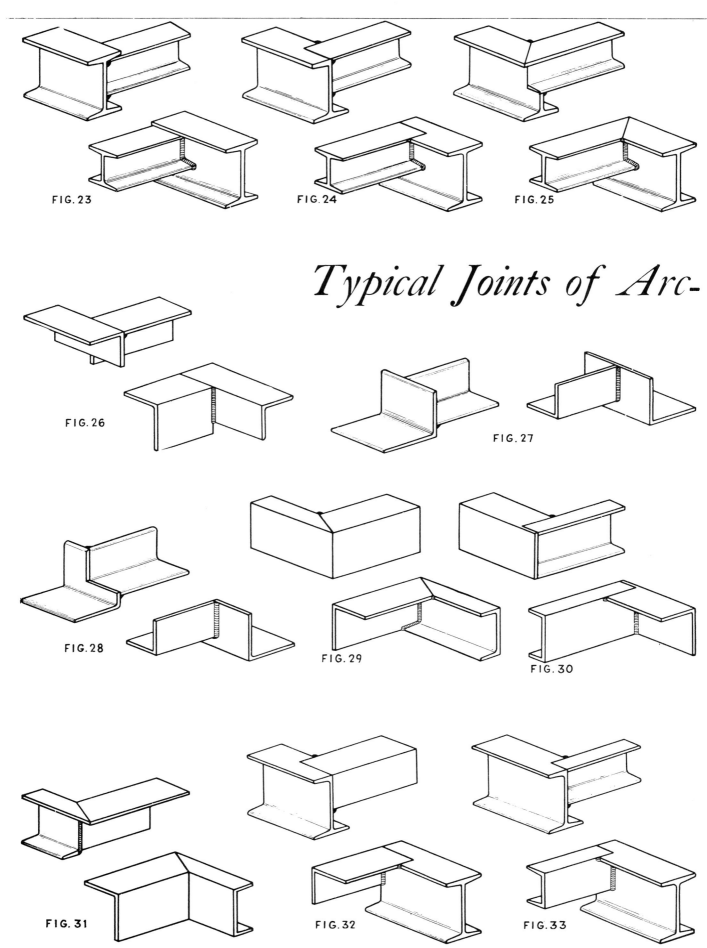

FIG. 23

FIG. 24

FIG. 25

*Typical Joints of Arc-*

FIG. 26

FIG. 27

FIG. 28

FIG. 29

FIG. 30

FIG. 31

FIG. 32

FIG. 33

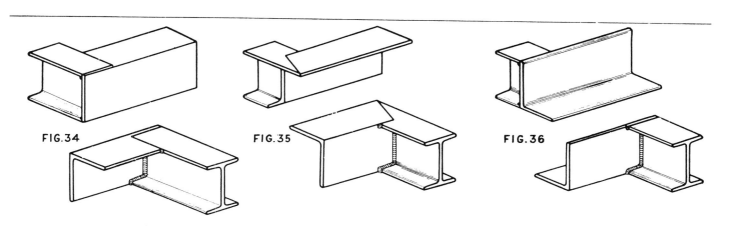

FIG. 34

FIG. 35

FIG. 36

# *W elded Structurals—II*

R. A. GAST
*The Lincoln Electric Company*

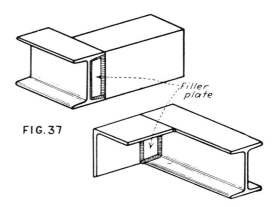

FIG. 37

*Filler plate*

FIG. 38

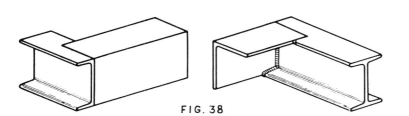

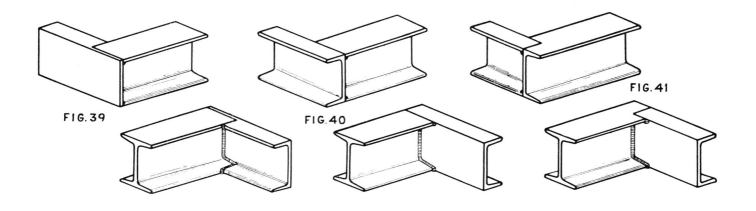

FIG. 39

FIG. 40

FIG. 41

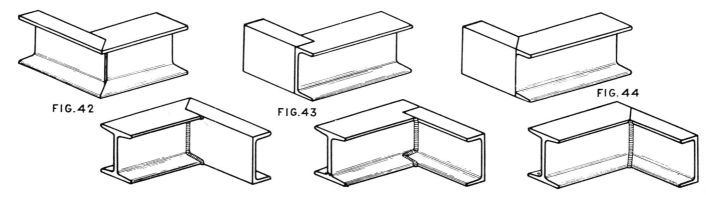

FIG. 42

FIG. 43

FIG. 44

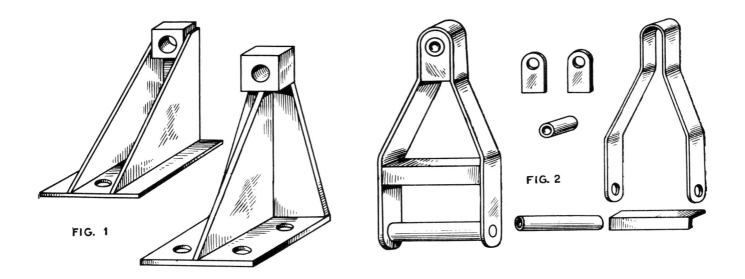

# *Typical Welded Bases*

### The purpose of the welded constructions shown here is to indicate types of designs rather than recommended finished products

Fig. 1—Two forms of brackets for an adjusting screw, using only straight cuts on the plates. Appearance, as in all designs shown here, can be improved by rounding the corners and curving the edges.

Fig. 2—Welded connector, made of a bent flat and standard shapes, for two shafts perpendicular to each other. Pipes, later to be bushed or babbitted, serve for the bearings.

Fig. 3—Bearing support for special equipment, made entirely from stock parts requiring only square cuts. A short piece of drilled round bar is used in place of the square block used in Fig. 1.

*(The Lincoln Electric Company)*

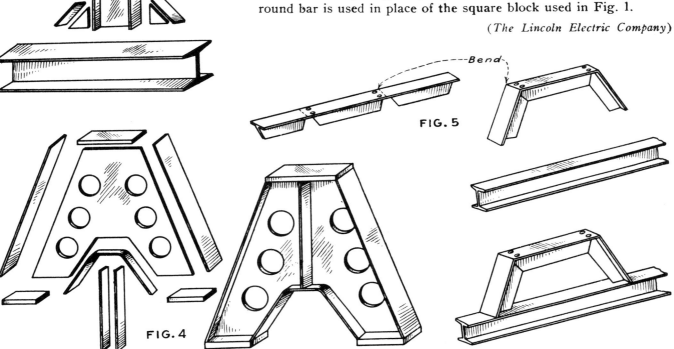

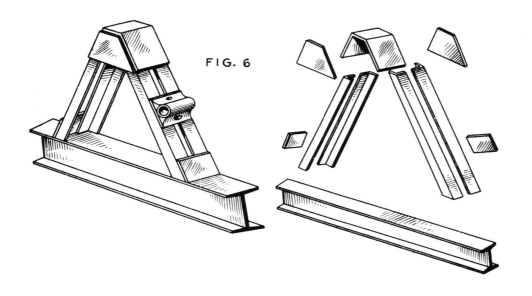

FIG. 6

# and Pedestals-I

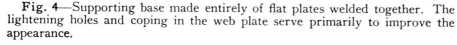

FIG. 7

**Fig. 4**—Supporting base made entirely of flat plates welded together. The lightening holes and coping in the web plate serve primarily to improve the appearance.

**Fig. 5**—Inexpensive bearing support suitable for other than extreme loads, using either a T-bar or a split I-beam for the upper section.

**Fig. 6**—Design of support wherein the slot between the angles permits adjustment of the bearing position. T-head bolts are used for holding the bearing.

**Fig. 7**—Two channels make a box section for each column of this bearing support. For appreciable thrust loads, a wide base plate would be used in place of the two narrow feet.

**Fig. 8**—For heavy loads an assembly of I-beams can be used, the I-beam webs being split to make T-bars.

**Fig. 9**—For a bearing support of medium height it may not be feasible to use an I-beam. Two flat and one bent plate will achieve the same purpose. The pipes add strength and rigidity and also serve as guide holes for the holding-down bolts.

*(The Lincoln Electric Company)*

Channels for box section

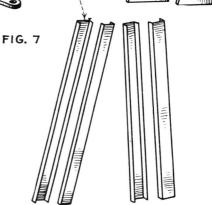

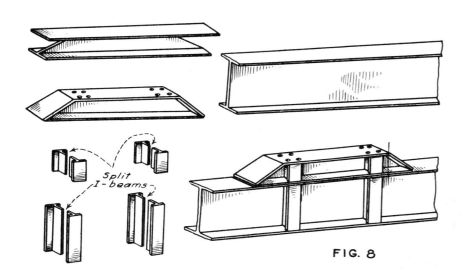

Split I-beams

FIG. 8

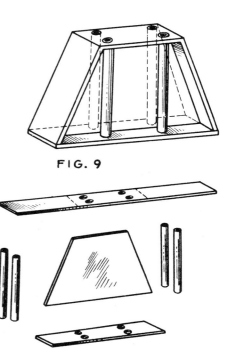

FIG. 9

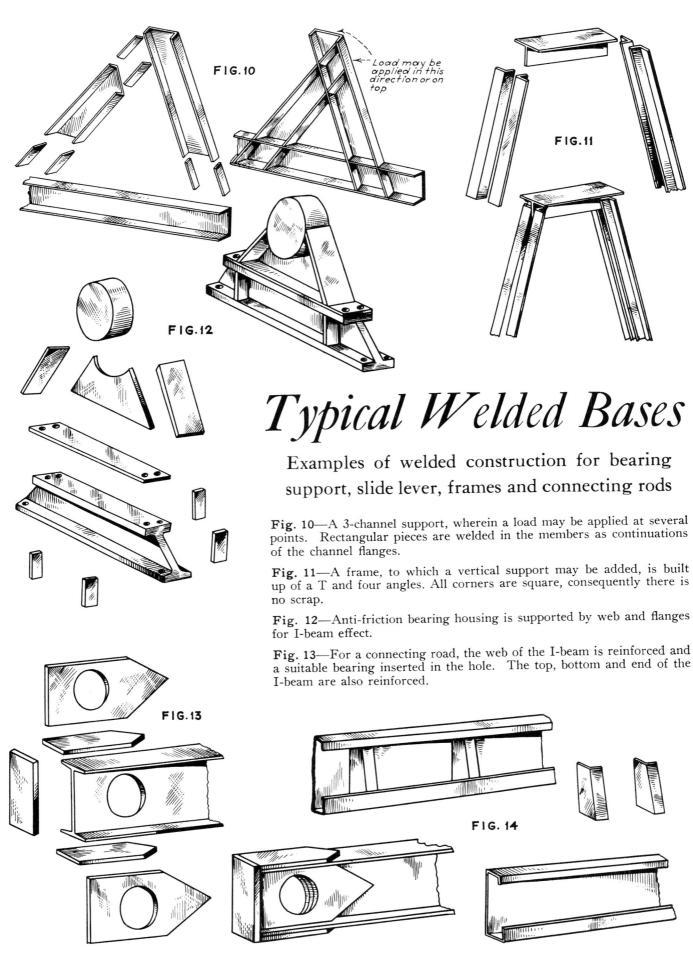

FIG. 10

Load may be applied in this direction or on top

FIG. 11

FIG. 12

# *Typical Welded Bases*

### Examples of welded construction for bearing support, slide lever, frames and connecting rods

**Fig. 10**—A 3-channel support, wherein a load may be applied at several points. Rectangular pieces are welded in the members as continuations of the channel flanges.

**Fig. 11**—A frame, to which a vertical support may be added, is built up of a T and four angles. All corners are square, consequently there is no scrap.

**Fig. 12**—Anti-friction bearing housing is supported by web and flanges for I-beam effect.

**Fig. 13**—For a connecting road, the web of the I-beam is reinforced and a suitable bearing inserted in the hole. The top, bottom and end of the I-beam are also reinforced.

FIG. 13

FIG. 14

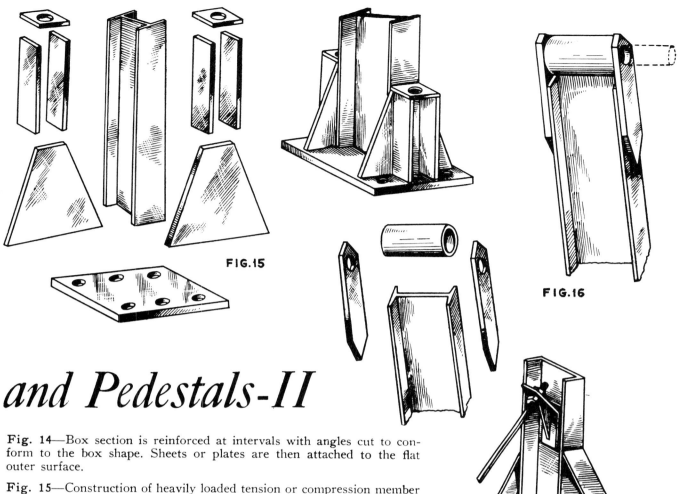

# and Pedestals-II

**Fig. 14**—Box section is reinforced at intervals with angles cut to conform to the box shape. Sheets or plates are then attached to the flat outer surface.

**Fig. 15**—Construction of heavily loaded tension or compression member to which easily removed parts are assembled. All connection holes are outside the main support.

**Fig. 16**—Two plates, a tube and I-beam are used to form the connection for a boom to mast on small derrick or hoist.

**Fig. 17**—Built-up bracket for adjustable traverse tie-rod is welded within channel flanges, angles being used to brace the channel. Load is applied to plate at top (not shown).

**Fig. 18**—Slide lever built up from plates, two of which are shaped, slotted and drilled. Rectangular plates are welded at two places on each formed member.

*(The Lincoln Electric Company)*

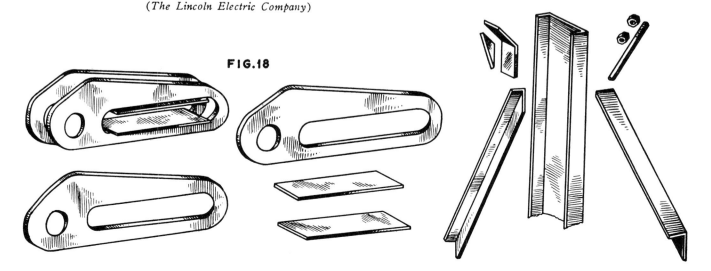

Fig. 1—Fabricated compressor housing assembled by a combination of arc and stud welding. The studs are located by means of sheet metal templates. A tripod on the welding gun insures perpendicular location and simplifies the stud welding operation.

Fig. 2—Enlarged cross section of an end-welded stud showing the fusion between the stud and the parent metal. The strength of such welds depends primarily on the type of stud used, on the stud material and diameter, and on the base material.

# Design Details for Stud Welding

Minimum plate thicknesses for different sizes of studs, strength of studs, required clearances for the welding gun, methods of stud location, and basic functional advantages of the process.

### R. W. MURDOCK
Nelson Stud Welding Division
Morton-Gregory Corporation

BECAUSE OF REPLACEMENT REQUIREMENTS, maintenance purposes, or for basic design considerations, metal parts often must be assembled with removable type fasteners. In heavier construction, the conventional way of attaching such fasteners is to drill and tap holes through the plate or structure and insert studs, but this method may limit the design of the finished assembly so that it is neither the most efficient nor practical. As a result, such methods of attachment frequently increase production costs and manufacturing difficulties.

If such is the case, stud welding can be used to advantage. With this process, the fastener can be end-welded to the surface without prior drilling and tapping. The equipment consists of a special welding gun, a timer and control unit, a d-c welding generator, special fluxed studs of weldable material, and ceramic ferrules.

When a weld is made, the stud and protective ferrule are chucked in the gun and pressed against the work. The switch on the gun is pulled, and a solenoid lifts the stud $\frac{1}{16}$ in. above the work to create an arc between the stud and the base metal. The timer unit controls the length of the weld cycle; at the proper time the solenoid is automatically de-energized and the stud plunged into the pool of molten metal. The ceramic ferrule, which surrounds the stud tip and butts up against the work, functions to (1) shield the molten metal to prevent oxidation; (2) to contain the molten metal in the weld area; (3) to control the form of the fillet resulting from the weld; (4) to concentrate the heat in the weld area, and (5) to shield the arc. Because of the shielding effect of the ferrule, in conjunction with the use of self-contained flux in the studs, stud welding may be classed as a

shielded-arc welding process. As seen by the cross-section illustration, Fig. 2, complete fusion results between the stud and the parent metal.

The controlled welding cycle makes for rapid, semi-automatic stud application. Other major advantages of the process are: (1) all work can be done from the outside of the structure; (2) no surface preparation is required; (3) design simplification and improvement in appearance are often feasible; and (4) the interior of the structure remains smooth.

## Design Considerations

The conditions that must be met before stud welding can be considered can be grouped into three general categories. Obviously, the stud and the structure to which it is to be joined must be weldable. Secondly, the size and shape of the stud must be such that a ferrule can be used, the stud can be chucked in the welding gun, and sufficient power is available to heat the metal to a welding temperature. And lastly, certain details, such as clearance for the welding gun and the stud, flatness of surface, thickness of the plate, and others—must be

## Table I—Minimum Plate Thicknesses for Different Sizes of Stud[1]

| Stud Dia., in. | Plate Material, in. | | | |
|---|---|---|---|---|
| | Mild Steel | | Stainless Steel | |
| | With Back-up | Without Back-up | With Back-up | Without Back-up |
| 1/8 | 0.036 | 0.036 | 0.030 | 0.036 |
| 3/16 | 0.036 | 0.036 | 0.036 | 0.059 |
| 1/4 | 0.036 | 0.048 | 0.048 | 0.059 |
| 5/16 | 0.048 | 0.054 | 0.048 | 0.075 |
| 3/8 | 0.054 | 0.060 | 0.059 | 0.075 |
| 7/16 | 0.078 | 0.090 | 0.075 | 0.105 |
| 1/2 | 0.090 | 0.105 | 0.105 | 0.135 |
| 5/8 | 0.125 | 0.125 | 0.135 | 0.188 |
| 3/4 | 0.156 | 0.156 | 0.188 | 0.250 |

[1]For welding without burn-through or excessive distortion. Heavier sheets may be necessary to realize the full strength of the threaded section.

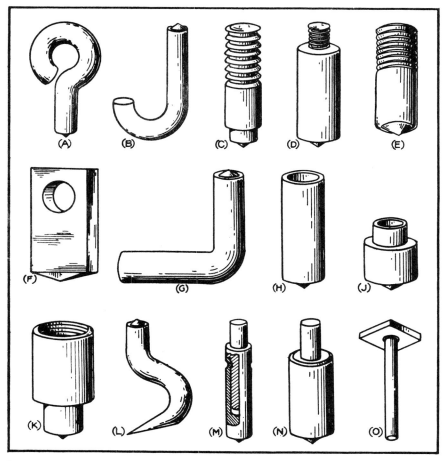

Fig. 3—Typical stud shapes: (A) eye-bolt, (B) J-bolt, (C) standard M-G, (D) threaded shoulder, (E) straight threaded, (F) rectangular, (G) bent, (H) female drive screw, (J) female shoulder, (K) female threaded reduced base, (L) meat hook, (M) composite aluminum rivweld, (N) rivweld, (O) square head. Only requirements are that the stud can be chucked and that a ferrule can be used.

309, 310 and 347 are satisfactory. In addition, stainless studs can be welded to either mild or stainless steel with a power increase of about 10 percent over that required for welding mild steel studs.

Low alloy, high tensile steel can also be welded without preheat if the carbon content is held to 0.12 percent maximum, and some success has been had with other ferrous alloys. For example, Monel studs have been joined to Monel sheet where corrosive conditions warranted the additional cost. Some progress also has been made in the non-ferrous field, but such applications still are considered as being in the more or less "special" category.

Of course, not all sizes of studs can be welded to all gages of light sheet. Limiting factors are the type of material, the strength required, and the amount of distortion that can be tolerated. In Table I are shown the relationships between stud diameter and minimum sheet thickness for mild and stainless steels. Although these minimum thicknesses may have to be increased for maximum strength, they are satisfactory for welding without burn-through or excessive distortion.

Standard shapes in which studs are formed are straight, hooked, rectangular, and special-purpose, which includes those such as retaining pad types for holding insulation or firebrick in furnace applications, insulated types for electrical applications, or split types. Sketches of some of these are shown in Fig. 3.

Straight, mild-steel threaded types range from $\frac{1}{8}$ to $\frac{3}{4}$ in. in diameter, and from $\frac{1}{4}$ to 8 in. or longer in length; the maximum diameter of stainless steel types is $\frac{3}{4}$ in. Critical dimensions of studs and ferrules are given in Table II. Actually, the limit on stud diameter is governed not by the capacity of the welding gun, but by the size of welding generator that is available: a NEMA d-c generator rated at 400 amperes is required for studs up to $\frac{1}{2}$ in. diameter.

Inasmuch as a portion of the stud is melted at the same time a molten pool is created in the plate by the welding arc, there will be some loss in stud length, according to the time and heat used in the welding cycle. Normally $\frac{1}{8}$ in. is allowed for burnoff. This allowance may decrease when studs are applied to very thin plate and the cycle is short; on the other hand, it may increase when studs are welded to medium carbon steel and an extra amount of heat is used to slow the cooling rate of the weldment.

Other points that will be noted in Fig. 3 are that either blank studs or threaded types—American Standard

taken into consideration in the design stage.

Insofar as materials are concerned, the same general limitations that apply to arc welding also apply to stud welding. Mild steels up to 0.30 percent carbon can be joined without preheat, and higher carbon steels can be welded provided that the area is preheated before striking the arc. Stainless steels either of the austenitic or martensitic type can be welded, although the austenitic types are preferred. AISI grades 302, 304, 307,

## Table II—Critical Dimensions of Studs and Ferrules

### STUDS

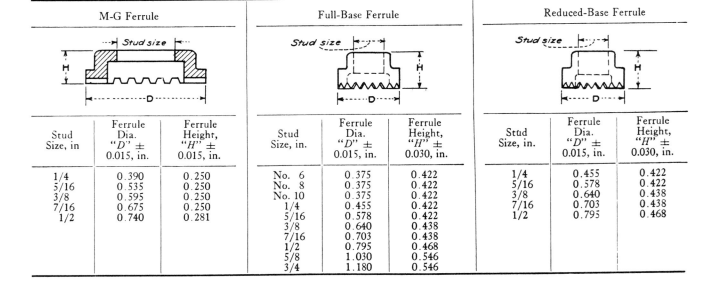

| Standard M-G Studs | Stud Dia. in. | Stud Length "L", in. | | Threads per in. | Thread Length "B", in. | | Burn Off, in. ("C" ± 1/32 in.) | Fillet Dia. ("D" + 0.02 in.) |
|---|---|---|---|---|---|---|---|---|
| | | Min. | Max. | | Stud Length Up to 2 1/2 in. | Stud Length Over 2 1/2 in. | | |
| | 1/4 | 1.0 | 3.0 | 20 | L— 3/8 in. | 2.0 | 1/16 | 0.275 |
| | 5/16 | 1.0 | 3.0 | 18 | L— 3/8 in. | 2.0 | 3/32 | 0.330 |
| | 3/8 | 1.0 | 3.0 | 16 | L— 3/8 in. | 2.0 | 3/32 | 0.406 |
| | 7/16 | 1.0 | 3.0 | 14 | L— 3/8 in. | 2.0 | 1/8 | 0.468 |
| | 1/2 | 1.0 | 3.5 | 13 | L— 13/32 in. | 2.0 | 1/8 | 0.546 |

| Full-base Studs | Stud Dia. in. | Stud Length "L" in. | | Threads per inch | | Thread Length "B", in. | | | Burn Off ("C" ± 1/32 in.) | Fillet Dia. ("D" + 0.02 in. |
|---|---|---|---|---|---|---|---|---|---|---|
| | | Min. | Max. | NC | NF | Stud Length Up to 1.0 in. | Stud Length 1 1/8 to 1 7/16 in. | Stud Length 1 1/2 in. or Over | | |
| | No. 6 | 13/16 | 8.0 | 32 | 40 | L— 3/16 | 1.0 | 1 1/4 | 3/32 | 0.190 |
| | No. 8 | 13/16 | 8.0 | 32 | 36 | L— 3/16 | 1.0 | 1 1/4 | 3/32 | 0.214 |
| | No. 10 | 13/16 | 8.0 | 24 | 32 | L— 3/16 | 1.0 | 1 1/4 | 3/32 | 0.262 |
| | 1/4 | 13/16 | 8.0 | 20 | 28 | L— 3/16 | 1.0 | 1 1/4 | 1/8 | 0.330 |
| | 5/16 | 13/16 | 8.0 | 18 | 24 | L— 3/16 | 1.0 | 1 1/4 | 1/8 | 0.406 |
| | 3/8 | 13/16 | 8.0 | 16 | 24 | L— 3/16 | 1.0 | 1 1/4 | 1/8 | 0.468 |
| | 7/16 | 13/16 | 8.0 | 14 | 20 | L— 3/16 | 1.0 | 1 1/4 | 1/8 | 0.546 |
| | 1/2 | 7/8 | 8.0 | 13 | 20 | L— 3/16 | 1.0 | 1 1/4 | 1/8 | 0.613 |
| | 5/8 | 15/16 | 8.0 | 11 | 18 | L— 1/4[1] | ... | 1 1/2[3] | 1/8 | 0.765 |
| | 3/4 | 1 1/4 | 8.0 | 10 | 16 | L— 1/4[2] | ... | 1 3/4[4] | 1/8 | 0.890 |

[1]For stud length 1 1/16 in. or less
[2]For stud length 1 15/16 in. or less
[3]For stud length 1 1/2 in. or over
[4]For stud length 1 3/4 in. or over

| Reduced-base Studs | Stud Dia., in. | Stud Length "L", in. | | Length of Base in. "K" | Weld Dia. "E" | Threads per inch | | Thread Length "B", in. | | | |
|---|---|---|---|---|---|---|---|---|---|---|---|
| | | Min. | Max. | | | NC | NF | Stud Length Up to 1 3/8 in. | Stud Length 1 1/2 in. or over | Burn Off ("C" ± 1/32 in.) | Fillet Diameter ("D", + 0.02 in.) |
| | No. 8 | 13/16 | 8.0 | 9/64 | 1/8 | 32 | 36 | L-K | 1 1/4 | 1/16 | 0.169 |
| | No. 10 | 13/16 | 8.0 | 9/64 | 9/64 | 24 | 32 | L-K | 1 1/4 | 1/16 | 0.192 |
| | 1/4 | 13/16 | 8.0 | 5/32 | 3/16 | 20 | 28 | L-K | 1 1/4 | 1/16 | 0.255 |
| | 5/16 | 13/16 | 8.0 | 1/4 | 1/4 | 18 | 24 | L-K | 1 1/4 | 3/32 | 0.343 |
| | 3/8 | 13/16 | 8.0 | 1/4 | 5/16 | 16 | 24 | L-K | 1 1/4 | 3/32 | 0.406 |
| | 7/16 | 13/16 | 8.0 | 9/32 | 3/8 | 14 | 20 | L-K | 1 1/4 | 1/8 | 0.468 |
| | 1/2 | 7/8 | 8.0 | 9/32 | 7/16 | 13 | 20 | L-K | 1 1/4 | 1/8 | 0.560 |

### FERRULES

| M-G Ferrule | | | | Full-Base Ferrule | | | | Reduced-Base Ferrule | | |
|---|---|---|---|---|---|---|---|---|---|---|
| Stud Size, in | Ferrule Dia. "D" ± 0.015, in. | Ferrule Height, "H" ± 0.015, in. | | Stud Size, in. | Ferrule Dia. "D" ± 0.015, in. | Ferrule Height, "H" ± 0.030, in. | | Stud Size, in. | Ferrule Dia. "D" ± 0.015, in. | Ferrule Height, "H" ± 0.030, in. |
| 1/4 | 0.390 | 0.250 | | No. 6 | 0.375 | 0.422 | | 1/4 | 0.455 | 0.422 |
| 5/16 | 0.535 | 0.250 | | No. 8 | 0.375 | 0.422 | | 5/16 | 0.578 | 0.422 |
| 3/8 | 0.595 | 0.250 | | No. 10 | 0.375 | 0.422 | | 3/8 | 0.640 | 0.438 |
| 7/16 | 0.675 | 0.250 | | 1/4 | 0.455 | 0.422 | | 7/16 | 0.703 | 0.438 |
| 1/2 | 0.740 | 0.281 | | 5/16 | 0.578 | 0.422 | | 1/2 | 0.795 | 0.468 |
| | | | | 3/8 | 0.640 | 0.438 | | | | |
| | | | | 7/16 | 0.703 | 0.438 | | | | |
| | | | | 1/2 | 0.795 | 0.468 | | | | |
| | | | | 5/8 | 1.030 | 0.546 | | | | |
| | | | | 3/4 | 1.180 | 0.546 | | | | |

## Table III—Average Fracture Strength of Stud Welds

| Type of Stud | Load at Fracture (tension, lb.; torsion, in.-lb.) | | | | | | | | | |
|---|---|---|---|---|---|---|---|---|---|---|
| | 1/4 in Stud | | 3/8 in. Stud | | 1/2 in. Stud | | 5/8 in. Stud | | 3/4 in. Stud | |
| | Tension | Torsion | Tension | Torsion | Tension | Torsion | Tension | Torsion | Tension | Torsion |
| Blank stud, full diameter........ | 3,700 | 250 | 8,300 | 840 | 14,700 | 1,980 | 23,000 | 3,300 | 33,000 | 5,800 |
| Blank stud, 1/2 reduced base..... | 2,700 | 155 | 7,800 | 740 | 14,000 | 1,560 | 22,400 | 3,180 | 32,400 | 5,180 |
| Blank stud, full reduced base..... | 1,250 | 50 | 5,500 | 310 | 13,300 | 1,300 | 19,900 | 1,880 | 25,400 | 3,200 |
| Threaded stud, U. S. Std. Coarse.. | 3,300 | 170 | 5,200 | 590 | 13,200 | 1,400 | 20,200 | 2,400 | 30,600 | 4,100 |

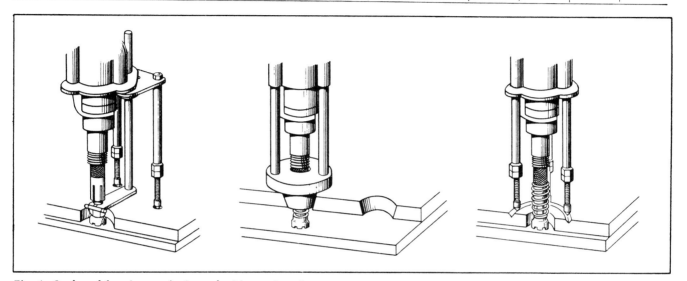

Fig. 4—Studs and ferrules may be located with templates by any of several methods: by means of holes in the template for gun adapter legs, left; by a tapered hole in the template for another type of gun adapter, center; or by a concentric groove.

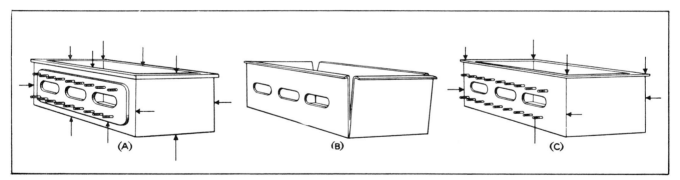

Fig. 5—The use of end-welded studs and sheet metal construction saves weight and manufacturing costs in the production of these switchgear boxes. The conventional design (upper left) requires heavy flanges and bosses to obtain sufficient tapping depth. The flange at the top is replaced by bending the side plates to form the gasketing surface, and studs end-welded to the plate material eliminate the need for the heavy bosses on the side of the box. The appearance also is cleaner than before.

NC or NF threads—are available, and that the diameter may be full or reduced at the base. Principal advantage of the reduced base type is that it minimizes the problem of clearance caused by the welding fillet. For example, a standard ½ in. stud produces a fillet diameter of 0.613 in. An M-G of the same diameter has a fillet diameter only 0.046 in. greater than the stud; but a reduced base stud has an even smaller fillet—although it is obtained at some sacrifice in strength, as indicated by the values in Table III.

There are, of course, other ways of designing around this weld fillet. If two metal plates are to be joined without an intervening gasket, counterboring will take care of it. When gaskets are required, careful selection of the material and the dimensions will minimize the fillet problem. Other ways of accommodating the weld fillet are by an oversized hole in the cover plate, or by dogs or clamps to hold the plate in position.

Partly because of the weld fillet and partly because of the clearance re-

quired for the ceramic ferrule and the welding gun, spacing between studs and minimum distances between studs and openings in the plate are limited. For the same reasons, the proximity of studs to flanges and other raised elements is limited. Minimum recommended clearance dimensions for common types of studs are indicated in Table IV. Height clearance problems are minimized, as is the handling of extra-length studs, by use of accessory offset chucks.

Positioning the studs on the work is

accomplished by any of several methods, the simplest of which is to center punch the proper stud location on the work. Accuracies of $\frac{1}{32}$ in. are possible with this method.

When closer tolerances are desired, templates can be made of light gage metal. Holes are drilled in the template to locate the ferrule—which, in turn, locates the stud—and the template is then positioned over the work with pins, slots, or other devices. A minimum of $\frac{1}{16}$ in. between the template and the work piece is required to allow the gases to escape. Other techniques may be applied, Fig. 4, whereby the stud is located indirectly by referencing gun legs or special adaptors that are attached to the gun. The method used will be determined by the requirements of the particular application. Note that the techniques illustrated not only locate the stud, but provide a means for maintaining perpendicularity as well. When offset legs are used for positioning the stud, the hole drilled in the template for the stud and ferrule is made large enough to provide adequate venting of the hot gases, and the template then fits flush against the work; accuracies of 0.025 in. are obtainable.

In some instances it is preferable to establish a fixed production unit for use in end welding studs to other components. Push buttons and hydraulic cylinders replace manual positioning and trigger actuation of the hand welding gun. As in the case of templates used with the portable gun, the degree of accuracy required and the amount and type of work to be done determine the size and character of the production unit. A simple production unit can be made by attaching a portable gun to a permanent stand such as a drill press. With a locating jig for the work, it is possible to accurately weld studs to small components with considerable speed.

When higher production rates make feasible a greater degree of automaticity, single or multiple-gun production units of a wide range of size can be designed to accommodate individual manufacturing requirements. Automatic indexing and feed controls, positioning devices, and similar features make possible production rates of 20 or 30 welds per minutes on some designs. Because of the rigidity of the mounting structure, tolerances of 0.005 in. on location and 0.010 in. in height are practicable. In one automotive application, a fixed production unit is used to weld studs at a slight angle to a sharply curved bumper guard surface. Somewhat similar setups have been used to weld studs to convex or concave surfaces having a

diameter as small as $\frac{3}{4}$ in. Besides several other automotive applications, fixed production units have been used in the manufacture of large pressure vessels and for welding pins and teeth to combing machines. In applications like the latter, the production unit is arranged to move the work so that the studs are applied in a particular path or pattern.

The strength of stud welded fasteners varies with the material of which the stud is made, the material of the plate, the size of the stud, the welding cycle employed, the shape of the stud, and on numerous other factors. Mild steel, which is commonly used for studs, has a tensile strength of 75,000 psi and a yield strength of 60,000 psi, an elongation of 24 percent in 2.0 in., and a reduction in area of 58 percent. The fracture strength of welds on this material are listed in Table III.

Tests show that the ultimate strength of a properly welded stud is determined by the smallest cross-section of the stud; stud failure may thus be anticipated before weld failure. Comparative tests between stud welding and hand arc welding indicate that the stud welded joint is usually superior in strength to a hand welded joint in static tension, impact tension and torsion. The increase in strength is attributable to the fact that the controlled stud welding cycle produces a fusion weld across the entire base of the stud.

### Advantages of the Process

If proper attention is given to design details, there are numerous advantages that are obtained by substituting welded studs for those that are

attached by drilling and tapping through-holes. These advantages can be summarized as follows:

PRODUCTION TIME. Reduced production time is a feature of stud welding, not only because drilling and tapping is unnecessary and no surface preparation is required, but also because the only jigs and fixtures required are of simple construction and hence set-up time is reduced. Production rates average 5-6 welds per minute for a hand-operated welding gun, or 6-30 welds per minute for an automatic unit.

MANUFACTURING COSTS. Cost reductions through stud welding often are appreciable. Of equal importance in many cases is the fact that weight of the workpiece itself is considerably lowered. These points are illustrated by the switchgear housing, Fig. 5. Heavy bosses and flanges usually must be added to the conventional box, A, to insure that there is sufficient depth of material to withstand the loads imposed on tapped threads. In the redesigned model, the flanges at the top are formed by bending the side plates on a press brake, and end-welded studs on the side C eliminate the need for heavy bosses.

LOAD DISTRIBUTION. Studs can be placed in proper relation to the load each must carry, which often is impractical if work must be done from the blind side. For example, if a container is to be drilled and tapped for through bolts, account must be taken of possible interference from some internal structure or condition when inserting the bolts—and consequently, such bolts cannot always be so placed

### Table IV—Minimum Stud Clearances

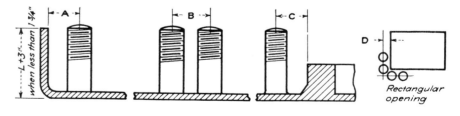

| Stud Dia., in. | Clearance, in. | | | |
|---|---|---|---|---|
| | A | B | C | D |
| 3/16 | Bend radius + 5/16 | 1/2 | Weld width + 1/4 | 1/2 |
| 1/4 | Bend radius + 5/16 | 9/16 | Weld width + 1/4 | 9/16 |
| 5/16 | Bend radius + 3/8 | 11/16 | Weld width + 5/16 | 11/16 |
| 3/8 | Bend radius + 3/8 | 3/4 | Weld width + 5/16 | 3/4 |
| 7/16 | Bend radius + 13/32 | 13/16 | Weld width + 3/8 | 13/16 |
| 1/2 | Bend radius + 15/32 | 15/16 | Weld width + 7/16 | 15/16 |
| 5/8 | Bend radius + 9/16 | 1 3/32 | Weld width + 1/2 | 1 3/32 |
| 3/4 | Bend radius + 5/8 | 1 7/32 | Weld width + 9/16 | 1 7/32 |

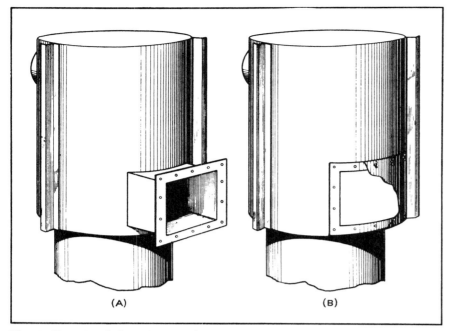

Fig. 6—How the design of access doors can be simplified by stud welding. Conventional construction *A*, has a rectangular opening welded to the main structure; the inspection cover is then bolted to the flange. Simplified construction *B* has studs welded directly on the surface; the cover plate is fastened in place by wing nuts.

that they carry their proper share of the total load on the structure.

INTERIOR SURFACES. Since no drilling is involved interior surfaces of tanks, blowers, and pressure vessels are smooth and unobstructed. This is especially important in the fabrication of large industrial fans, because internal projections interfere with the normal flow of the air stream, and promote the collection of dirt accumulations which further reduce efficiency.

A related advantage occurs when studs for covers of access doors or inspection openings are welded to pressure vessels or furnaces. Good design practice—and some national safety codes—prohibit drilling and tapping bolt holes in the casings of such equipment. Also, stud welded fasteners can be used to hold insulation, firebrick, or similar materials to interior or exterior surfaces; for such applications, spe-

cially designed studs are available.

Still another application where smooth internal surfaces are important is in the production of cold walls for food processing equipment. External plug welding provides the necessary spacing for walls for milk coolers and pasteurizers, for example, without effecting the inner surface.

CORROSION. Elimination of "through" holes also minimize the problem of corrosion in pressure vessels and fluid-handling equipment of all kinds. When a smooth unbroken internal surface is maintained, no convenient toehold is provided for damaging corrosion. For example, better corrosion protection was obtained on underground switchboxes for communication equipment. The former construction involved a cast housing and extensive drilling and tapping operations; the redesigned units are made of stainless

steel plates, on which studs are end-welded.

DESIGN SIMPLIFICATION. Mention has already been made of examples of design simplification, for decrease in cost and product improvement usually follow design improvement. An obvious example is the furnace cleanout access door shown in Fig. 6. As indicated in the sketch, the former construction consisted of a box-like structure hand-welded to the boiler. The inspection cover was then bolted to the flange around the box. Necessary because internal holes would introduce the possibility of gas leakage, this external flange arrangement was a difficult and costly one and, further, greatly limited accessibility to the interior of the furnace. The built-up components was replaced by studs which are end welded to the boiler surface. The cover plate was then fastened in place with wing nuts.

BROADER APPLICATION RANGE. When conventional studs are used, both the size of structure involved and the point in the manufacturing cycle at which studs can be applied may be limited by the fact that drilling and tapping are necessary preliminary operations. Studs may be conveniently applied in a large structure in the assembled state, for example, much more simply than in the separate components.

Boiler and processing equipment manufacturers, on the other hand, may apply stud welding in the field to complete the assembly of separate components. The five-pound stud welding gun may be operated with 300 feet or more of cable in any position, on the other hand, which greatly broadens its application range.

Under the proper conditions, the work may even be used in assembly as a locating template to position studs to complete fabrication, eliminating troublesome problems involved in supplying precisely dimensioned prefabricated components.

# INDEX